Issues in Therapeutic Recreation:
A Profession in Transition

David M. Compton, Ed.
University of Utah

Sagamore
Publishing
a division of
Management Learning Laboratories

Champaign, Illinois 61820

Printed in the United States of America

Cover Design: Michelle R. Dressen
Text Design: Susan M. Williams

ISBN: 0-915611-20-1
Library of Congress Catalog Card Number: 89-060963

photo courtesy of San Francisco Recreation Center for the Handicapped

We need not be immobilized by our debates. We must continue to move forward for the sake of our ideals of quality of care to our clients, our constituencies, and ourselves as professionals.

—Peg Connolly

CONTENTS

Part III: Issues Related to Practice

Part IV: National and International Issues

FOREWORD

The "profession in transition," the "emerging profession"—these and many other terms applied to the field of therapeutic recreation imply the dynamics of growth, development, and change—and along with this change is a natural state of uncertainty. We have seen a struggle toward defining our profession and our services, and we have seen history repeat itself as this debate about who we are has gone on and on from the 1950s to the debates of the 1980s.

I dare say these debates will continue in the future as they show evidence of a concern for bringing meaning and defining the potential of our field. My hope for the profession is that we recognize this struggle for identity as a positive means of continually evaluating our worth as a profession, and defining areas in which we wish to improve our professional services. We will probably never have 100 percent agreement amongst ourselves as to a solitary purpose, function, and outcome for our field, but I believe we need not be immobilized by our debates, and that we must continue to move forward for the sake of our ideals of quality of care to our clients, our constituencies, and ourselves as professionals.

You have before you a collection of articles that portray our thinking on the critical issues facing our field at this time. While the articles may seem diverse and complicated, they are intricately related and reflective of the global issues concerning the quality of our services and our profession. One cannot separate philosophical issues from reimbursement, or from credentialing, as there is a connectedness between these and many of the other topics covered in this book. While we may study the issues such as reimbursement or ethics in a singular fashion, please attempt to recognize how each is related to the other issues of professionalism. As you read and ponder the enclosed information, seek to understand the concept, and to then perceive it within the perspective of the total profession.

We and other health care/human service professions face some incredible dilemmas in the next two decades. We will experience an increase in health care opportunities in our country through the year 2000. The U.S. Bureau of Labor Statistics projects that there will be a

3 percent growth in health services and a 2 percent growth in social services between 1986 and 2000. While the fastest employment growth will be in business, health services will provide as many or more jobs than the business sector. In 1986, there were 7.6 million jobs in health services and by the year 2000 that number is expected to grow to over 10 million jobs. Of all health services jobs, those in hospitals will remain high at 42 percent, and provide 2 of every 5 jobs in the health service arena. In 1988 alone, over 200,000 positions were added in hospitals in the United States. The next highest growing areas will be physician offices and nursing homes.

At the same time that we will experience more opportunities for our field, there is a dramatic shortage of personnel to fill these increased health care positions, in all health care professions. Part of this is explainable by our population census, which for the first time is experiencing a reduction in the 16-24 age labor force. Traditionally, this age group has filled many entry-level positions. However, because of low birth rates in 1960, we will not see an increase in this age group for the labor force until 1992-2000 when the baby-boomers' babies come into the 16-24 age bracket. So who will fill these entry-level positions that are so essential to health care? It is projected that all professions must re-examine their entry-level workforce. Our future workforce will include more women and minorities. However, it will be our responsibility to recruit and train these individuals for access to our field.

While we have not conducted a comprehensive supply-demand study of our own field at this time, the U.S. Department of Labor Statistics projects that there were approximately 29,000 positions in Recreation Therapy as in 1986. It is further projected that positions in our field will grow at the rate of 20 percent through the year 2000. The field is healthy, then, in a labor and occupational outlook, but how will we fill these employment needs?

At this time of transition in our field, we must not only look at critical issues and professional tradition, but examine how we will provide our services in the future. It is time to take a critical look at our current values concerning personnel and professional service delivery. The shortage of qualified therapeutic recreation personnel in this country is significant, and at the same time, there seems to be an increased demand for our services as evidenced by increased job opportunities in the field. Related to this is the reduced pool of therapeutic recreation educators to fill academic positions that are so critical to the future training needs of our profession.

I believe it is time to examine our service provision practices and to consider career ladder opportunities. It is time to stop the lip-service regarding increased involvement of minorities and to actively create educational opportunities that allow the non-traditional entry-level person the opportunity to complete training and education requirements while being actively employed in service delivery.

Considering the critical issues facing our field, the need for greater sophistication in, our techniques of practice, our methods of research and evaluation, and in our professional concepts, it is sometimes frustrating to imagine a lesser reliance on professional level personnel and a greater use of extender or assistant staff who develop their skills via on-the-job training and certificate programs. On the other hand, the labor supply of entry-level personnel willing to enter educational programs in the health care professions is at the lowest level ever in our society and we must be creative in our efforts to recruit and develop our own entry-level labor pool who may progress through levels of education throughout their work careers. Further, while we examine these non-traditional methods of personnel use in our field, we must continue to strive for improved quality in our services.

I believe we can look at this stage and transition in our profession in a positive light. I believe we will be able to adequately address the critical issues we now identify and ponder, and at the same time, we will be able to address the personnel needs for our field. Our focus must remain on the development and delivery of quality services. Our energies may need to be directed to creative and non-traditional methods of educating our future professionals. But our hopes for our profession should remain high. We have accomplished so much in the past ten years that it has made us aware of all that remains to be accomplished and we have not lessened our vigor with which we face our challenges as a profession. Please read, ponder, and think of your own contribution in this process. Each of us has much to contribute to the advancement of the therapeutic recreation profession.

References

U.S. Department of Labor, Bureau of Labor Statistics. *Occupational Outlook Handbook, 1988-89 Edition.*

U.S. Department of Labor, Bureau of Labor Statistics. *Projections 2000: Revised Employment, Output, and Demand for the Year 2000.*

Peg Connolly, Ph.D.
Executive Director
National Council for Therapeutic Recreation Certification

ACKNOWLEDGMENTS

This book is the result of a dream to assemble the very best authors and address the issues facing the therapeutic recreation profession. A work as complex as this sometimes loses importance if perseverance and belief in the project are not constant. Sincere appreciation is expressed to Dr. Joseph Bannon, President, Management Learning Laboratories, Ltd. and Sagamore Publishing, who kept the project on target. His foresight in creating the Rehabilitation and Human Development Series allowed a project such as this to become a reality. Many more quality publications serving the allied health, rehabilitation and human development arenas will follow.

Appreciation is extended to all the authors who gave of their time, talents and convictions. Each has given our profession a rare perspective of his or her given issue. These individuals represent the past and current leadership of the profession. They also represent the most prolific and provocative writers in our scholarly journals. Finally, they represent the intellectual, moral, and learned frontiers of the profession. Each has challenged the practitioner, student, and faculty member to think deeply about the issues facing the profession. Their candor and provocative manner can only yield solutions, answers and progress.

In any project, there are people in the trenches who do much to make it a success. Sincere appreciation is expressed to Susan Williams and Michelle Dressen of Sagamore Publishing for their editorial and marketing expertise. Appreciation is also expressed to Mrs. Verla Hagen, Assistant to the Dean, College of Health, University of Utah, who assisted me throughout the project. One of my stalwarts has been Rachel Lohmeyer, Research Assistant, College of Health, University of Utah. Her efforts to assemble the final pieces of the manuscript were invaluable. In addition, she and Marlene Valentine, a TEAM-TR student, were instrumental in pulling together the resource section.

This project would not have been possible to complete without the support of key people in the University of Utah administration. During the summer of 1988, I was granted a research leave to work on several projects. I want to personally express my thanks to: Chase N. Peterson, M.D., President; Dr. James L. Clayton, Provost; Don E. Detmer, M.D., former Vice President for Health Sciences and Cecil O. Samuelson, Jr., M.D., for allowing me to take the time to work on this project. Quality time is a precious commodity for administrators. Their faith in this project was extremely gratifying.

Special appreciation is extended to Janet Pomeroy, Founder and Director, San Francisco Recreation Center for the Handicapped, Gary Robb, Director, Bradford Woods Outdoor Education Center at Indiana University, and John Chambers, Director, Special Programs, Recreation and Park Department, City of Las Vegas, for providing us with excellent photos to depict the practice of therapeutic recreation. We are deeply indebted to the children, teens and adults who are depicted in the pictures. They provide the reader with provocative evidence that through one's recreation anything is possible.

David M. Compton, Ed.D.
Dean and Professor
University of Utah

Philosophical and Historical Issues

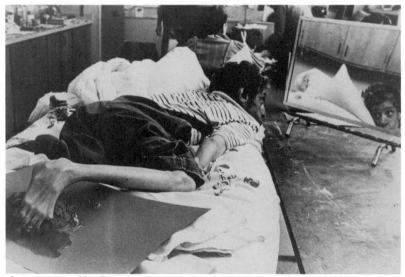

photo courtesty of San Francisco Recreation Center for the Handicapped

All serious daring starts from within.
—Eudora Welty

IMPRESSIONS OF THE INTELLECTUAL PAST AND FUTURE OF THERAPEUTIC RECREATION:
Implications for Professionalization

Charles D. Sylvester

Introduction

Scholars have debated at length the attributes of a profession and which occupations qualify to what degree along an idealized scale ranging from "nonprofession" to "profession." They have consequently discussed what constitutes a profession, exactly, and which occupations qualify to what degree along an idealized scale ranging from "nonprofession" at one extreme to "profession" at the other (e.g., Cogan, 1953; Etzioni, 1969; Flexner, 1915; Goode, 1960; Greenwood, 1966; Hughes, 1963; Vollmer & Mills, 1966). In his classic analysis, Flexner claimed that professions are distinguished by (1) intellectual operations; (2) science and learning; (3) clear, unambiguous practical ends; (4) teachable techniques transmitted through professional education; (5) strong internal organization; and (6) unselfish devotion to the public good. Flexner was particularly emphatic that professions are essentially altruistic and intellectual, asserting that "the real character of the activity is the thinking process; a free, resourceful and unhampered intelligence applied to problems and seeking to understand and master them—that is in the first instance characteristic of a profession" (p. 902). Although all occupations involve some type of skill, Greenwood (1966) also asserts that the crucial distinction between a professional occupation and a nonprofessional one rests in the former's "fund of knowledge that has been organized into an internally consistent system, called a *body of theory* . . . a feature virtually absent in the training of the nonprofessional" (p. 11).

The primary role of theoretical knowledge in professional education can be traced to Plato's *Republic* (Sabine, 1961), and the autonomous use of theory-based knowledge to meet individual and social needs dates back to the sixteenth century (Charlton, 1973). The intellectual basis of professions also has wide and ample modern support. Turner and Hodge (1970) call the essential underpinning of theory a "ubiquitous assumption in writings on professions" (p.26). Millerson (1964) found that skill based on theoretical knowledge was among the most frequently cited characteristics of a profession. Assessing the status of therapeutic recreation, Reynolds and O'Morrow (1985) also confirm that in addition to publicly sanctioned authority to practice and mechanisms to protect the public, professions are characterized by "both a general and specialized body of knowledge that can be used to benefit the consumer" (p. 11). A profession, therefore, is based on a body of theory-based knowledge, which is founded on and funded by ideas. Without legitimate foundational ideas (basic beliefs and values) to explicate presuppositions, justify fundamental goals, and serve as guides to research and practice, a body of knowledge would not be possible. And without a valid body of knowledge, practitioners would literally have no idea of what to do, how to do it, and, most importantly, why they do it. Ideas are the soil from which all professional activities sprout, including ethics, research, standards, curricula, and credentialing.

The complex idea of a body of knowledge implies three interrelated parts. First it suggests *theory,* which is an explicative system of ideas that provides the basis for professional knowledge and activity. The goal of theory is knowledge itself, including the laws, facts, values, and principles that direct practice. *Practice* refers to organized moral and political activity. It is the social field of action where abstract knowledge (theory) is structured and applied to achieve concrete goals. Finally, *technique* involves specific skills used to make or to do something related to practice. Its concern is how to apply skills to achieve practical purposes. None of these elements may be ignored without weakening the structural integrity of a profession.

Whether therapeutic recreation sufficiently demonstrates the attributes of a profession, especially the basic qualities of service and theory, has been a prominent issue (see Peterson, 1981; Reynolds & Morrow, 1985; Rowthorn, 1978). Therapeutic recreation has undoubtedly served the public; but despite admirable attempts (e.g., Avedon, 1974; Ball, 1970; Meyer, 1976), false starts, and occasional pretense, it does not yet have the intellectual character comparable to the systematic bodies of knowledge evidenced by such bona fide professions as law, medicine, and engineering. Consequently, it is an occupation whose professional aspirations have been frustrated by intellectual insufficiency and by excessive reliance on other disciplines for most of its theoretical knowledge.

As I elucidate this situation, I will trace several of therapeutic recreation's intellectual moments, regretful that I cannot cover them all. But my purpose is not to write a chronology of its leading ideas, resulting in a superficial account. Limited by space, I have selected instructive episodes in the intellectual history of therapeutic recreation as a way of framing and clarifying the problem. After supporting my thesis, I will conclude by urging an intellectual awakening in therapeutic recreation.

Intellectual Moments in Therapeutic Recreation

Benefits and values of play, leisure, and recreation have been recognized since antiquity (e.g., Plato's, *The Republic*, Aristotle's *Politics*). However, spurred by immigration, urbanization, and industrialization – and fostered by Progressivism– play, leisure, and recreation received truly broad attention in relation to human welfare and well-being only in the twentieth century (e.g., Addams, 1923; Alger, 1925; Cabot, 1911; Lee, 1911a, 1911b, 1915; Patrick, 1916; Scott, 1913). Furthermore, it wasn't until after World War II, following the formation of the Hospital Recreation Section of the American Recreation Society in 1948, that a semblance of sustained intellectual dialogue emerged.

The Basic Concepts Committee of the Hospital Recreation Section was appointed in 1950 to study the conceptual foundations of "hospital recreation." Its first major project involved surveying professionals from the fields of recreation and medicine on recreation-related subjects. The committee's "Statement of Tenet" (Hospital Recreation Section, 1953) was one of the first concerted attempts to form a philosophical foundation for recreation services in hospitals and institutions (Reynolds & O'Morrow, 1985). The Basic Concepts Committee reported again a decade later (Hospital Recreation Section, no date). Conceptual dilemmas which continue to vex therapeutic recreation, such as the difficult means/end debate[1] (see Mobily, Hunnicutt, & Weissinger, 1987), were evident in the report. For example, recreation was defined as "*voluntary* participation in any wholesome activity for the personal enjoyment and satisfaction *derived from the doing* [italics added] (p. 3). Conversely, "medical recreation" involved prescriptive treatment delivered under the "ultimate authority" of the physician. Basic assumptions guiding the theory and practice of recreation in hospitals also complied with the medical model, revealing the pervasive influence of medicine. One assumption pronounced "The patient and the recreator are governed by medical philosophy and regulatory practices" (p. 3), plainly suggesting that recreation was chiefly a technical broker for medicine and had marginal autonomy of its own.

It was not uncommon for physicians to interpret and justify therapeutic recreation during its early formative period (e.g., Haun, 1965; Meyer, 1962; Rusk, 1960), provoking occasional criticism. Hunnicutt (no date) asserted that by accepting medicine's view, "The NTRS [National Therapeutic Recreation Society] . . . surrendered a good portion of their ability to formulate their own standards and goals" (p. 19). Rowthorn (1978) argued that "recreators have been guided too much by views and opinions of medical colleagues, and not enough by the substance of their own beliefs . . . " (p.158). More recently, Lahey (1987) explained that therapeutic recreation, lacking an indigenous body of knowledge, has borrowed its logic and language out of expediency from various medical and clinical sources. Consequently, therapeutic recreation has grown without substantive foundational ideas of its own, impairing its capacity for self-understanding and professional development.

The late sixties and early seventies showed signs of increased intellectual activity, as recreationists assumed greater responsibility for interpreting and justifying therapeutic recreation (e.g., Ball, 1970; Frye & Peters, 1972; Gootzeit, 1967; Robb, 1975; Shivers, 1971; Southern Regional Institute, 1969; Witt, 1977). Nevertheless, most writings lacked the rigorous, disciplined, and systematic quality of philosophical argument (see Hemingway, 1987, p. 2). As a result, they were unable to sustain the intellectual mood and momentum needed to create a conceptual foundation upon which to erect a body of knowledge.

Organizational exigencies and growing demands for therapeutic recreation services, however, exerted pressure for greater conceptual clarity and a stronger sense of occupational function and identity. Among leaders recognizing the need to define therapeutic recreation's scope of service, NTRS President Gary Robb (1977-78) used the Presidential Commission on Assessment of Critical Issues to begin developing a definition and philosophical statement. Soon afterward, Lee Meyer (1980), chair of the Philosophical Statement Task Force, made a major contribution with his ground-breaking research on the philosophical bases of therapeutic recreation service (as distinguished from therapeutic recreation theory). Adapting the results of Meyer's study, the Philosophical Issues Task Force polled the NTRS membership on which of four positions it preferred to represent its field of service. Position A held that the purpose of therapeutic recreation was to provide opportunities for persons with special needs to experience recreation. Position B viewed recreation services as treatment for enhancing the total functioning of the individual. Position D included Positions A (recreation) and B (treatment). Finally, Position C, which was not among the final alternatives identified in Meyer's study consisted of a continuum of services, including treatment, education, and recreation. It was subsequently favored by the majority of members who responded to the survey and was accepted in May 1982 as the NTRS Philosophical Position Statement.

Concerns were soon expressed, however, about the need for further interpretation of the NTRS Philosophical Position Statement. O'Morrow (1986) stated, "It was recommended that deliberations and research projects be encouraged to continue to probe the validity of the position" (p. 20). Moreover, Humphrey and Reynolds (1981) observed that the "continuum alternative,"[2] which provides the framework for the NTRS Philosophical Position Statement, is not a discrete philosophy, but rather "an operational concept within which any philosophical position may be placed" (p. 4). Implying that the continuum alternative lacked explicit theoretical underpinnings, they urged therapeutic recreation to build a professional philosophy using constructs legitimized through philosophical method.

Nevertheless, discerning analysis of the NTRS Philosophical Position Statement has not occurred. Its key terms—*play, leisure, recreation, education, treatment,* and *appropriate leisure lifestyle*— have been examined descriptively rather than discursively. Values inquiry, an intellectual operation, has also been neglected despite the presence of such value-saturated terms as *appropriate leisure lifestyle, leisure ability,* and *quality of life.* It also leaves unexplained significant political claims, such as the "right to, and a need for, leisure involvement as a necessary aspect of the human experience." (NTRS, 1982). The conceptual strength of the NTRS Philosophical Statement to foster theoretical development, therefore, has been negligible.

Formed during a period when organizational stability was crucial, the NTRS Philosophical Position Statement has served an important developmental function. By defining occupational roles and relationships, it has provided direction for such activities as ethics, research, standards, education, and credentialing, none of which can be pursued logically and credibly without at least the appearance of theory to guide them. After all, a profession claims to know better than others what its aims and operations should be. Accordingly, a basis was needed to provide professional identity and to determine which course of action to follow in favor of other reasonable alternatives. Insofar as the NTRS Philosophical Position Statement served as a compass showing "here is therapeutic recreation," it gave guidance to practice and impetus to professionalization.

Yet the process of legitimizing foundational ideas and theoretical knowledge is not achieved by the democratic method of majority opinion—in short, by a head count. It is accomplished using the intellectual methods of philosophy and science conjointly, which prior to the nineteenth century were not treated as separate departments of inquiry (see Sylvester, 1987, pp. 182-185). Although the NTRS Philosophical Position Statement defined the scope and arrangement of services, it did not ordain therapeutic recreation a profession. Its historical significance, therefore, has been political rather than intellectual. Although instrumental in the evolution of therapeutic recreation, the NTRS Philosophical Position Statement is not a body of theoretical knowledge, nor has it generated the philosophical grounds upon which to erect one. Anticipating the ramifications of confusing an occupational blueprint for theoretical knowledge, Meyer (1980), in his study on the professionalization of therapeutic recreation, cautioned that

> the various views of therapeutic recreation and NTRS ... do not have any particular implications for the achievement of this attribute of professionalism—a body of systematic applied knowledge. Rather this attribute is the basis upon which the occupation claims its professionhood. (p. 46).

In other words, the comfort and security of having a set of occupational beliefs is not evidence of validity. Regardless of the position selected, the lengthy and difficult process of developing a legitimate theoretical basis for practice awaits therapeutic recreation. Yet, with few exceptions (e.g., Dattilo & Barnett, 1985; Mobily, 1985a, 1985b; Witt & Ellis, 1986), therapeutic recreation has not attended to its intellectual chores, preoccupying itself instead with immediate concerns of practice.

An instructive example of the issue of immediacy versus theory development (Beck, 1963) is available in the history of guidance counseling. Wrenn (1959) observed that early guidance counseling, busy with the social and organizational demands of a developing profession, understandably had little opportunity for systematic philosophical writings. The immediate requirements of practice preceded and delayed attempts to formulate and legitimize theory and its philosophical presuppositions. Peterson (1976) concurred that guidance counseling developed without the benefit of a sound philosophy, forcing practitioners to rely on inadequate models borrowed from other disciplines (cf. Lahey, 1987). The situation was exacerbated by the dearth of practitioners with adequate background in philosophical method. Consequently, the field was not prepared to mold an intellectual foundation capable of supporting a body of knowledge.

Wrenn compared this predicament to a new city that tries to keep pace with growing requests for services without an adequate infrastructure. Lacking a substantial foundation, a poorly planned city simply cannot bear the weight of public demand. Before long it deteriorates, and it eventually collapses. Similarly, soon after the shock of rapid organizational growth, a field pays for conceptual neglect. Edifices unfortified by legitimate philosophical constructs and valid theoretical knowledge decay and crumble under the pressure of critical analysis and external evaluation (cf. Witmann & Shank, 1987, p. 41.) Aware of this predicament, guidance counseling has steadily improved its intellectual dimension over the past 40 years.

Therapeutic recreation has also been justifiably occupied providing services and attending to organizational business. Consequently, as was once the case with guidance counseling, its theoretical development has suffered. Of course, professions exist to serve people, not ideas. But professional services are ideas in action! Without the benefit of dynamic theory, practice gradually retreats into self-serving habit and convention, the stuff of medieval guilds, not professions. If professionalism is to become a reality, then philosophical, historical, and scientific study–concertedly aimed at answering questions about therapeutic recreation–is imperative.

Unfortunately, the intellectual history of therapeutic recreation has been marked by *reconciliation* rather than *resolution*. To reconcile implies settling differences. It is an adaptive process directed at harmony. Conversely, to resolve suggests finding a valid answer. Its process is analytic and its purpose is truth. Guided by the chief criterion of validity rather than harmony or expediency, a body of knowledge requires resolution using methods of rational inquiry. Both processes are important.

However, reconciliation has militated against resolution during critical periods of therapeutic recreation's history. For instance, Meyer

(1976) posited that the term *therapeutic recreation* may have resulted from attempts to settle differences between early proponents of the term *hospital recreation*, who supported recreation as an end, and advocates of *recreation therapy*, who promoted recreation as treatment. Consequently, needed intellectual inquiry may have been further impeded by the appearance of philosophical unity. Similarly, the selection of Position C as the official philosophy of the NTRS reconciled terminology by inclusively defining the range of therapeutic recreation services. But it did not resolve vital conceptual questions that should be answered prior to justifying a body of knowledge (see Mobily, 1985b, p. 15).

Compromises of this sort may appear prudent at first. In fact, they can be prudent for immediate purposes, such as stabilizing a fledgling organization like the NTRS at a precarious point in its history. But Beck (1963) warned that apparent agreement achieved in terminology—or, as in the case of therapeutic recreation, the selection of a service model—may result in mere verbal agreement, "glossing over . . . seriously incompatible, bedrock differences" (p. 6). Beck's insight is supported by the presence of two professional organizations (National Therapeutic Recreation Society and American Therapeutic Association) and major philosophical differences dating back over three decades which were not resolved by either the formation of the NTRS or the acceptance of the NTRS Philosophical Position Statement.

If serious about professionalism, therapeutic recreation would seem eager to establish a substantial intellectual movement. There are indications, however, of actual disdain for ideas.[3] Curricular research by Stumbo (1986) reveals an alarming disregard for theory and philosophy of practice. Respondents ranked "theories and philosophies of therapeutic recreation" and "theories and philosophies of play, leisure, and recreation" 15th and 27th in importance out of 37 entry-level knowledge content areas. These results are tantamount to doctors ignoring precepts of health, educators disregarding principles of learning, and judges neglecting tenets of justice.

Furthermore, the first edition of *Therapeutic Recreation Program Design* (Gunn & Peterson, 1978) contains the following statement:

> We can no longer afford to spend valuable classroom time attempting to defend our existence by debating such issues as (1) "Is all recreation therapeutic?" (And, if so, all recreation specialists are therapeutic recreators.) Or (2) "Can recreation prescribed in therapy really be recreation?" (And, if not, how can we call ourselves recreators?)

"Although these types of inquiry can provide hours of mental amusement, their resolution in no way affects the important work that has been, is being, and needs to be done in our field" (emphasis added) (p. 11)[4]

Yet, these are precisely the sort of questions that every profession must necessarily raise, interpret, and resolve in order to construct and enhance its body of knowledge. Theory and practice are not frozen in time and place, conveniently ready to heat and serve at any time. They occur in social contexts, systemically influenced by economic, cultural, political, and intellectual factors. Freudian psychology, for example, was at first dismissed by many authorities, later embraced in mind and habit on two continents, and today continues dynamically to affect thought and behavior, at the same time being transformed by modern interpretation.

Democratic ideals of natural rights and egalitarianism combined favorably with the civil rights movement to benefit the civil rights of disabled persons, which broadened the conception and practice of therapeutic recreation. More recently, resurgence of the term *recreation therapy* in the field's vocabulary reflects the trend toward a narrower interpretation of recreation and intervention, one that is especially amenable to clinical practice and the politics of health care. Finally, reflecting on the power of machines to prolong life, Callahan (1987) argues that the medical-care system should reconsider its monolithic goal of inexorably extending biological life for the elderly, instead exploring alternative interventions that improve the quality of a limited life span. Such rethinking of health care and the quality of life would have significant theoretical and practical implications for therapeutic recreation.

In short, therapeutic recreation, as one element of a greater social whole, can no more stop "thinking" about such critical ideas as health, leisure, recreation, treatment, and quality of life than responsible citizens can cease reflecting on their beliefs, values, and actions in relation to the larger society. Moreover, not only does the sociology of knowledge apply to therapeutic recreation, but thinking ossifies without critical analysis, impeding the refinements and innovations needed to build and fuel a body of knowledge. Greenwood (1966) argues that the spirit of critical thinking is a uniquely essential aspect of professions, producing "an intellectually stimulating milieu that is in marked contrast to the milieu of a nonprofessional occupation" (p. 12). All conceptual foundations must be examined, therefore, no matter how suitable they may appear at the moment (Hampshire, 1982). Far from a waste of time, scrutinizing theory and practice strengthens professionalism through the acquisition of knowledge and protects against the dogmatism brought on by custom and intellectual antipathy and neglect.

Toward an Intellectual Awakening

A more probingly comprehensive study would be necessary before I could reach any firm conclusions about the intellectual state of therapeutic recreation and its influence on professionalization. But if my impressions are plausible, it is doubtful whether therapeutic recreation presently qualifies as even a nascent profession. Of course, this assertion may be truly bitter food for thought. Being fervent believers in therapeutic recreation, we wish to celebrate heartily its professional coming of age. Our minds, though, should not submit to zealotry, for to embrace what may not be true for the insidious sake of appearances and self-interest only exacerbates matters and delays professionalization. It takes time and knowledge to become a profession. Therapeutic recreation is struggling with the same developmental tasks and growing pains experienced historically by education, social work, and guidance counseling. An aspiring profession, therefore, must inexorably pursue knowledge, which will be periodically disconcerting, discouraging, and even divisive, but over time will prove enlightening, leading to genuine professional growth.

Moreover, as bleak a scene as I may have sketched, the quest for professionalism is not at all hopeless. There are, in fact, promising signs of an intellectual awakening in therapeutic recreation, including several critically provocative and conceptually substantive discussions (e.g., Hemingway, 1986, 1987; Lahey, 1987; Mobily, 1985a, 1985b, 1985c; Mobily, Hunnicutt, & Weissinger, 1987). Reynolds and O'Morrow's 1985 text on professional issues is also an intellectual advance, as are the comments about philosophical thinking made in an introductory text by Carter, Van Andel, and Robb (1985, p. 57-59). Wittman and Shank's 1987 study of state leaders' perceptions of professionalization offers further hope that the field is beginning to recognize the importance of a strong intellectual dimension. In particular, state leaders considered the development of a central mission—an intellectual task entailing the discovery of fundamental beliefs and values—to be paramount among 14 characteristics of professionalization. Mastery of theoretical knowledge and use of practical knowledge were also highly regarded. Joined by central mission and formal training, they were perceived as the highest priorities for professionalization. Yet despite these apparently encouraging results, Wittman and Shank's caution that therapeutic recreation must "become more effective at describing what is done, how it is done, and why it matters" (p. 40) should remind us of the difficult challenge at hand, which can only be met through a substantial intellectual awakening.

Still, if these events are indicative of an inchoate intellectual movement, I am cautiously optimistic about professionalism. But to cultivate its small intellectual plot toward that large end, therapeutic recreation requires a dramatic change, returning us a final time to the meaning of a profession.

The Enlightened Professional

The quintessence of a profession is formed by two core qualities. First, the seed of professional life is the altruistic calling to serve an area of public concern. Fain (1985) observed, and I agree, that therapeutic recreation has passed this test of authenticity exceptionally well, historically placing public service above self-aggrandizement. While at times ignored, misunderstood, and inadequately supported, therapeutic recreation has steadfastly answered its calling.

Answering the call of public service, however, is not enough. Volunteers regularly respond unselfishly to the needs of others without necessarily qualifying as professionals. The second core attribute of a genuine profession, then, is understanding what is called for, using practices and techniques derived from theoretical knowledge to meet a definite public need, such as health, justice, education, or recreation. The calling to perform good works is joined by a body of working knowledge, which together serve the end of excellent services for the good of others. Inseparable, they are the discriminating measure of a profession, one which not every occupation can achieve. Accordingly, in addition to its present devotion to the public good, therapeutic recreation must develop a valid theoretical basis for intelligent action. This will require an intellectual awakening led by enlightened professionals.

Professionalism, and becoming an enlightened professional, is not an issue of skill per se. It principally involves the ability of practitioners to comprehend the implications of and be responsible for the consequences of their actions. Professions affect the course of people's lives, presumably for the better but sometimes, unfortunately, for the worse. As such, they are moral enterprises that demand reasoned judgment reached through ethical, historical, and scientific knowledge of the relationship between theory, purposes, practice, technology, and human well-being. Consequently, a foundation for understanding the moral, social, cultural, economic, and political dimensions of service is necessary for a profession to execute its calling with expertise and wisdom.

Yet the technocratic and positivistic character of therapeutic recreation—and its disinclination for philosophical and historical meaning—restricts its social perspective. Limited knowledge and outlook in turn reduce therapeutic recreation's capacity to discover, understand, and articulate social contributions and public policy. For example, when was the last time a wave of social concern swelled over leisure education; or when has a national study alerted an alarmed public to the impoverished condition of recreation for many people, disabled and nondisabled? How often do journalists and social critics comment on the broader issue of recreation and leisure in modern society?

In short, therapeutic recreation and leisure services are rapidly becoming social nonissues, which was not always the case. Leisure and recreation were once national concerns discussed by prominent thinkers (see Cardinal Principles of Secondary Education, 1918; Cutten, 1926; Kraus, 1986; Lee, 1911a; Lindeman, 1939; Scott, 1913). But excessive focus on the internal affairs of practice and the paucity of intellectual activity capable of interpreting pertinent moral and sociopolitical roles have impaired professionalization. As a result, both fields have been seen clinging to medical and entrepreneurial bandwagons to carry them through the gates of "professiondom."

The only antidote for this ignorance, and the main source of professional enlightenment, is education. E.L. Boyer (1987), president of the Carnegie Foundation for the Advancement of Teaching, concurs that the modern crisis is not rooted in the lack of technical competence but instead stems from a vacuous social and historical perspective (see Ortega, 1932; Rowthorn, 1978, pp. 319-320). Boyer specifically recommends designing and implementing "enriched majors" which allow undergraduates to place their specialized fields in social perspective. Grounded in general education, enriched majors will:

respond to three essential questions: What is the history and tradition of the field to be examined? What are the social and economic implications to be understood? What are the ethical and moral issues to be confronted? (p. 110)

Specialized education must hence "be conceived in a liberal spirit as a real intellectual enlightenment in regard to principles applied and services rendered" (Whitehead, 1929, p. 55). Undergraduate curriculum should be squarely set in liberal education, therefore, with concomitant opportunities for specialization. The moment specialization becomes the cardinal principle of curriculum development, however, undergraduate programs of therapeutic recreation should be ousted from colleges and universities and placed in trade schools. Students doubtlessly need to learn performance skills related to their calling. But what they above all require is liberally imbued learning, enlightening them along intellectual and humanistic paths to handle the career-long and socially complex demands of a calling.

Whether an intellectual awakening led by enlightened professionals will be sufficient to meet the rigors of professionalization remains to be seen. The road is arduous, and few occupations actually make it. Yet if therapeutic recreation does arrive, it will exemplify the alliance of altruism and wisdom, standing above the crowd of aspirants and pretenders as an exemplar among the handful of genuine professions. I hope, then, that we choose the more difficult route, for in this case, the hard road is also the high road.

Notes

[1] The means/end debate concerns whether the value of recreation is principally intrinsic (good for its own sake), extrinsic (good as a means to achieve other purposes), or both intrinsic and extrinsic. Much of the confusion stems from carelessly lumping together the ideas of play, leisure, and recreation without regard for their conceptual differences and from failing to consider or from misinterpreting pertinent philosophical literature. Play, leisure, and recreation have been treated by moral philosophers, yet their illuminating discussions are virtually ignored in the therapeutic recreation literature (see Sylvester, 1987).

[2] See Peterson and Gunn (1984), pages 1-52, for a thorough explanation of the continuum alternative.

[3] Disdain for ideas is not peculiar to therapeutic recreation. Hofstadter (1963) examines the persistent theme of anti-intellectualism in American history in his acclaimed book *Anti-Intellectualism in American Life*.

[4] This statement was removed for the second edition of *Therapeutic Recreation Programming* (Peterson & Gunn, 1984).

Study Questions

1. Does your program of study mostly focus on how to perform specialized skills, or is there greater emphasis on theory and critical thinking? Is there a blend between theory, practice, and technique? In what ways do you consider your program of study to be "enlightened"? Do you believe you have the advantage of an "enriched major," enabling you to better understand the moral social, cultural, political, and economic implications of therapeutic recreation?

2. The following quotes are from Joseph Wood Krutch (1959) and Dugald Arbuckle (1960), respectively. Discuss them in relation to this chapter and to the issue of anti-intellectualism.

    > Know-how is a dubious endowment unless it is accompanied by other "knows" —by "know what," "know why," and—most important of all at the present– "know whether!" (p. 210).

    > We train technicians who ask the more empirical question "how," but only the educated man can ask the more philosophic question "why." If counseling is concerned with human dignity, and freedom, and integrity, then surely the "why" of our counseling takes precedence over the "how." We need more counselors, possibly, who know how to do things, but we need in vastly greater numbers those who know why they do what they do. (p. 14)

3. The thesis of this chapter is that therapeutic recreation is not presently a profession due to its mostly barren intellectual history. Accordingly, consider the following activities:

    a.   Research the intellectual history of therapeutic recreation and write a paper refuting the thesis of this chapter.

    b.   Conduct a class debate. For: Therapeutic recreation is a profession. Against:Therapeutic recreation is not a profession. Of course, both sides should be very intellectual.

    c.   Lurking between the lines of this chapter is the audacious, if not outrageous, assertion that the field must become "smarter"—wiser, if you will—if it hopes to become a profession. Write a three- page paper discussing ways in which you can become more "enlightened" and how you can contribute to an intellectual awakening in therapeutic recreation.

4.   Some readers may be wondering, "What's the fuss?" when it comes to the meaning of a profession. Who cares what therapeutic recreation is called as long as its practitioners perform their job? Indeed, what difference does it make to examine the meaning of such ideas as health, profession, leisure, and freedom? After all, they're just words. It's not as if they're real. Or are they?

References

Addams, J. (1923). *Twenty Years at Hull House*. E.W. Case (Ed.). New York: Macmillan.

Alger, G.W. (1925). Leisure—For What? *Atlantic Monthly, 135,* 483-492.

Arbuckle, D. (1960, September). Counseling: Philosophy or science? *Personnel and Guidance Journal,* 11-14.

Aristotle. (1946). *Politics*. (E. Barker, Trans.) London: Oxford University Press.

Avedon, E.M. (1974). *Therapeutic Recreation Service: An Applied Behavioral Approach*. Englewood Cliffs, NJ: Prentice-Hall.

Ball, E.L. (1970). The Meaning of Therapeutic Recreation. *Therapeutic Recreation Journal, 7*(1), 17-18.

Beck, C.E. (1963). *Philosophical Foundations of Guidance.* Englewood Cliffs, NJ: Prentice-Hall.

Boyer, E.L. (1987). *College: The Undergraduate Experience in America.* New York: Harper and Row.

Cabot, R. C. (1911). The Soul of Play. *Playground, 4,* 285-292.

Callahan, D. (1987). *Setting Limits: Medical Goals in an Aging Society.* New York: Simon and Schuster.

Cardinal Principles of Secondary Education: Report of the Commission on the Reorganization of Secondary Education of the National Education Association. (1918). *Bureau of Education Bulletin No. 35.* Washington, DC: Department of the Interior.

Carter, M.J., Van Andel, G.E., & Robb, G.M. (9185). *Therapeutic Recreation: A Practical Approach.* St. Louis: Times Mirror/ Mosby.

Charlton, K. (1973). The Education of the Professions in the Sixteenth Century. In T.G. Cook (Ed.), *Education and the Professions (pp. 19-27).* London: Methuen.

Cogan, M.L. (1953). Toward a Definition of a Profession. *Harvard Educational Review, 23,* 33-50.

Cutten, G.B. (1926). *The Threat of Leisure.* New Haven, CT: Yale University Press.

Dattilo, J., & Barnett, L.A. (1985). Therapeutic Recreation For Individuals with Severe Handicaps: An Analysis of the Relationship Between Choice and Pleasure. *Therapeutic Recreation Journal, 19*(3), 79-91.

Etziono, A. (Ed.). (1969). *The Semi-Professions and Their Organization.* New York: The Free Press.

Fain, G.S. (1985). Guest Editorial: Special Issue on Ethics. *Therapeutic Recreation Journal, 19*(4), 6-7.

Flexner, A. (1915). Is Social Work a Profession? *School and Society, 1*(26), 901-911.

Frye, V., & Peters, M. (1972). *Therapeutic Recreation: Its Theory, Philosophy and Practice.* Harrisburg, PA: Stackpole Books.

Goode, W.J. (1960). Encroachment, Charlatanism, and the Emerging Professions: Psychology, Sociology, and Medicine. *American Sociological Review, 25,* 902-914.

Gootzeit, J.M. (1967). Therapeutic Recreation vs. Rrecreation for the Handicapped. *Therapeutic Recreation Journal, 1*(2), 6-9, 30-31.

Greenwood, E. (1966). Attributes of a profession. In H.M. Vollmer & D.L. Mills (Eds.), *Professionalization* (pp. 10-19). Englewood Cliffs, NJ: Prentice Hall.

Gunn, S.L., & Peterson, C.A. (1978). *Therapeutic Recreation Program Design: Principles and Procedures.* Englewood Cliffs, NJ: Prentice-Hall.

Hampshire, S. (1982). *Thought and Action.* South Bend, IN: University of Notre Dame Press.

Haun, P. (1965). *Recreation: A Medical Viewpoint* (E.M. Avedon & F.B. Arje, Eds.). New York: Teachers College Press.

Hemingway, J.L. (1986). The Therapeutic in Recreation. *Therapeutic Recreation Journal, 20*(2), 59-68.

Hemingway J.L. (1987). Building a Philosophical Defense of Therapeutic Recreation: The Case of Distributive Justice. In C. Sylvester, J. Hemingway, R. Howe-Murphy, K. Mobily, and P Shank. (Eds.). *Philosophy of Therapeutic Recreation: Ideas and Issues* (pp. 1-16). Alexandria, VA: National Recreation and Park Association.

Hofstadter, R. (1963). *Anti-intellectualism in American life.* New York: Vintage Books.

Hospital Recreation Section, American Recreation Society. (1953). *Basic Concepts of Hospital Recreation.* Washington, DC: American Recreation Society.

Hospital Recreation Section, American Recreation Society. (n.d.) *Report of the Committee on Basic Concepts, 1960-1961, 1961-1962.* Washington,DC: American Recreation Society.

Hughes, E.C. (1963). Professions. *Daedalus,92*, 655-668.

Humphrey, F., & Reynolds, R. (1981). The Editors' Viewpoint. *Therapeutic Recreation Journal, 15*(2), 4-6.

Hunnicutt, B.K. (no date). *A Brief History of Therapeutic Recreation: Its Concepts and Organization.* Unpublished manuscript, University of North Carolina, Chapel Hill.

Kraus, R. (1986). Recreation and Leisure in a Post-industrial Society: Transformation in Values. In *Proceedings of the 1986 Symposium on Leisure Research* (pp. 67-69). Alexandria, VA: National Recreation and Park Association.

Krutch, J.W. (1959). *Human Nature and the Human Condition.* New York: Random House.

Lahey, M.D. (1987, September). *Foundation Questions in Therapeutic Recreation.* Paper presented at the Leisure Research Symposium, New Orleans, LA.

Lee, J. (1911a). Play As An Antidote to Civilization. *Playground, 5,* 110-126.

Lee, J. (1911b). Play as Medicine. *Playground, 5,* 289-302.

Lee, J. (1915). *Play in Education.* New York: MacMillan.

Lindeman, E.C. (1939). *Leisure: A National Issue.* New York: American Association for the Study of Group Work.

Meyer, L.E. (1976). A View of Therapeutic Recreation: Its Foundations, Objectives and Challenges. In G.C. Zaso (Ed.), *Therapeutic Recreation Dialogues in Development: Concepts and Action* (pp. 13-27). Durham, NH: University of New Hampshire School of Health Studies, Recreation and Parks Program.

Meyer, L.E. (1980, May). *Philosophical Alternatives an the Professionalization of Therapeutic Recreation.* Paper submitted as part of the Philosophical Statement Task Force to the National Therapeutic Recreation Society.

Meyer, M.W. (1962). The rationale of recreation as therapy. *Recreation in Treatment Centers, 1* (September), 23-24.

Millerson, G. (1964). *The Qualifying Associations: A Study of Professionalization.* London: Routledge and Kegan.

Mobily, K. (1985a). A Philosophical Analysis of Therapeutic Recreation: What Does it Mean to Say "We Can be Therapeutic?" Part I. *Therapeutic Recreation Journal, 19*(1), 14-26.

Mobily, K. (1985b). A Philosophical Analysis of Therapeutic Recreation: What Does it Mean to Say "We Can be Therapeutic"? Part II. *Therapeutic Recreation Journal, 19*(2), 7-14.

Mobily, K. (1985c). The Ethical Dilemma of Freedom in Therapeutic Recreation. *Therapeutic Recreation Journal, 19*(4), 22-30.

Mobily, K., Hunnicutt, B.K., & Weissinger, E. (1987). The Means/End Controversy: A Framework for Understanding the Value Potential of TR. *Therapeutic Recreation Journal, 21*(3), 7-13.

National Therapeutic Recreation Society. (1982). *Philosophical Position Statement of the National Therapeutic Recreation Society.* Alexandria, VA: National Recreation and Park Association.

Ortega, J. (1932). *The Revolt of the Masses.* New York: W.W. Norton.

Patrick, G.T.W. (1916). *The Psychology of Relaxation.* Boston: Houghton-Mifflin.

Plato. (1953). The Republic. In *The Dialogues of Plato, Vol. II* (B. Jowett, Trans.). Oxford, England: Oxford University Press.

Peterson,C.A. (1981). Pride and Progress in Professionalism. In G.L. Hitzhusen (Ed.) *Expanding Horizons in Therapeutic Recreation VIII,* (pp. 1-9). Columbus, MO: Curators, University of Missouri.

Peterson,J.A. (1976). *Counseling and Values.* Cranston, RI: Carroll Press.

Peterson, C.A., & Gunn, S.L. (1984) *Therapeutic Recreation Program Design: Principles and Procedures* (2nd ed.). Englewood Cliffs, NJ: Prentice-Hall.

O'Morrow, G.S. (1986). *Twenty-year History of the National Therapeutic Recreation Society.* Alexandria, VA: National Recreation and Park Association .

Reynolds, R.P., & O'Morrow, G.S. (1985). *Problems, Issues and Concepts in Therapeutic Recreation.* Englewood Cliffs, NJ: Prentice-Hall.

Robb, G. (1975). Therapeutic Recreation: Stagnation in a Time of Change. *Therapeutic Recreation Journal, 9*(2), 47-53.

Rowthorn, A.W. (1978). *A History of the Evolution and Development of Therapeutic Recreation Services for Special Populations in the United States from 1918 to 1977.* Unpublished doctoral dissertation, New York University, New York City.

Rusk, H. (1960, April). Therapeutic Recreation. *Hospital Management,* 35-36.

Sabine, G.H. (1961). *A History of Political Theory* (3rd ed.). New York: Holt, Rhinehart, and Winston.

Scott, T. (1913). *The Use of Leisure.* New York: B.W. Huebsch.

Shivers, J.S. (1971). One Concept of Therapeutic Recreational Service. *Therapeutic Recreation Journal, 5*(2), 51-53, 93.

Southern Regional Institute. (1969). *Therapeutic Recreation Position Paper.* University of North Carolina, Chapel Hill.

Stumbo, N.J. (1986). A Definition of Entry-Level Knowledge for Therapeutic Recreation Practice. *Therapeutic Recreation Journal, 20*(4), 15-30.

Sylvester, C.D. (1987). The Ethics of Play, Leisure, and Recreation in the Twentieth Century, 1900-1983. *Leisure Sciences, 9,* 173-188.

Turner, C., & Hodge, M.N. (1970). Occupations and Professions. In J.A. Jackson (Ed.), *Professions and Professionalization* (pp. 19-50). New York: Cambridge University Press.

Vollmer, H.M., & Mills, D.L. (1966). *Professionalization.* Englewood Cliffs, NJ: Prentice-Hall.

Whitehead, A.N. (1929). *The Aims of Education.* New York: Macmillan.

Witman, J.P., & Shank, J.W. (1987). Professionalization in Therapeutic Recreation; State Leaders' Perceptions of Progress, Priorities and Strategies. *Therapeutic Recreation Journal, 21*(4), 32-42.

Witt, P.A. (1977). Therapeutic Recreation: The Outmoded Label. *Therapeutic Recreation Journal, 11*(2), 39-41.

Witt, P.A., & Ellis, G.D. (1986). The leisure diagnostic battery: Past, present, and future. *Therapeutic Recreation Journal, 20*(4), 31-47.

Wrenn, C.G. (1959). Philosophical and psychological bases of personnel services in education. In Nelson B. Henry (Ed.), *Personnel Services in Education Yearbook of the National Society for the Study of Education, Part II* (pp. 41-81). Chicago: University of Chicago Press.

THE DILEMMA OF PHILOSOPHY

Carol Ann Peterson

Introduction

When the topic of philosophy in therapeutic recreation is brought up, it seems to result in heated discussion, debate, and disagreement. It is one issue on which there appears to be little agreement or consensus, but always a great deal of interest and opinion. The title of this chapter may say it all, for most certainly there is a dilemma surrounding the issue of philosophy. Whether we are discussing the need for philosophy, the content of philosophy, or even the nature of philosophy, we have a dilemma.

A dilemma is defined as a problem that appears incapable of a solution or as a situation involving choice between equally unsatisfactory solutions. It does appear that we are locked into a dilemma regarding philosophy. The years of discussion over this issue have resulted in little consensus and at times fierce disagreement. But why is the issue so significant? What contributes to its centrality in the profession? What are the factors that must be addressed and resolved relative to the philosophical issue? This chapter attempts to bring into focus the multitude of complex factors that surround the philosophical issue and make it such a volatile and high-priority topic.

The Need for Philosophy in Therapeutic Recreation

Professions exist to the extent that they are recognized and acknowledged for making some significant contribution to the needs of people. The contribution must be identified and sanctioned by the society at large. Sanctioning refers to a recognized authority's confirming the activities and actions of that profession. Further, the profession must receive the support of associated professions; in our case, this includes the multitude of other human and health professional fields. And last, but not least, the clients who are the recipients of the professional service must perceive the service as valuable, credible, and worthy of trust. Satisfying this large and diverse audience is no small task, especially for an area of service which has somewhat recently entered the professional arena and struggles for acceptance (as do all new professions). To the difficulties of being an emerging profession in the already competitive professional market, add a specialized focus on any aspect of leisure, and we find a major challenge on our hands.

Although it is true that leisure is far more acknowledged as an important aspect of the human condition than it once was, its acceptance as an essential human behavior and thus deserving of professional attention is still not widespread. Nor has the use of activity as a therapeutic intervention been unconditionally endorsed by the medical establishment. Thus, the fact that our profession deals with a marginally accepted area of human need is an issue.

However, this issue is not nearly as large a barrier as is our own internal (and at times appearing eternal) dilemma over philosophy. The inability or unwillingness of the profession to take a stand on philosophical content issues appears to be a major stumbling block in the recognition, acceptance, and marketing of the field as a legitimate profession. The profession needs to resolve its own long-standing debate on philosophy. Until this resolution occurs, it is highly unlikely that full professional acceptance can, will, or should be awarded. A united front, a commonly accepted and supported philosophical approach, is imperative.

While it is useful to examine, explore, and expand our own understanding of therapeutic recreation, this type of analytical endeavor does nothing for the outside world, which has little understanding of our field in general and even less patience for our own internal debates and discussion. Note carefully that these few sentences are not suggesting an absolute definition or acceptance of a philosophy or narrowly described set of procedures. Rather, what is called for is the acceptance of a basic conceptual approach. Stated quite simply, we need to decide whether our basic contribution to society is in the domain of leisure or in the domain of therapy. This seems to be an old, familiar area of controversy.

Why is it important to select an approach and to unify behind that approach? The reasons are many, and each brings to focus a facet of the complexity of the issue. First, the absence of a single definition has resulted in widespread confusion of the role, nature, and contribution of therapeutic recreation. When all practitioners are free to define therapeutic recreation for themselves and within their settings, there is no opportunity for the field to be understood and acknowledged in any broader, more significant way. It is thus not surprising that the medical, psychiatric, and human service professions have little understanding of, and often less respect for, our profession. For over 40 years, the field has floundered because of loosely defined services. The focus has been on specific programs in local agencies, with no national direction or interpretation. This is not to say that services within a given agency have been weak; it is only to highlight that there has been little opportunity for national identity to emerge. Meanwhile, the longer this situation continues, the harder it is to bring people together in purpose and direction. In the earlier years, this may not have been terribly problematic. Today it creates a tremendous obstacle. As the sophistication of human and health care increases, the problem of identity becomes even more difficult.

Consider the following professional situations. Each time a piece of legislation is introduced that in some way affects the inclusion or the delivery of therapeutic recreation services, we struggle to define therapeutic recreation in that context. Valuable time of professionals is lost, not to mention the confusing image that this must project to other professions, lawmakers, and the assorted bureaucratic agencies and personnel we deal with. Our involvement with accrediting bodies such as the Joint Commission on Accreditation of Health Care Organizations and the Commission on Accreditation of Rehabilitation Facilities is likewise impeded when we attempt to initiate or respond to proposed standards or revisions.

Whether we are trying to define "qualified therapeutic recreation specialist," describing our involvement with treatment teams, or defining the nature or contribution of our services, we struggle for agreement within our own profession. The decisions made are often based on which person is heading what committee at the time that new or revised standards are being circulated. This inconsistency is both appalling and damaging to our credibility and, thus, acceptance. Simply stated, a supported common definition of our field would allow such professional advancement work to proceed in an orderly manner, with the task requiring only the appropriate response related to the issues and context of the legislation or standards instead of our continual hassling over content as well.

In the past several years, the issue of third-party reimbursement has been a major issue and concern. We have had a more than difficult time trying to determine and describe our contribution to the treatment outcomes of clients. Our ability to claim the right to reimbursement is dependent on this knowledge. Unfortunately, much of what we have to offer as "contribution" is opinion, intuitive feelings of the "goodness" of therapeutic recreation, and an occasional clinical observation that has not been adequately documented. None of this serves as evidence, which is what is required by third-party insurance carriers. We simply lack the necessary efficacy research to back our claims of impact on treatment or rehabilitation outcomes. Again, a major part of the problem is the absence of an agreed-upon philosophical approach, which would have enabled directed efficacy research. Thus, the absence of the needed evidence for third-party reimbursement has been dangerously delayed. Stated another way, we cannot demonstrate efficacy of therapeutic recreation services until we are willing to define therapeutic recreation and then systematically conduct the needed research addressing that definition.

Another major concern is that of professional preparation and the content as well as quality of the knowledge of the entry-level professional. The diverse approaches to philosophy taught in the more than 200 schools that claim options in therapeutic recreation only magnifies the problem. Philosophy is the foundation of all other content. Whether the content is assessment, treatment plans, program development, implementation and evaluation, or intervention techniques, the philosophical approach used by the faculty directs the nature of the knowledge and skills presented. In our current situation, there is little similarity in the therapeutic recreation content being taught in our undergraduate or graduate programs. Thus, instead of representing a profession that has a commonly held body of knowledge, we continue to graduate hundreds of new professionals each year who perpetuate the diversity of opinions regarding the role, nature, and techniques of the field. Consequently, two undergraduates from two different schools find that they have little knowledge in common. This appears to negatively affect their confidence in themselves, their professional preparation, and the profession in general. Employers, as well, complain about the preparation level and most often hire based on the personal characteristics of the applicant since there is no stable or similar approach, content, procedures, or techniques on which they can depend.

This lack of a commonly accepted philosophical approach also impairs greatly the development and testing of our knowledge base. Research is an acknowledged major need in our field. We have all too few qualified researchers working on our body of knowledge or advising graduate students in their research projects. Our lack of definition and purpose in TR results in diffused research efforts, which more often than not limits our knowledge base rather than expands upon identified areas of need that would result in a more targeted and thus intensified body of knowledge.

All of the above factors also lead into the professional issue of credentialing. Under our current system (the National Council for Therapeutic Recreation Certification), there is no difficulty with the philosophical issue since certification is granted based on a review of transcripts, which focuses on the number of courses taken in various categories (therapeutic recreation, general recreation, support courses, and a practicum supervised by a certified therapeutic recreation specialist). However, future efforts to move toward a more sophisticated method of credentialing must look at the content or body of knowledge held by the individual. At that point, whether an examination is employed or not, philosophy will become a pivotal point in credentialing. Indeed, it will be impossible to move toward an examination phase if the profession is unwilling to define itself and specify the knowledge and job-related tasks on which to test and thus determine basic competence.

The preceding paragraphs have discussed professional issues that feel the impact of the absence of a commonly held and supported philosophical approach. Equally important, if not more significant, is the issue of service to clients. How do we determine the nature of the services we provide to clients? More fundamentally, what needs of clients do we address? The whole area of determining the direction and content of programs is based on philosophical foundations. Directly tied into this issue is the concern for assessment. What tools do we have? What tools do we need to develop? The content of our assessment tools must parallel our philosophical orientation and program offerings. Simply stated, determining and addressing the needs of clients is a philosophical consideration. For the most part, we have avoided the centrality of this issue of client needs and philosophical concerns in the development and delivery of therapeutic recreation service.

The last issue to be addressed is simply that of advocacy. How do we effectively market our profession, its services, and its contributions when there is so little agreement on who we are and what we do? At the current time our advocacy efforts have been very limited. This seems to be due to the scarce financial base for professional advocacy work through our professional organizations. The fact remains, it would be difficult to develop a national-level advocacy and marketing strategy for the profession without a clear and supported understanding of the nature and contribution of our services.

It becomes apparent that our profession has an identity problem. Philosophical disagreement and indifference contribute to this identity crisis. Although our history may help explain the existence and even the necessity of diverse opinions and approaches, our current situation is not helped by the continued lack of unity and direction.

The Essence of the Dilemma

What is the essence of the philosophical issue? What is at the core of the dilemma? In order to put the dilemma in some context, a review of some of the literature is necessary, as is some discussion of the professional organizations and their support for various philosophical approaches.

From the beginning, it appears, there has been a debate over the basic issue of whether therapeutic recreation is or should be therapy oriented or leisure oriented. Much of our literature both historically and currently addresses this debate. The content has been primarily opinion, with attempts to build cases by using logic, description, and preference. Little theory or theory-based research has been presented in support of one or the other of the approaches. From the early works of such people as Haun (1965), Martin (1962), and Frye and Peters (1972) to the more contemporary works of such people as Sylvester (1985a,b), Mobily, Weissinger, and Hunnicutt (1987), and Hemingway (1987), there has been a continual debate in the literature over the means/end, therapy/recreation issues. This type of literature has kept alive the debate and directed our attention to the issue. It also appears to have kept us from moving on into the serious work of developing theory, theory testing, and evaluating the effects of theory-based applications. We spin our wheels with the continual arguments. Newer and more sophisticated arguments appear, but the central conflict focus remains the same.

More recently we have seen a new area of content and discussion in the therapeutic recreation literature. Several articles have appeared that address topics such as what philosophy is, why our current body of literature on philosophy really isn't philosophy, and what the nature of philosophy and philosophical inquiry is. Halberg and Howe-Murphy (1985), Sylvester (1985a,b), and Shank (1987) are examples of this type of presentation and discussion. These contributions have helped us think about the nature of philosophy and have given us some direction regarding the stages and criteria involved in the construction and definition of philosophy. They have also broadened our perception of what all may be considered within philosophical inquiry. However, they have not as yet resulted in the use of such information in the development of therapeutic recreation philosophy. Thus, the basic question of therapeutic recreation philosophical content remains unsolved.

 As is the case in most professions, we have a segment of our literature that focuses on the analysis and criticism of the current philosophical approaches and contributions. Reynolds and O'Morrow (1985), Sylvester (1985a,b), Halberg and Howe-Murphy (1985), Shank and Kinney (1987), and the introductory sections of many articles on therapeutic recreation employ this approach. This is a necessary and healthy self-examination and -exploration. It may, however, become a self-defeating activity and obsession if new philosophical content, insight, or direction is not an outcome.

Some of our literature is also devoted to presenting, describing, and expanding approaches that are currently in use. The Leisure Ability Model (Peterson & Gunn, 1984) exemplifies this type of literature, as does Howe-Murphy and Charboneau's ecological perspective (1987). These models both propose a leisure philosophical orientation and go on to develop and describe procedures for the implementation of practice based on that philosophical orientation. Other components of our textbook literature appear to skirt the philosophical issue by presenting an overview of theory and philosophy and then going on to describe the profession and its services, procedures, and issues independent of a specific philosophical approach. Kraus (1983), Carter, Van Andel, and Robb (1985), and O'Morrow (1980) are examples of this type of literature.

The literature contains diverse content and approaches to the philosophical issue. That is the nature of publications, vehicles for the expression of thought and opinion. What is more important in this discussion is what the profession chooses to do with the information. The people who call themselves therapeutic recreators are the ones who collectively select a philosophical approach and translate it into professional practice. Most often this is done through professional organizations. Thus, our attention is drawn to the professional organization's actions related to the philosophical issue.

The National Therapeutic Recreation Society in the late 70s identified the significance and importance of the philosophical dilemma by commissioning a task force to study the issue. The comprehensive work of the commission over several years and the major analysis and written contributions of Meyer (1981) resulted in NTRS' endorsing the Leisure Ability approach in 1981. This action, however, did not seem to resolve the philosophical conflict, although it has provided definition and direction for a significant number of practitioners and educators in the field.

Confusing the situation, although initially unrelated to the topic of philosophy, was the emergence of a new national professional organization–the American Therapeutic Recreation Association (ATRA). This new organization reestablished the philosophical issue as a necessary part of its defining itself and establishing its statement of purpose. The selected purpose of ATRA is "to promote independent functioning and to enhance optimal health and well being of individuals with illnesses and/or disabling conditions" (ATRA, 1984). This statement reflects a philosophical orientation in the direction of therapy. The situation now facing the field of therapeutic recreation is even more complicated. The interests of the profession are split between two national-level organizations, and each organization is supporting a different philosophical approach to service. The overall identity issue, as well as the philosophical dilemma of the entire field, becomes more complex because of the professional organization situation.

The dilemma of the profession's philosophical issue continues. Is there a solution or resolution? This writer believes that the resolution will not simply emerge on its own and, further, if left unresolved could lead to the demise of the profession as a viable field of specialization. What is felt to be needed is a decision by the profession to endorse, support, and develop within one of the two basic orientations–therapy or leisure. The leisure orientation implies that the ultimate outcome or guiding set of beliefs is related to leisure behavior, and the orientation draws on the existing body of knowledge related to leisure as its source and foundation. The therapy orientation, on the other hand, indicates change or improvement of functional behaviors as the desired end and draws from the medical, psychiatric, psychological, and human development body of knowledge.

Efficacy Research–Theory and Philosophy

The following framework is presented as a strategy for helping us understand the relationship of philosophy and theory building. Before efficacy research can be meaningfully undertaken, it is important to build a context which helps to focus such research efforts. It appears that currently much of our research is diverse, fragmented, and lacking a perspective of the bigger picture. Thus, many of the findings are very limited in their application and usefulness. The suggested framework facilitates efficacy research by constructing a hierarchy which attempts to take into account the fundamental nature of philosophy and theory. It also indirectly deals with some of the criticism surrounding the philosophical conflict by putting it into the context of the larger issues.

The first concern is the attempt to differentiate between philosophy and theory building. This writer sees philosophy as a more general framework, and theory building as sequential to philosophy and more specific in content. Thus, it makes sense to first establish a philosophy or, stated more accurately, a philosophical approach, which then would be followed by the development of specific theories within that approach. These theories would be directed to aspects of the overall philosophical foundation and be developed and tested as they were related to specific populations, components, interventions, and procedures. The body of knowledge is thus systematically built by focusing on manageable but necessary parts.

Theory building and testing appears most appropriately and feasibly done in such stepwise and part-specific stages. Mobily (1985a) would appear to support this approach when he states, "Because a sound philosophy should not only guide practice, but also give direction to research, we should develop a reasonable philosophical framework before proceeding with empirical research" (p. 15). Hemingway (1987) concurs by stating, "Justification thus becomes a process of analyzing the values guiding practice, articulating them so they can be discussed and understood, and then seeking empirical verification not of the values themselves, but of the techniques to realize them in practice" (p. 3).

The point to be made is that specific theory testing follows the acceptance of a generalized philosophical approach. The nature of the theory testing we need for efficacy or impact research is possible only once we select an overall philosophical framework and then work within it. The philosophical framework itself is neither right or wrong, nor can one be proven right. It can only be chosen and then specific theory can be developed and tested within it.

Let's illustrate this concept of generalized philosophy and specific theory building. For the sake of discussion and familiarity, I'll use Leisure Ability as an example. Of the two alternative orientations, leisure and therapy, we select the leisure-based orientation. This basic leisure orientation is then conceptually developed into a model and an approach appropriate for practice. Leisure Ability (Peterson & Gunn, 1984) is an example of this conceptual refinement of a leisure-oriented philosophy appropriate for therapeutic recreation. It states that the purpose of therapeutic recreation is "to facilitate the development, maintenance, and expression of an appropriate leisure lifestyle" (p. 3). The approach then goes on to describe a model that gives specification to the types of components that are seen as useful in determining needs of clients (improved functional behaviors, leisure awareness, knowledge, attitudes and skills, and opportunities for self-directed leisure participation and expression) and categories of services to address these needs (therapy, leisure education, and recreation participation). Thus, there is a conceptual design and description related to a generalized leisure orientation. We'll call this the "philosophical approach."

With the leisure orientation and the philosophical framework selected, we can move into specific theory building and testing. It is only when we move to this level that we can demonstrate or determine the specific information related to what works in practice or what the impact or efficacy of service is. Three research studies illustrate this valuable model of theory building within a philosophical and conceptual scheme: Sneegas (1986) investigated social competence related to leisure and life satisfaction with elderly individuals; Dattilo and Barnett (1985) explored the issue of choice in leisure with severely retarded children; and Hedrick (1985) tested a specific instructional intervention with physically disabled teenagers to determine the most appropriate context for integration. Each of these studies focuses on a specific population and some component of the Leisure Ability Model, thus systematically building the body of knowledge within a given philosophical orientation and conceptual approach.

Obviously, this overall approach–accept a generalized orientation and build a theory related to a segment of the approach–can and should be used within other orientations. Mobily's (1985 a, 1985b) work, related to the therapeutic dimensions of therapeutic recreation using existentialism and Rogerian client-centered concepts and techniques with psychiatric clients, is an illustration of this approach to theory construction within a therapy orientation.

Where does this take us in relation to the philosophical dilemma? We need to know what works in practice. We need to know the efficacy and impact of what we do. There is no rightness or wrongness in either a leisure or a therapy orientation. We can build and test theories only once we accept a basic orientation; refine, describe and build models within those orientations; and then review and utilize the findings. Thus, the solution to the philosophical dilemma becomes one not of goodness, but rather one of choice. What do we choose to do? What do we in therapeutic recreation want to have as our major identification and area of contribution? Our choice of contribution now appears to be influenced by two factors: appropriateness and feasibility. Appropriateness is related to what is suitable and fits well; feasibility is related to what is capable of being accomplished (*Webster's*, 1962).

Each of these factors can be analyzed and explored. We have historical roots and contemporary practice from which to view the issue. We can study our professional organizations and our professional preparation structures. We can make a decision about our future and get on with the essential work of being a profession and building a reputable body of knowledge. But we must make a decision. Our philosophical dilemma is simply our own inability or unwillingness to choose.

Study Questions

1. How important is a "unique contribution" of service, the establishment, development for and recognition of a profession?

2. Identify various factors of appropriateness and feasibility of the different philosophical orientations, leisure and therapy as they are related to the selection or support of one position for the profession.

3. How much should the selection and support of a philosophical position be influenced by the demands of current health care situations such as reimbursement and health care accreditation standards?

4. What new populations, settings, and arenas of service do you see as possible areas for therapeutic recreation focus in the future? Which philosophical orientation do you see as fitting into these new horizons, and how?

5. How would you propose to resolve the philosophical dilemma?

References

American Therapeutic Recreation Association. (1984). Membership Application Materials. Washington DC

Carter, M., Van Andel, G., & Robb, G. (1985). *Therapeutic Recreation: A Practical Approach.* St. Louis, MO: Times Mirror/ Mosby College Publishing.

Dattilo, J., & Barnett, L. (1985). Therapeutic Recreation for Individuals with Severe Handicaps: An Analysis of the Relationship Between Choice and Pleasure. *Therapeutic Recreation Journal, 19*(3),79- 91.

Frye,V., & Peters, M. (1972). *Therapeutic Recreation: Its Theory, Philosophy and Practice.* Harrison, PA: Stackpole Books.

Halberg, K. J., & Howe-Murphy, R. (1985). The Dilemma of an Unresolved Philosophy in Therapeutic Recreation. *Therapeutic Recreation Journal, 19*(3), 7-16.

Haun, P. (1965). *Recreation: A Medical Viewpoint.* New York: Columbia University Bureau of Publications.

Hedrick, B. N. (1985). The Effect of Wheelchair Tennis Participation and Mainstreaming Upon the Perceptions of Competence of Physically Disabled Adolescents. *Therapeutic Recreation Journal, 19*(2), 34-46.

Hemingway, J.L. (1987). Building a Philosophical Defense of Therapeutic Recreation: The Case of Distributive Justice. In C. Sylvester, J.L. Hemingway, R. Howe-Murphy, K. Mobily, & P. Shank (Eds.), *Philosophy of Therapeutic Recreation: Ideas and Issues* (pp. 1-16). Alexandria, VA: National Recreation and Park Association.

Howe-Murphy, R., & Charboneau, B. (1987). *Therapeutic Recreation Intervention: An Ecological Approach.* Englewood Cliffs, NJ: Prentice-Hall.

Kraus, R. (1983). *Therapeutic Recreation Service: Principles and Practices.* Philadelphia, PA: W.B. Saunders.

Martin, A.R. (1962). A Philosophy of Recreation. In *The Doctors and Recreation in the Hospital Setting* (Bulletin No. 30 pp 5-8, 10, 14.) Raleigh, NC: The North Carolina Recreation Commission.

Meyer, L.E. (1981). Three Philosophical Positions of Therapeutic Recreation and Their Implications for Professionalization and NTRS/NRPA. *Therapeutic Recreation Journal, 15*(2), 7-16.

Mobily, K.E., Weissinger, E., & Hunnicutt, B.K. (1987). The Means/ end Controversy: A Framework For Understanding the Value Potential of Therapeutic Recreation. *Therapeutic Recreation Journal, 21*(3), 7-13.

Mobily, K.E. (1985a). A Philosophical Analysis of Therapeutic Recreation: What Does it Mean to Say "We Can Be Therapeutic?" Part I. *Therapeutic Recreation Journal,19*(1), 14-26.

Mobily, K.E. (1985c). The Ethical Dilemma of Freedom. *Therapeutic Recreation Journal, 19*(4), 22-30.

O'Morrow, G. (1980). *Therapeutic Recreation: A Helping Profession* (2nd ed.). Reston, VA: Reston Publishing.

Peterson, C.A., & Gunn, S.L. (1984). *Therapeutic Recreation Program Design* (2nd ed.). Englewood Cliffs, NJ: Prentice-Hall.

Reynolds, R.P., & O'Morrow, G.S. (1985). *Problems, Issues and Concepts in Therapeutic Recreation.* Englewood Cliffs, NJ: Prentice-Hall.

Sneegas, J. (1986). Components of Life Satisfaction in Middle and Later Life Adults: Perceived Social Competence, Leisure Participation and Leisure Satisfaction. *Journal of Leisure Research, 18*(4), 248-258.

Shank, J., & Kinney, T. (1987). On the Neglect of Clinical Practice. In C. Sylvester, J.L. Hemingway, R.Howe-Murphy, K. Mobily, & P.S. Shank (Eds.), *Philosophy of Therapeutic Recreation: Ideas and Issues* (pp.65-75). Alexandria, VA: National Recreation and Park Association.

Shank, P. (1987). Therapeutic Recreation Philosophy: A State of Cacophony. In C. Sylvester, J.L. Hemingway, R. Howe-Murphy, K. Mobily, & P.A. Shank (Eds.), *Philosophy of Therapeutic Recreation: Ideas and Issues* (pp.27-40). Alexandria, VA: National Recreation and Park Association.

Sylvester, C.D. (1985). Freedom, Leisure and Therapeutic Recreation: A Philosophical View. *Therapeutic Recreation Journal, 19*(1), 6-13.

Sylvester, C.D. (1985). Wonder, Doubt, and Thoughtfulness in Therapeutic Recreation. Therapeutic Recreation Journal, 20(3), 6-10.

Webster's New World Dictionary. (1962). New York: World Publishing.

Issues Related to Professional Affiliation and Organizations

photo courtesy of San Francisco Recreation Center for the Handicapped

The therapeutic recreation profession must become active participants in coalitions and other groups that have a regulatory or quality service focus, so as to advocate for those we serve, as well as the profession.

—Michal Anne Lord

PROFESSIONAL LEADERSHIP:
Honor or Responsibility?

M. Jean Keller

Introduction

It is now over 150 years since Alex de Tocqueville, a young French nobleman and an acute observer of American life, returned to his native France and published his observations about his experiences in the United States. Among his many perceptive comments about America was the following:

> Americans of all ages, all stations in life, and all types of disposition are forever forming associations. There are not only commercial and industrial associations in which all take part, but others of a thousand different types–religious, moral, serious, futile, very general, and very limited, immensely large and very minute. Americans combine to give fetes, found seminaries, build churches, distribute books and send missionaries to the antipodes. Hospitals, prisons and schools take shape that way. Finally, if they want to proclaim a truth or propagate some feeling by the encouragement of a great example, they form an association (de Tocqueville, 1979, p.10.)

Associations for therapeutic recreation provide strong contemporary support for de Tocqueville's thesis.

Professional Associations and Leaders

What are professional therapeutic recreation associations? Why do they exist? What do they do? Should professionals be concerned about them? Most therapeutic recreation professionals have asked or will ask themselves some of these questions. Each question is deserving of thoughtful consideration.

Professional associations are organizations formed voluntarily by persons working in a profession, primarily for the purpose of organizing the resources of the members for effective service to others, advancing the quality and standards of the profession and its members, and advancing the welfare of the members. The continued development of a profession and its members does not just happen. Recognizing that concerted, purposeful, and planned action is needed, members voluntarily form professional organizations in order to serve more effectively than they could as individuals or small groups. It is a characteristic of the time-honored professions that they accept responsibility for the quality of their service, standards of professional practice, and behavior of members (O'Morrow, 1976).

Professional associations require professional belonging. Once a professional association is formed, it requires people to belong and provide it with service and leadership. While not everyone desires a leadership role in a professional association, some must so serve to enable the association to flourish.

Some might say that volunteering for a therapeutic recreation association leadership position is too much trouble, too much responsibility, and too large a time commitment—especially for men and women who have careers, families, and outside interests. Yet busy men and women volunteer in our professional associations every year. Why? A sense of duty? Moral imperative? Personal altruism? To make a meaningful contribution to their profession and to society? More than likely all of these are possible reasons for professional belonging. Muhammad Ali once said, "Service to others is the rent I pay for my room on earth." It may seem unusual to compare a heavyweight prizefighter to leaders of therapeutic recreation associations, but after talking with volunteer leaders across the country, it was discovered many men and women share their talents, resources, ideals, and optimism for the betterment of their associations, professions, and society for a similar reason.

A convenience survey of 15 leaders of state, regional, and national therapeutic recreation associations were asked the question "What motivates volunteers to serve their professional associations?" Nearly all the respondents felt the therapeutic recreation profession was important to them and that they had a responsibility to give something back. Nearly all the leaders felt that they received more from their associations when they gave more of themselves. Several volunteer leaders were motivated by the honor and recognition it gave them and their agencies. The opportunity to meet peers and colleagues, to network with those who can provide support for the profession, and to seek challenge and personal growth were among other reasons for volunteering for associations' leadership positions.

As these 15 leaders responded to questions, it became clear that being a volunteer leader of a therapeutic recreation association is more than an honor–it requires dedication and commitment. Several associations required their leaders to spend several days at a time traveling to meetings and giving speeches. Even when in their agencies, these professional association leaders would spend hours each week reading and responding to correspondence, making phone calls, and staying at the forefront of the field. All of the leaders indicated that they must continually juggle the demands of the association and the requirements of their work and other responsibilities.

Although the need to balance work, association, and other commitments discourages some potential volunteers, it did not discourage any of the leaders surveyed. To nearly half (7) of the leaders, the time and energy required to fulfill their responsibilities came as a surprise. Yet, it was not a deterrent. Each respondent indicated in his or her own way that one must learn to coordinate volunteer and professional roles. The respondents stressed the importance of establishing priorities for paid and volunteer work, learning to effectively delegate, and obtaining the understanding and backing of employers before accepting volunteer responsibilities. One third (5) of the respondents felt that to get the work done, they devoted more time to the association and less to family life and personal interests. Interestingly, all of the leaders felt they gained energy and enthusiasm from their volunteer work and became better time managers. The majority (12) felt each volunteer position they had held in their professional association was a pleasurable and leisure experience. While all 15 volunteer professional association leaders gave of their time and sacrificed personal interests, they all admitted to receiving intrinsic rewards–such as a sense of being a part of something bigger than themselves, achievement, pride, accomplishment, stimulation, and self-esteem–in return. The experience of serving in a leadership role is demanding; yet, according to Stratton (1979) in an article in *Leadership,* a publication for volunteer association leaders, the feeling of personal satisfaction in knowing one has contributed to a profession makes it all worthwhile (Stratton, 1979).

With some insight into why and how people participate in leadership roles in professional therapeutic recreation associations, it appears just as important to understand why people do not belong to or remain inactive in professional associations. Professional belonging isn't what it used to be, according to Olson (1986), chairman of the board of the American Society of Association Executives. Membership and leadership in professional associations is changing.

Touche Ross and Company, an international accounting and management consulting firm, polled 308 volunteer leaders in 1980 on their views of volunteer leadership as it is today and as it might become in the future (Jorpeland, 1980). Three major issues were expressed by the respondents regarding professional involvement in leadership roles in their associations: time, money, and commitment. "More than ever before, volunteer professional association leaders need to demonstrate a commitment to the organization's purpose, a strong business orientation for wise use of funds and time, and an increased sensitivity to the organizations various constituencies" (p. 45).

Fifteen nationally certified or licensed therapeutic recreation specialists who were either not members (5) or had never served in any leadership roles (10) in their state or national professional associations were also surveyed. The 5 respondents who did not belong to state or national professional associations felt there was very little associations could do for them personally. Two of the respondents had never belonged, and 3 had allowed their memberships to expire because of increased dues and perceived decreased services. As Touche Ross and Company discovered among other professional volunteers, therapeutic recreation specialists also indicated they were no longer members of professional associations simply because of a commitment and loyalty to the profession. They were interested in "value"–what the cost was in relationship to the services provided.

The 10 therapeutic recreation specialists who had held memberships in their professionals associations (on the average for 8 years) yet had not held leadership roles of any kind, expressed the following reasons for non-participation: 40 percent said they did not have enough time, money, or interest to make a commitment to their professional associations; 30 percent expressed that they did not know how to get involved or what was expected; and another 30 percent indicated they did not have leadership skills, were not in agreement with an association's policies, or were afraid of legal liability.

Touche Ross and Company (Jorpeland, 1980) concluded that the responsibility of leaders in professional associations ia growing, and with increased responsibility comes great demands on time. Individuals must be committed enough to find the time and money to serve their associations, and it does not appear this will change in the future. Future leaders of professional associations will need to be more responsive to their members and their needs, and willing to spend more time on their associations' fiscal matters, planning their future, and empowering and assisting the membership to get involved with the associations. Interestingly, there were similar findings among the therapeutic recreation specialists who responded to the survey.

Professional belonging is indeed a complex and multifaceted phenomena. For nearly 20 years, such well-respected leaders in therapeutic recreation as Frye (1969), Ball (1970), Humphrey (1970), Park (1974), Meyer (1978), Peterson and Connolly (1981), and Reynolds and O'Morrow (1985) have reflected and commented on the role of therapeutic recreation professional associations and their relationships to the development of the profession. Each leader has concluded that the discipline of therapeutic recreation is emerging as a profession and a great deal of the struggle to obtain professional status has rested with our professional associations and their members. Thus, professional associations are vital to the professionalization of therapeutic recreation–to its mission, service, and practice. However, it appears that it is time to seek new ways to involve individuals in professional therapeutic recreation associations.

Involvement in Professional Associations: A Paradigm for Participation

Most therapeutic recreation professionals would subscribe to the concept that it is of utmost importance to foster and develop the fullest possible life. Most would also agree that the motivating force for involvement in any life activity is derived from within the individual. Thus, professional association participation comes through an inner commitment and involvement of individuals working with one another.

The question facing leaders of professional associations is how to encourage and develop participation. The key to unlocking the membership's participation in professional associations is a complex and multifaceted task. An important variable is the types of individual behavior necessary for an effective and purposeful association. These behaviors are classified into four operating aspects. In order for professional associations to be effective, each aspect must be in place, because they are sequential and interlocking.

The first aspect of participation is the interaction of the individual in a "contract to belong" and to be a part of the association. The second aspect is the interaction of a member of the association working with others in a team or committee relationship in order to accomplish a task. The third aspect is the interaction of committees or intra-association activities to produce work functions within the association. The final aspect is the association's action as a single actor in an external environment, garnering resources from that environment and contributing products or services back to the environment and its individual members (see Figure 1). For a professional association to tap its human resources, it must enable and empower its members to operate in these four distinct areas. The following ideas are offered as possible means to encourage and develop leadership and involvement in therapeutic recreation professional associations among its members.

Individual belonging and leadership

Professional associations and their leaders need to begin to change their thinking. Professional commitment will remain a valid reason for some individuals to continue their involvement. However, there is a need for leaders to reflect as to how people are motivated in different situations and at different times in their adult lives. "The more ownership and awareness that an individual has of his/her life, the more capable he/she is of contributing his/her unique aspects which are so necessary for associations to change and develop" (Lippitt, 1982, p. 397).

A key intervention on the individual level for obtaining professional belonging and leadership is an assessment with the individual of the dynamics of his or her life, work, and family stages in relationship to the association's needs and the benefits he or she can receive from involvement. This technique is based on helping individuals see how professional belonging and leadership can be meshed with experiences, needs, interests, and values. By working with individuals to assess their responsibilities, interests, and needs, professional associations can help them discover a level of professional involvement or leadership that can produce the greatest sense of satisfaction for them. This technique can be used in the setting of a contract between members and their professional associations to maximize the contributions and benefits to all.

Other interventions that professional associations might consider are focusing on particular individual issues that are unique to persons in the therapeutic recreation field. For example, some professionals feel they do not have adequate leadership and political skills, while others may need help with time management, dual careers, or stress management. Programs should be offered by associations to develop potential leaders.

With an individual assessment process, association leaders will understand what is happening within their membership and the impact of all their other roles and responsibilities on their professional involvement. Then professional association leaders can help individuals integrate professional belonging and leadership into their lives.

Figure 1
Involvement in Professional Associations:
A Paradigm for Participation

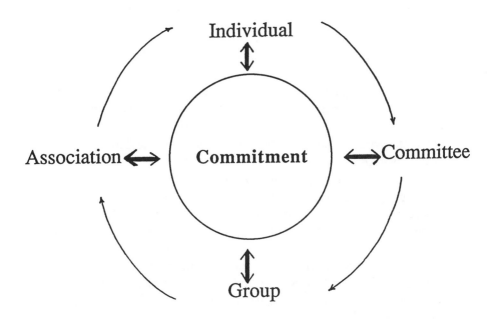

Committee involvement

From the individual's perspective, entry into a professional association's activity generally involves interfacing with other individuals on a committee. Think about a functioning committee: What are the face-to-face interactions with other committee members like? Does the committee have a well-defined purpose, and can all the committee members agree on the committee's common work objectives? Do the members know what their duties are? Do the members understand how the committee fits into the whole association? Do members know how well the committee has assisted the association? How well does each member feel his or her time and energy was expended on committee work? Committees are the backbone of a professional association and in this way determine its strength and height.

An individual's task within the committee is that of performing as a team member. Having a sense of belonging, an individual can contribute to the collective venture of the team, or committee. The task is that the committee should have significant output to the overall association's mission. Accordingly, the committee chairperson's function is to facilitate the committee in its awareness, reflection, and learning on this level. By giving the committee feedback, chairpersons can facilitate the determination of errors and the consequent avoidance of dysfunctional expenditure of effort. It is critical for a committee to develop the appropriate skills of self-reflection and of correcting its own dysfunctions. Such skills typically constitute the definition of a successful committee.

The committee process thus focuses on the committee's becoming a functioning work unit to build on successes and learn from mistakes. Difficulties arise from the lack of such reflective and corrective skills. Discovery of negative information is not valued in many associations and committees. In most associations, performance is not measured at the committee level. Committees in professional associations often lack continuity and longevity, which makes it difficult to build on successes and learn from mistakes. Professional associations may unconsciously structure rewards which may be divisive for committees, break up committees through the transfer of successful individual members, and impose restrictive norms and procedures on the committees. Surprisingly, many professional associations fail to see the importance of creating and developing strong committees.

The key intervention on the committee level consists of formally building up team or committee skills. Friedlander and Schett (1981) provide such a framework. This framework focuses on committee skills in

- setting goals and priorities,
- analyzing and allocating work,
- examining the committee's process, and
- examining the interpersonal relationships of the commit tee members.

Within every committee, there are different roles and perspectives on each of these activities. There are leader, member, outcome, and association issues. The dynamics between these four activities and four roles are complex and comprehensive. Thus, leaders are challenged to help committee members develop process skills in decision making, problem solving, and committee communication and evaluation.

Committee development can provide a framework for understanding the growth stages of the collective personality that makes up the committee and what the committee's relationship to the association and its members is. The basic viability and well-being of many professional associations is dependent on what happens in their committees. In order to foster professional belonging and leadership, it is necessary for an association to devote time, energy, and resources to building and evaluating its various committees and their members.

The role of groups

From the committee's point of view, to be effective and enter the association's life is to work within a larger system, such as a section, society, branch, or division. Functional groups are made up of committees which constitute subunits, whether geographic or strategic work units, of the larger association. The group must have the ability to sense critical information and to pass it beyond the barriers of individual committees in order to implement programs and project at a range beyond its direct contact. In large, complex associations, where size and distance dissolve immediate personal relationships, it is imperative that this level function well. The committees' task within the group is to perform as a team while having a sense of belonging to the group from which each of the committees receive the scarce resources, enabling it to function.

This process of performing a complex function and making the right distribution of scarce resources, such as talent and money, is the key venture of the group level. As a group, this amorphic mass must be capable of finding its own dysfunctions. The correction process includes the mapping of the flow of transferring information and partially completed work or services from one group to the next. The entire function must be viewed, understood, and successfully handled in order to produce the work of the group. Because of the large number of individuals who work on a particular task in complex associations, this process can be very opaque. The group's process then must focus on becoming a functioning work unit to build on successes and to learn from mistakes.

Difficulties arise from the lack of reflective and corrective skills at this level, too. Discovery of negative information is difficult because often it is hidden in the interfaces that exist between one group and the next. An association's rewards system often does not reflect the actual needs of particular working groups within the association. At times a group's needs may change, requiring more resources, yet the group may be slow to change and incapable of restructuring itself effectively to meet its needs.

The key intervention on the group level consists of internal mapping, in which individual group leaders are asked to plot the work flow through their groups, and to do this in such a way that from the beginning of a work process until its finish, all the intermediate links passing between different functioning committees are plotted out. Further, all members of the group have a chance jointly to own dysfunctional areas and work in small task forces to fix the dysfunctions. Severe dysfunctions on the group level must often be solved through the use of an organizational development consultant or an outside facilitator who can help the group reconfigure its information and processes, and restructure itself, if necessary, to a new configuration.

The association, especially in its nature as a large aggregate of groups, develops its own culture out of the experience of success in dealing with problems of internal integration and external adaptation. Culture exists on three levels, according to Schein (1985): the creation level, the values level, and the basic assumptions level. Each of these levels must be understood; however, rarely is much time devoted to discussing and sharing the creation and history of a group or to exploring and reflecting on the values and purpose of a group. The third level is the most difficult to uncover because basic assumptions are taken for granted and, therefore, not readily available. How effectively the group level functions is somewhat contingent on what basic assumptions are operating at this level. Uncovering the layers of basic assumptions is difficult and time consuming, but necessary in order for the group to efficiently function.

The association as a whole

The association's tasks are simply to be whole, to live in a competitive environment, and to exchange services for the reception of scarce resources. The association then has an appropriate contract with its membership, through which the exchange is mutually benefiting. The association is then required to chart its internal groups and available resources as well as to assess the external climate for the opportunities and challenges facing the association. Effectiveness, then, is the maximizing of opportunities for overcoming challenges to provide a healthy, growing association.

Thus, the basic goals of an association are membership involvement and participation in such a way that the association works as a unit and has the ability to respond to all exigencies. One of the difficulties that exists at this level is that most associations are biased toward growth. This growth can be the death of an association when it keeps moving to a certain size which becomes dysfunctional, and it no longer enjoys the economy of scale that a smaller size once held for it. A second serious dysfunction occurs when the economic or the service climate has changed dramatically and the association does not know how to deal with the group conflict and fault-finding that may be the response to this change within the association. The key intervention for growth at this level is that of open systems planning, performed in terms of core mission of the total association with the constituencies, both internal and external, that make demands on an association. This process leads to an understanding of an association's desired future state, and it maps the processes and structures by which the association can arrive at the state. Ultimately, an association that has an understanding of itself can create a positive internal environment, and those working with the association will foster goodwill in the external environment.

Summary

The interrelationships between the four aspects discussed in this participation paradigm are complex, important, and in need of further study. Professional associations are founded on the effective utilization of human resources and are challenged to help professionals develop and grow in order to serve their professions, professional associations, themselves, and society. Lucille Maddalena (1980), editor of *Encouraging Voluntarism and Volunteers,* indicates that evolving social mores, economic patterns, and personal needs have brought about significant change in the roles and responsibilities of volunteers. She also expresses the need for both professional staff members and volunteer leaders to reckon their inheritance by recognizing changes, meeting new demands, and developing procedures to effectively implement programs and services vital to the continued operation of professional associations.

The profession of therapeutic recreation is emerging with assistance from its professional associations. As with any period of development, there will be struggles and conflicts. Yet, there appears one item where there will be little disagreement: the need for professional involvement in the growth and development of therapeutic recreation. Possibly there is more to professional belonging and leadership than responsibility or honor. It appears that the hallmark of the success of the therapeutic recreation profession and its professional associations is when professionals see commitment to their profession as a responsibility and honor.

Study Questions

1. Discuss the purpose of professional associations in therapeutic recreation. Consider why they exist, what their functions are, and how they operate.

2. What would you consider important when making the decision whether to become involved in a professional therapeutic recreation association?

3. Discuss some of the benefits you and others could derive from serving in a leadership role in a professional therapeutic recreation association.

4. What are some factors that you should consider when accepting a leadership role in a professional association? Why?

5. You have been asked to chair a committee within your state therapeutic recreation professional association. Review the various aspects you need to consider in chairing this committee and discuss why they are important.

6. Discuss the strength and weakness in using the proposed paradigm for participation in professional associations outlined in this chapter. Suggest other means to involve the membership in professional associations.

7. How do you think therapeutic recreation professional associations will be different in the year 2010? Consider structure, professional involvement, and purpose.

References

Ball, E.L. (1970). The Meaning of Therapeutic Recreation. *Therapeutic Recreation Journal, 4* (1), 17-1.

de Tocqueville, A. (1979). Profiles in Leadership. *Leadership,* November, 10-16.

Friedlander, F., & Schott, B. (1981). The Use of Task Groups and Task Forces in Organizational Change. In R. Payne and C.L. Cooper (Eds.), *Groups at Work.* New York: Wiley. 148-169.

Frye, V. (1969). A Philosophical Statement on Therapeutic Recreation Service. *Therapeutic Recreation Journal, 3* (4), 11-14.

Frye, V., & Peters, M. (1972). *Therapeutic Recreation: Its Theory, Philosophy, and Practice.* Harrisburg, PA: Stackpole Books.

Hillman, W.A. (1970). Therapeutic Recreation as a Profession: A Status Report. *Therapeutic Recreation Annual, 7,* 1-7.

Humphrey, F. (1970). Therapeutic Recreation and the 1970s. *Therapeutic Recreation Annual, 7,* 8-13.

Jorpeland, E. (1980). Leadership Qualities: What to Look For In Potential Board Candidates. *Leadership,* March, 23-25.

Lipitt, R. (1982). The Changing Leader-Follower Relationship of the 1980s. *Journal of Applied Behavioral Science, 18,* 395-403.

Maddalena, L.A. (Ed.). (1980). *Encouraging Voluntarism and Volunteers.* San Francisco, CA: Jossey-Bass.

Meyer, L.E. (1978). *An Analysis of Views of Recreation Professionals Toward Therapeutic Recreation and its Professionalization.* Unpublished doctoral dissertation, University of North Carolina at Chapel Hill.

Olson, M.S. (1986). A letter from the chairman. *Leadership, 10.*

O'Morrow, G.S. (1976). *Therapeutic Recreation: A Helping Profession.* Reston, VA: Reston Publishing.

Park, D.C. (1974). The Challenge of Professionalism in Therapeutic Recreation. In J.D. Kelley (Ed.), *Expanding Horizons in Therapeutic Recreation* . (Vol. 2). Champaign, IL: University of Illinois, Office of Recreation and Park Resources, 63-68.

Peterson,C.A., & Connolly, P. (1981). Professional Preparation In Therapeutic Recreation. *Therapeutic Recreation Journal, 15* (12), 41.

Reynold, R.P., & O'Morrow, G.S. (1985). *Problems, Issues, and Concepts in Therapeutic Recreation.* Englewood Cliffs, NJ: Prentice-Hall.

Schein, E.H. (1985). *Organizational Culture and Leadership.* San Francisco, CA: Jossey-Bass.

Stratton, D.J. (1979). Profiles in Leadership. *Leadership*, November, 10-16.

ORGANIZATIONAL NETWORKING

Michal Anne Lord

"Perhaps there are no Heroes anymore. . .
. . . because the times do not permit.
Perhaps there's greatness not in large concerns but small . . .
Not in how one acts before the searching eye . . .
. . . or in public view . . .
But how one acts when no one sees or hears or knows . . . or
even cares.

There are no Heroes anymore? There are . . .
. . . just look about, there are.
Greatness is not the sole possession . . .
. . . of the great.
Potentials reside in each of us . . .
. . . if we but tap the source.
If we but recognize it . . . in ourselves . . .
. . . and in our peers.

First, let us define it, if we can . . .
. . . what Greatness is.
Concern for others. A quiet helpfulness.
A reaching out.
Philosophies which go beyond material things.
A reaching up.
Doing well what one decides to do . . .
. . . Integrity combined with skill."
(Excerpts from "There Are No Heroes Anymore,"
written for Mutual of New York by Earl Fultz.)

Perhaps there are no heroes anymore; yet within the field of therapeutic recreation and, for that matter, within most human services and allied health professions, we stand at the threshold of a new era of heroes. Not individual heroes riding their white steeds, but rather a group of individuals joining together for a common cause, riding the horse called networking.

As professionals in a field that is constantly being challenged as to its validity, its relevancy and its contribution to mankind, we in therapeutic recreation must develop our networks with respect to legislation, research, and professional and program standards, as well as programming trends. We must stay informed and keep our peers informed within and outside the field of therapeutic recreation. Therapeutic recreation professionals must be the leaders in foregoing the battles of turf and become the champions of the multidisciplinary treatment approach and team management, for the ultimate good and betterment of those we serve.

Purpose of Networking

In *Reinventing the Corporation,* Naisbitt and Aburdene (1985) state that the corporation is an analogue for the rest of society, although typically more responsive to change than education, health care, politics, or any other social structures within the "new information society,"

a society that is information-rich, decentralized yet global, multi-optioned that emphasizes the values of high tech/high touch, networking, participatory democracy, self reliance and a long-term view. (p.4)

Networking implies that individuals from a variety of backgrounds, professional disciplines, agencies, and organizations can benefit by pooling information, resources, and technical assistance. Networking suggest, that through a sharing process, common goals might be achieved, credibility, and public awareness increased.

Intra- and Interorganizational Networks

Organizational networking takes place predominantly on two planes: intraorganizational and interorganizational. Intraorganizational networking refers to the series of networks that operate, individually and collectively, within an organization for a shared goal and, thus, the betterment of the organization. For example, within the National Therapeutic Recreation Society (NTRS) there are the Board of Directors, the States and Regional Advisory Council, and individual committees. Members of all these entities must communicate with each other to ensure progress and efficiency within the organization.

Interorganizational networking refers to the networking between organizations who share similar characteristics, such as populations served, service delivery system, goals, or issues. For example, the Consortium of Citizens with Developmental Disabilities is a formalized national network that focuses on regulatory and legislative issues; members include the National Easter Seal Society, National Recreation and Park Association/National Therapeutic Recreation Society, American Occupational Therapy Association, the National Education Association, and the American Foundation for the Blind, to mention just a few.

By networking, organizations can demonstrate a greater number of individuals involved; a broader scope of involvement, which may reflect geographic, education, and professional preparation, or financial qualities; and interpersonal, political, or social relationships. Both levels of networking are important and usually operate simultaneously.

Benefits of Networking

Traditionally the guiding principle for networking has been *communications,* or *information sharing.* A second principle or benefit to emerge has been that of *advocacy.* A third benefit, yet to reach maturity, is that of *professional development.* Networking is a facet of participative management and is fundamental to an organization's progress.

Information sharing

Although networking is not a new concept, the need for it today is even greater, given reduced resources and given that human capital has replaced dollar capital as the most strategic resource (Naisbitt, 1985). It is therefore important that individuals share experiences with others who have similar concerns; there is no need to reinvent the wheel. By using networks, individuals or organizations find the strength and confidence to pursue a cause or an innovative idea. This kind of cooperation and support is not automatic. Networks must be nurtured to really work, giving time, care, and commitment. Network members must share information, and communicate needs and accomplishments, if the relationship is to be meaningful; otherwise, a network can become superficial (Loden, 1985).

Advocacy

Since the "squeaky wheel gets the oil" and "there is strength in numbers," organizational networking is the ideal vehicle for mobilizing any advocacy effort. An effective organizational network provides a rippling effect on all network members and then, to some degree, society at large.

Figure 1 illustrates the "advocacy rippling effect." A message enters the network at the interorganization level. Each organization (1, 2, 3, etc.) receives the initial notification of information, call for action, or instruction to stand-by for further information. The rippling effect occurs as each organization in turn extends the network to the intraorganization level by notifying its appropriate components (A, B, C, etc.), including committees, task forces, individual members, consumer groups, and so on. Certainly each component within the intra-organizational level might further the information sharing by incorporating its own personal networks, such as co-workers and advisory boards.

Thus, networking and its advocacy rippling effect has the capability of truly mobilizing a large constituency to voice concerns and issues to policymakers, to demonstrate the impact and value of service delivery, and to heighten public awareness.

Professional development

The new information society of today warrants a change in management, the way of doing business, whether business is done within a corporation, a governmental agency, or professional society. Corporations no longer need managers but leaders who will assist in developing teams or other small group units in which the functions of leadership are shared, leaders who can recognize the needs, inspire the dreams, communicate the values, and ultimately mobilize the potential of others.

A *quality circle* is a form of participative management. A group of individuals, usually less than 10 members, voluntarily meet on a regular basis to define, analyze, and solve problems by idea sharing. As a form of networking, this type of management fosters cooperation, communication, self-development, and increased productivity in the workplace (Wilhite, Terry, Yoshioke, & McLean, 1983).

> Personal growth and development is positively affected through the Quality Circle process. A continuing education philosophy is inherent in this concept. The individuals involved in the Circle not only learn things that allow them to perform their jobs better, they also

Figure 1
Advocacy Rippling Effect

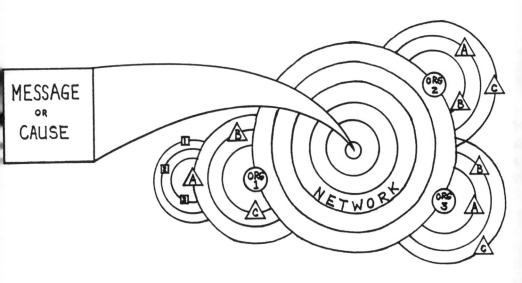

develop in areas of interpersonal and public communication, analytical deliberation, organization of ideas, and self-confidence. (p.9)

Illustration

These three benefits of networking are perhaps best illustrated by the critical issues involved in nursing home reform and the subsequent events centering around legislative action with respect to Senate Bill 1108, the Medicare and Medicaid Nursing Home Quality Care Amendments of 1987. Although the author of Senate Bill 1108 originally intended to facilitate improvements to nursing home care, the actual working of the bill modified the conditions of participation for skilled nursing facilities and intermediate care facilities. The bill seemingly weakened the existing requirements pertaining to recreation services by excluding "activities" as a required service, requiring assessments but without an activities component, and eliminating the activity professional under standards regulating qualified personnel.

By professionals initiating both intra- and interorganizational networks and implementing the information-sharing process, awareness was created, clarification was provided, and substantial support for recreation/activities programming in nursing homes was noted. On the intraorganizational level, the key leadership within NTRS (Board of Directors, the States and Regional Advisory Council, and state TR society presidents) was provided appropriate information and notified of the need for action. In addition, on the interorganizational level, the members of the Legislative Coalition for Therapeutic Recreation—which includes NTRS, the American Therapeutic Recreation Association (ATRA), and the National Consortium on Physical Education and Recreation for the Handicapped (NCPERH), were informed of events and action requested. Ongoing communications between NRPA/NTRS and the National Association for Activity Professionals (NAAP) were maintained so as to effect change as well.

Issues

Whereas we may all recognize the potential benefits of networking, we may not all be aware of its importance within the therapeutic recreation profession. Discussion of some of the critical issues within the field today follows.

Ideology vs. organizational structure

> Therapeutic recreation is unique because it rests on recreation's subjective quality (the individual and his own state of mind–his fun) at the same time that it provides tangible evidence that real medical and health goals are served through recreation. But without its subjective, human, intangible, individual, and even "irrational" component, TR becomes just another therapy which, like occupational therapy, is absorbed by the gigantic health field. (Hunnicutt, 1978, p. 18)

Certainly philosophy or ideology is fundamental to the operation and development of not only the profession but its professional organizations (Austin & Hunnicutt, 1978; Halberg & Howe-Murphy, 1985) and thus, ultimately, their linkages and participation in various organizational networks. As Hunnicutt (1978) indicated, therapeutic recreation was and is unique in that it embraces two professional groups, recreators and health professionals, within one ideology. Therapeutic recreation, in fact, bridges the chasm between the two, forming a continuum of service through the leisure education process. This dynamic tension gives life to therapeutic recreation, although at the same time it can inhibit or at least cloud decision making with respect to affiliations with any organizational network.

When networks are implemented in the real world, often more questions may be raised than answered. For example, an organization must determine whether it is an advisory or governing body, or somewhere in between, like a quasi-policy-making entity. An organization must define its constituents and what role they will play within the network at the intraorganizational level as well. Role definition is particularly important if constituents include disabled consumers. Understanding who you are and what you do should be prerequisites to identifying and becoming involved in any interorganizational network.

Cooperation vs. competition

Today we live in a world where competition for scarce resources has become a struggle for survival among individuals, organizations, and nations; where winning and losing can have profound consequences; where competition must be balanced by an increased emphasis on collaboration. (Loden, 1985, p. 180)

Hopefully, the days of "them" against "us" are over, and cooperation rather than competition has become the way to success. Certainly cooperation is a key factor in building successful organizational networks. A cooperative environment is achieved by encouraging greater participation and shared accountability by all members.

When critical legislative or regulatory issues surface, when survival seems paramount, the desire for control takes over from the fostering of compromise among parties. Such was the case within many states as therapeutic recreation professionals responded to the occupational therapy licensure movement. Because most state therapeutic recreation professionals and/or state professional societies had not maintained liaisons with the occupational therapists or effective legislative networks within their states, they were caught offguard and unprepared to work with the occupational therapists and their efforts to obtain licensure. Thus, therapeutic recreation professionals appeared competitive rather than cooperative.

Marilyn Loden (1985) recognized the strengths of a cooperative work climate given similar conditions when she said,

> It can be put to best use when a long-term approach to influencing events is required, when facts and expert information are critical to the effort, and where the quality of relationships within the work groups is an important consideration. (p.94)

Traditionally, the competitive way–the need to win and control–rules more heavily with the interorganizational networks. However, the nearly opposite way is being recognized and accepted as the mode of the eighties and nineties, that is, the desire to design "win-win" situations and foster consensus building and shared decision making amongst the ranks.

So in the case of licensure, therapeutic recreation professionals should develop networks that not only include the therapeutic recreation professionals and paraprofessionals but also hospital and agency administrators, disabled consumers, and other advocates, and most importantly other allied health and human service professionals, such as occupational therapists, physical therapists, and representatives from the creative art therapies. By sharing information far in advance of any legislative action with respect to licensure, assuming a cooperative attitude rather than a competitive one, the following would hopefully result:

1. Other allied health and human service professionals would be educated as to what therapeutic recreation is, the unique skills of qualified professionals and paraprofessional staff, and how therapeutic recreation service is related to and complements other services. This might prevent defeat of a therapeutic recreation licensure bill due to another profession's uninformed lobbying.
2. Therapeutic recreation professionals would benefit from the experience of other professions who have already achieved licensure.
3. Initial public awareness would be achieved prior to submission of licensure legislation. In other words, consumers, administrators, and other professionals would be informed so as to speak on the therapeutic recreation profession's behalf during state lobbying efforts.

As an effort to ensure quality service delivery to the consumer, licensure is important to all allied health related professions; if supported by all appropriate professions and factions (consumers, administrators), it guarantees a win-win situation for all.

Reactive vs. proactive

> From the organization's standpoint, the most difficult person to manage is the person who has no idea what he or she wants to do. (Naisbitt & Alburdene, 1985, p.87)

The same can be said for an organization as a whole. If a group has no sense of self and what it wants to accomplish, it will be difficult for it to chart a course of action. This scenario is dramatically pointed out within the networking process. An organization which is not clear as to its mission, its objectives, its timetables, and how they interface with other members of the network will ultimately become an isolated and ineffective link in the system and therefore potentially reduce the effectiveness of the overall network. Thus, planning is a prerequisite to entering into a network, so as to define one's role and to facilitate a proactive rather than a reactive posture within the network's activities. A systematic approach to planning, being proactive, enables a network and individual members within the network to maximize resources, thereby enhancing one's credibility.

Reduced resources vs. increased demands

Halberg and Howe-Murphy (1985) point out that today's society is concerned with accountability, cost effectiveness, productivity, and reduced government support at all levels for human, social, and educational services. At the same time society demands the enhancement of the quality of life for all people. In effect, society is asking the professions and all human services to do more with less.

> The fact remains: competing in the professional arena today requires more than dedication and concern of [professional organization's] members. Strong professional organizations with resources and capable staff with various types of expertise are needed to direct, monitor, and facilitate the growing demands of professional service in the human and health care fields. (Peterson, 1984, pp. 14-15).

In this information era, the most vital resources are information, knowledge, and creativity, and the only way to tap such resources is through people. Thus, human resources are an organization's competitive edge. Human resources can be maximized when placed in small teams with different talents and perspectives to work on a common problem (Naisbitt & Aburdene, 1985). People work not in isolation but rather in a "cross-pollination" environment.

Certainly a second issue to consider within the initial dilemma of reduced resources and increased demands is the level of effectiveness of volunteers as opposed to that of paid participants within a network. Peterson (1984) indicated that a profession attempting to gain credibility and recognition cannot do so solely with voluntary time and effort; that professional activities warrant paid staff.

The value of networking as a process is that it can respond to increased demands while honoring reduced resources, minimizing duplication, and promoting quality service delivery. Thus, while a profession, organization, or agency may be dependent on voluntary efforts to a large degree because of limited resources, it may foster its own development by joining forces with others who share or support like purposes, lack sufficient resources (dollars, facilities, equipment, or manpower) to accomplish tasks alone, and/or believe partnerships can enhance the quality of service.

Special Olympics has historically promoted the implementation and nurturing of networks at the local, area, and state levels to further the growth and development of the Special Olympics program. An area-level program within a state is the result of a network's commitment. The network may be solely volunteer in nature (e.g., service organizations, parents or family members, teachers, or professionals who give of their own time to coach or manage competition events), or it may be a combination of volunteer and paid staff effort. As examples of combined networking efforts, parks and recreation departments and school districts often designate staff and resources (facilities and equipment) for training programs and competition; television stations often donate staff time for the development of public service announcements (PSAs) for public awareness promotional material; and volunteers and staff often work together to raise funds to establish paid positions to coordinate area and local activities. No matter the number of paid staff, Special Olympics is still fundamentally a grass-roots organization and requires volunteer coaches, officials, fund-raisers, and event coordinators, and so on, and thus networking.

Summary

The therapeutic recreation profession must continue its efforts to network–to share information and to communicate to others, in and outside of the health care human services field, as to who we are and what we do! The therapeutic recreation profession must become active participants in coalitions and other groups that have a regulatory or quality service focus so as to advocate for those we serve, as well as for the profession. Not only must advocacy efforts continue on the national level, but advocacy of the therapeutic recreation profession on the state and local levels must be initiated and increased. Personal and professional growth and development are benefits of networking and the inherent quality circle process. It is through the exchange of information with peers within the field of therapeutic recreation and with professionals in other fields that allows one to take advantage of the professional development opportunities that are a result of networking.

As workers in a field striving for professional visibility and credibility, a field endeavoring to address critical issues of the day, therapeutic recreation professionals must embrace networking, not only as a trend of today but the way for tomorrow. Networking can build and maintain productive relationships. It provides for team decision making and, thus, ownership of a commitment to a cause or mission. However, to reap the dividends of networking, one must remember that networking requires the subordination of individual needs to the good of the whole.

Study Questions

1. It is sometimes difficult and time consuming to foster networks. How can the therapeutic recreation profession motivate professionals and other individuals to maintain intraorganizational and interorganizational networks?

2a. Should the professional organizations representing the field of therapeutic recreation narrow their focus and align their ideology with one profession (e.g., NTRS represents those professionals working in the public sector delivering recreation services to special populations or those who clearly identify their work with the recreation and park field; ATRA represents the therapists and those working in clinical programs); or should the therapeutic recreation profession join forces into one organization that provides a true continuum of service delivery? Which option would better define the direction and level of involvement within interorganizational networks? Why?

or

b. Today there are two professional organizations within the thera-
    peutic recreation profession: NTRS and ATRA. Discuss the
    ramifications of this on interorganizational networking.

3. Who has the authority to enter into formalized networks on behalf
    of the therapeutic recreation profession? How is accountability
    ensured?

4. In a given organization or work setting, how are intra- and
    interorganizational networks started and developed?   What
    makes them successful?

5. Suppose that a federal bill has been proposed that would elimi-
    nate funding for all transportation services for the elderly. De-
    scribe how an intraorganizational network within the therapeutic
    recreation profession would be activated. Name other organiza-
    tions that would be involved in an interorganizational network
    and describe the approach this network would take in stopping
    this legislation.

References

Austin, D., & Hunnicutt, B. (1978). National Therapeutic Recreation
    Society: The First Twelve Years. *Therapeutic Recreation Jour-
    nal, (11)*3, 4-11.
Halberg, K., & Howe-Murphy, R. (1985). "The Dilemma of an Unre-
    solved Philosophy in Therapeutic Recreation." *Therapeutic
    Recreation Journal, (19)*3, 7-16.
Hunnicutt, B. (1978). A Rejoinder to the Twelve-Year History of the
    National Therapeutic Recreation Society. *Therapeutic Recrea-
    tion Journal, (12)*3, 15-19.
Levy, J. (1987). TIP-OFF: A New Model for Interagency Networking.
    *Therapeutic Recreation Journal, (21)*2, 20-28.
Loden, M. (1985). *Feminine Leadership or How to Succeed in Business
    Without Being One of the Boys* (1st ed.). New York: Times
    Books.
Naisbitt, J., & Aburdene, P. (1985). *Reinventing the Corporation.*
    New York: Warner Books.

Peterson, C. (1984). A Matter of Priorities and Loyalties. *Therapeutic Recreation Journal, (28)*3, 11-16.

Wilhite, B., Terry, B., Yoshioke, C., & McLean, D. (1983). Exploring Quality Circles in the Provision of Therapeutic Recreation Services. *Therapeutic Recreation Journal, (27)*3, 6-13.

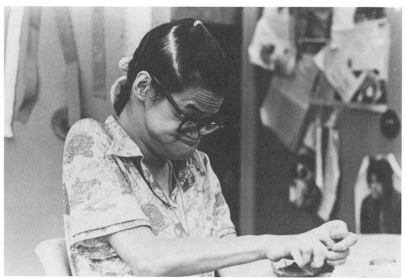

photo courtesy of San Francisco Recreation Center for the Handicapped

What indeed is it about the therapeutic recreation environment that causes the client's affective dispositions, cognitions, and perceptions to coalesce to bring about remediation of the psychological concomitants of some particular disease state?

—Kenneth G. Mobily

PART I

Issues of Meaning and Value

Summary

In youthful professions much attention is paid to the clarification of terms, roles, one's purpose for being and a host of other meaning and value oriented issues.   Sylvester aptly brings to our attention the problems with youthfulness when he asserts that therapeutic recreation lacks the "intellectual character suitable for the type of systematic body of knowledge evidenced by such bona fide professions as law, medicine, and engineering. Consequently, it is an occupation whose professional aspirations have been frustrated by intellectual insufficiency and by excessive reliance on other disciplines for most of its intellectual knowledge."

Sylvester suggests that there were periods when therapeutic recreation focused on philosophical and intellectual issues but these were rare. Efforts to address the philosophical issues were initiated by NTRS President Gary Robb during his term of office. His presidential critical issues committee to generate a philosophical statement was not only the first systematic effort to place clarity and meaning behind the terms "therapeutic recreation" but an important developmental and organizational statement.

The NTRS Philosophical Position Statement represented a "democratic method of majority opinion" according to Sylvester. Its historical significance must be considered political rather than philosophical. Sylvester suggests that "...the NTRS Philosophical Position Statement is not a body of theoretical knowledge, nor has it generated the philosophical grounds upon which to erect one." So where are we? It is apparent that we do not want to travel the path of guidance counseling. Neither do we wish to be an occupation. We cannot afford to continue a course of conciliation or reconciliation. Fundamental questions and ideas concerning "health, leisure, recreation, treatment, and quality of life" are essential to an "intellectual awakening."

Excessive attention to the internal political and working machinations of the organizations has led us past the essential issues of a profession and professionals. Fundamental changes in the education of therapeutic recreation professionals are required. The therapeutic recreation curriculum must move from specialization and technocracy, and become couched in a liberal education base. Choosing the right road will be of critical importance to creating an intellectual past worthy of citation, declaration and tradition.

In her discussion of the dilemma of philosophy, Peterson suggests that the need for philosophy is to achieve sanction from consumers/clients, recognized authorities and other professions. Central to the emergence of therapeutic recreation is "The inability or unwillingness of the profession to take a stand on philosophical content issues (which) appears to be a major stumbling block in the recognition, acceptance, and marketing of the field as a legitimate profession." Whether we are principally a part of the leisure or therapy profession is fundamental to the emergence and acceptance of a philosophy according to Peterson. Achieving unity in the definition of terms, purpose and a host of other matters (eg) legislation, third party reimbursements, standards for practice, etc., requires clarity and singularity of purpose. Our professional preparation programs are frought with diversity. Little resemblance exists between curricula, even with the advent of a national accreditation program. There is little ability to examine our knowledge base if the curricula persist in dispensing information which is inconsistent and incomplete. Implications for the emerging credentialling process are mind boggling. How can we conceivably test base level knowledge in such a diverse atmosphere?

Peterson closes by suggesting that there is little current theoretical development such as the Leisure Ability model or Howe-Murphy and Charboneau's ecological perspective. Sylvester might challenge the notion that either represents the explicit intellectual underpinning for theory development in the profession. If there is any commonality in this part, it is the clarion call for the unification of thought which should foster theoretical constructs upon which to build a profession. The words of Harry Lorayne in *Memory Makes Money* are poignant reminders of our dilemma, "Most problems precisely defined are already partially solved"

Numerous issues revolve around our professional affiliation and the organizations we tend to identify with on a daily or annual basis. Keller discusses the reasons why professional organizations exist and the requirements of their members. She goes to the heart of the issue by addressing the need for leadership in an organization. Several qualifications are discussed and reasons for belonging are offered. In articulating a position for engagement of the professional, Keller offers four keys to developing involvement and leadership in the profession-individual assessment of the persons life and needs, creating a sense of belonging through meaningful committee involvement and team building, establishing functional and guided committee work that is relevant to the overall improvement of the organization, and creating an environment in which there is mutual respect and interest of both the organization and the member for each other.

Lord offers some interesting options in the area of networking among organizations involved in or related to therapeutic recreation. Creating intra- and inter-organizational networks offers all participants the opportunity to increase communications, share information and professional development. She suggests that an era of cooperation is needed to address the numerous issues facing the profession. One must agree that our current "house divided" status does little to increase our power among the decision makers within or outside the profession.

Credentialing Issues

photo courtesy of City of Las Vegas

A license or credential to practice therapeutic recreation comes with heavy responsibility for the welfare of human beings entrusted unto the professional.

—Marcia Jean Carter

CREDENTIALING IN THERAPEUTIC RECREATION:
Issues in Ensuring the Minimal Competence of Professionals

Norma J. Stumbo

Introduction

What is professional competence? What types of programs are available to establish standards for professional competence? What are the specific mechanisms used to define and measure competence? And what are the advantages, disadvantages, and issues surounding these mechanisms? These are just a few of the many questions that abound when issues of ensuring professional competence are raised. There are no easy answers or solutions, and usually one decision merely unfolds many further layers of new issues and decisions to be made. The purpose of this chapter is to explore some of the issues and dilemmas of ensuring minimal competence of professionals, specifically relating these to therapeutic recreation practice. The reader will discover quickly that many issues and situations are yet to be confronted by our profession and hover on the immediate horizon. The decisions made and methods used will have impact on the profession for years to come.

The first portion of this chapter discusses the basic problems of defining and measuring professional competence. The second section outlines the four major types of programs that establish standards for professional competence, including advantages and disadvantages of each. The third section discusses different methods or options available for defining, measuring, and monitoring professional competence. One of these methods is examinations, which is the focus of the fourth part of the chapter. The last section outlines the current activities and developments within the National Council for Therapeutic Recreation Certification. At the end of the chapter are questions for further thought and dialogue. Each reader is encouraged to keep abreast of current developments as the profession of therapeutic recreation grapples with these issues and continues in its quest for greater professionalization.

The Definition and Measurement of
Professional Competence

The *measurement* of professional competence is hindered by the extreme difficulty in defining and operationalizing the *concept* of professional competence. Without an acceptable definition, measurement is impossible. "The word competence has become one of the most abused words in our professional vocabulary. It means capable, qualified or adequate for the purpose. The confusion comes when one attempts to assess the qualities in people" (Pottinger, 1979, p. 35). Competence in practice is a multifaceted phenomenon made more complex when one attempts to measure the qualifications of persons with varying backgrounds and degrees of abilities performing a multiplicity of job functions.

There are at least three complicating factors. The first addresses the variety of job functions professionals perform. Olson and Freeman (1979), among other authors, have asserted that the term *competence* may be too encompassing and instead have suggested a shift to identifying individual (but interrelated) competencies.

> The reason for the shift from competent to competencies is that one cannot, with science, say that a certain person "is a competent teacher in my school and of my children"; it is a social normative judgment. But one can, with science, say that she or he possesses certain behaviors and can perform them on call. (p. 6)

One avenue, then, is to define competence by delineating the specific and important components or areas of professional practice, that is, identifying the individual components of the whole. "These components must be identified as they relate to the individual's ability to achieve positive professional practice outcomes, particularly positive client outcomes" (Scofield, Berven, & Harrison, 1981, p. 34). The specification of components aids in the increased ability to measure the components and, in turn, the whole.

A second concern in defining and measuring competence is when and how the individual demonstrates competence. The major question is whether competence may be verified before or after the behavior is demonstrated. Olson and Freeman (1979) clarify this.

> These two ordinary uses of competent suggest two meanings in the context of licensing: one expresses certitude that a person can do a routine job, and the other expresses probability that a person can

handle a unique job (if anyone can). Conceptual confusion may result if competence [first definition], where what is done is repeatedly done and subject to judgments of competence after the act, is treated as [second definition], where what is done could only be done once and ability to do must be judged before the act. (p. 3)

This distinction becomes important because there exists a difference between measuring one's *potential* ability to perform a future activity and measuring one's *demonstrated* ability to provide competent service. This distinction is crucial in selecting an appropriate method of measuring competence (as will be seen in later sections of this chapter), and its importance proportionately increases with the profession's ability to harm or damage clients. That is, there are some professions in which the *demonstration* of competence prior to actual practice is paramount (for example, surgery).

The third issue, which receives even greater attention in the literature, is the difference between knowledge and skills or abilities. This concern revolves around whether competence is judged based on (a) a person's level of knowledge (one would predict, based on the person's knowledge, that he or she will perform competently) or (b) a person's ability (the person has demonstrated the ability, so it is therefore assumed that he or she has the requisite knowledge). The problems of definition and measurement in this case are assuring job relatedness versus ease of test development and administration. These issues will be discussed in greater depth in later sections of the chapter.

These three concerns are central to the delineation and assessment of professional competence, and their resolutions intertwine with a number of related factors. Two of these factors are the type of structure which is chosen to administer the program and the type(s) of methods utilized to directly assess individual competence. The next two sections contain discussions of these and their impact on the assessment of competence.

Program Structures

Four types of program structures are reviewed in this section; as a preface, it should be noted that one system is not necessarily preferable to any other but should be chosen by the profession involved based on the need for and purpose of the program. Each has a unique mission along with advantages and disadvantages. A second note is that many professions use the related terms interchangeably, so when reading other materials or conversing with other professionals, it is best to focus on the purpose of the program, not on the terms. The most common usage of each term is used in the following discussion.

Credentialing

Credentialing is an umbrella term used for any type of program which defines and recognizes professional competence. The four common types of credentialing programs are licensure, certification, registration, and accreditation. Utilization of one form does not preclude others, that is, any given profession may use two or more mechanisms for credentialing individuals based on the profession's needs. Most health-related professions do rely on two or more approaches.

Licensure

In 1977 the U.S. Department of Health, Education and Welfare defined licensure as

the process by which an agency of government grants permission to persons meeting predetermined qualifications to engage in a given occupation upon finding that the applicant had attained the minimal degree of competency necessary to ensure that the public health, safety, and welfare will be reasonably well-protected. (p. 4)

Licensure is the most restrictive form of credentialing because it requires a state government to enact legislation defining professional practice. Such pieces of legislation are often "referred to as 'practice acts' because they usually contain 'scope of practice' statements that define what a licensed practitioner may do" (Shimberg, 1981, p. 1138). In turn, practice acts also make it illegal for anyone not licensed to perform the activities defined in the scope of practice (Shimberg, 1984, p. 101). In addition, "a group proposing that it be licensed must usually convince a legislative body that the public is being harmed by the absence of regulation" (Shimberg, 1981, p. 1138–1139). The rationale used to promote passage of practice acts is "that they assure the public that practitioners are competent and protect the public against fraudulent or wrongful acts by the regulated providers" (Danish & Smyer, 1981, p. 16).

However, those who write in disfavor of licensure state that "it is instructive to add the evidence that licensing does not seem to be effective in preventing incompetent practice, and . . . there isn't much interest in the discipline of incompetent practitioners" (Gross, 1978, p. 1014). As such, some of these opponents "suggest that certification and registration arrangements could accomplish the protection of the public as well as the compulsory licensing of practice would" (Gross, p. 1014).

Certification

Certification "is the process by which a nongovernmental agency or association grants recognition to an individual who has met certain predetermined qualifications specified by that agency or association" (Pennell, 1972, p. 82–83). The National Commission on Health Certifying Agencies (NCHCA) (1980b, p. 4) has defined certification as "the awarding by a private agency of a credential and the right to use that credential, which attests to the competence of the individual engaged in the relevant scope of practice." Since, unlike licensure, certification is usually administered by nongovernmental agencies, it is usually referred to as "title control" (in contrast to licensure as "practice control"). Certification requirements do not prohibit uncertified individuals from practicing their occupations; rather, they prevent them from using the designated professional title(s) (Shimberg, 1981). Certification is usually a voluntary process not required for practice in the profession.

In the past, licensure requirements were typically representative of minimal competence, thereby denying the license to those individuals who may harm the public by their lack of qualifications; certification was usually set to designate competence well above entry level, as in the medical specialty certifications. However, in recent years these simplified distinctions have become less clear as a number of professions, including therapeutic recreation, have initiated programs which certify individuals who possess entry-level skills (Schmitt, 1987; Shimberg, 1984).

Registration

Registration is another term often associated with professional credentialing. Although the terms 'registration' and 'certification' are sometimes used interchangeably, registration generally means that " a law requires all individuals who wish to engage in a given occupation to register with a designated government agency" (Shimberg, 1982, p. 18). As a rule, "registration usually involves only listing one's name and address and payment of a fee...the law does not require the individual to pass an examination or show that he or she has met any predetermined standards" (Shimberg, 1982, p. 18). By this definition, registration does not aid in the definition or determination of professional competence.

Accreditation

Accreditation of educational programs may be used as a mechanism for upgrading and maintaining the quality of personnel entering a given profession. It is a mechanism for ensuring that educational programs have met certain standards of educational requirements, qualified faculty, and adequate resources. There are two types of accreditation: institutional and program specialization. Institutional accreditation for higher education facilities is implemented by regional associations that focus on the adequacy of the entire facility and personnel in terms of providing overall quality education (Reynolds & O'Morrow, 1985; Shimberg, 1984). Specialized program accreditation is usually conducted by the professional association and focuses on the narrower perspective of the preparation of students for a particular profession (Shimberg).

The major disadvantage of requiring graduation from an accredited program for credentialing lies in the fact that accreditation assesses the qualifications of the educational program, not the individual. As such, it is rarely used as the sole criterion for professional credentialing, but may be one of a number of requirements the individual must meet to be awarded a license or certificate.

Methods of Defining Professional Competence

In the previous sections, the difficulties of defining and measuring competence as well as administrative program structures have been discussed. Both of these have an impact on the decision of exactly how the definition of professional competence is operationalized into standards of entry. The primary concern with these methods or standards is that they should be *job-related*, although this proof is often lacking (Hogan, 1979; Shimberg, 1981, 1984). This concern should be kept in mind when reading the following material on requirements of personal characteristics, education, experience, and examinations. Most credentialing programs stipulate a combination of these requirements.

Personal characteristic requirements usually come under two categories. The first is citizenship status, which was predominantly found in licensure acts. The trend recently has been to remove this requirement from statutes because there has been no demonstrated evidence of job relatedness to it, and, in fact, under the Fourteenth Amendment it may be illegal (Shimberg, 1982). The second personal requirement often listed is "good moral character" or "no moral turpitude." The major weakness of such a requirement is the inherent vagueness of the terms. "However, to the ex-offender the meaning is quite clear. Both courts and licensing agencies have interpreted it to mean that if a person has a criminal record he lacks the requisite character for a license" (Grant, 1970, cited in Shimberg, p. 51). It is worthwhile to note that this requirement may receive greater attention in the years to come as criteria for disciplinary action are developed and enforced by credentialing bodies. At the December 1987 meeting of the National Commission on Health Certifying Agencies, several credentialing groups stated they were requesting this information on applications, and several sessions were presented on or discussed disciplinary procedures.

Education requirements may take three forms: years of schooling, specification of a degree, and graduation from an accredited program or university. Years of schooling are usually specified by those occupations which do not maintain typical college programs, such as cosmetology, which specifies years of high school education. However, there is debate whether these requirements are "related to safe practice and . . . serve a useful social purpose" (Shimberg, 1982, p. 38). These requirements are not typical of professions which require graduation from specific college degree programs.

Almost all professions that have a credentialing mechanism in place require graduation from a professional preparation program. Standards for the internal content of the program may be specified directly by the credentialing body or may be implied by requiring the educational program to be accredited. The general concerns in this area are that there is little empirical evidence demonstrating a correlation between competence and academic grades and that accreditation does not produce a valid standardization of curricula (Hogan, 1979; Pottinger, 1979; Shimberg, 1982). In spite of these arguments, the trend is currently to raise training requirements for entry (that is, to the master's or doctoral level). Opponents argue that additional training does not assure a higher quality of service provision and that the requirement unnecessarily restricts entry into the profession.

The third avenue used for defining and measuring competence is an experience requirement, traditionally in addition to a specific educational requirement. The underlying, and interesting, assumption of dictating experience appears to be the compensation for the inadequacy of training programs to properly prepare entering professionals. While few would argue against experience being beneficial, the question is one of defining the minimal amount considered to be entry-level. There is a wide disparity between professions, which require anywhere from 1 to 5 years of experience. An additional concern centers around measuring the quantity and quality of the experience (i.e. how much and at what level).

Examinations as a Method for Defining and Measuring Professional Competence

To overcome some of these limitations of requiring certain personal conditions and types of education and experience, another alternative, examinations, is often suggested. As with other methods, testing for competence is not a panacea and has its own set of problems and disadvantages. Because it is a method with intricate complexities and one chosen for therapeutic recreation, a more thorough discussion of utilizing examinations is needed.

Testing for professional competence is not a new concept, and in a "test-taking" society such as ours, it has the advantage of familiarity. However, as the saying goes, "familiarity breeds contempt": in recent years testing for various purposes has come under close scrutiny and criticism as sophistication of consumers and assertion of individual rights increase. This places new but not necessarily unreasonable demands on test development and implementation.

Whether a board uses a locally prepared written test or a national exam, it still has the responsibility of assuring (a) that the examination is a satisfactory measure of competence; (b) that it measures the critical or important knowledge, skills, and abilities prerequisite to performance on the job at a minimal level of competence deemed necessary for the public's protection; and (c) that it is capable of screening out those who lack the requisite level of competence (Shimberg, 1982)

It is no surprise that in the past, few examinations met these basic requirements, but attention to new developments and techniques is gaining momentum as credentialing bodies gain expertise and respond to the demands for accountability.

The concept of job-relatedness was discussed in introducing different methods of competence assessment. This concept is extremely important to examinations and relates to the measurement properties of validity, reliability, and fairness. Validity "refers to the extent to which the results of an evaluation procedure serve the particular uses for which they are intended" (Gronlund, 1981, p. 65). Validity indices determine whether the intended characteristic is actually measured or represented by the final results. Validity asks the question "Does the instrument measure what it is intended to measure?" In relation to credentialing exams, it asks whether the test measures the appropriate knowledge, skills, and abilities necessary for minimal competence in entry-level practice.

Reliability refers to the consistency or accuracy of the measurement results (Gronlund, 1981; Thorndike & Hagen, 1977). In credentialing tests, reliability indices report how consistent the results are from one administration to another, as well as how accurately the results of the test relate to the job in question.

Fairness, or nondiscrimination of protected classes, in testing is a difficult situation for measurement experts. On one hand, tests cannot be biased with regard to scores received by certain population sub-groups, that is, they cannot be unduly discriminatory (Educational Testing Service [ETS], 1987, p. 7). On the other hand, tests are constructed to determine differences in knowledge and abilities and to reflect these differences through test scores. In discussing a hearing on one method of minimizing test bias, Shimberg (1987a) highlights this dilemma.

> Many of the witnesses pointed out that the approach was based on the false assumption that when differences between groups are observed, the difference was attributable primarily to bias. What is overlooked, they argued, is the possibility that the differences may be due to real differences in ability or in knowledge of the field. (p. 5)

Major testing companies have developed specific procedures to reduce unreasonable test bias in response to this situation (e.g., ETS, 1986).

These three factors–validity, reliability and fairness–are over-riding concerns throughout the test development process. The process encompasses several decision points or issues including, (a) the content of the test, (b) the type of test, (c) test security, (d) the interpretation and use of results, and (e) sound measurement practices.

Content of the test

Once a decision has been made to use a test, the next, often overlooked, step is to determine what exactly is to be tested. The content and difficulty of the test are dependent on the purpose. Typically, in most licensing and certification programs, the purpose is directed to establishing minimal criteria for knowledge and skills, and differentiating between those practitioners who are likely to harm the public and those who are not. Certification and licensing tests are not intended to predict the most successful practitioners in job performance, as employee selection examinations are intended to do (Bryant, 1981; Burns, 1985). Determining minimal competence then becomes both the purpose and the "difficulty" of the examination.

The next step is to determine the parameters or content of the test. This is usually performed by conducting a formal job analysis. According to Burns 1985),

> a job analysis is a systematic method of determining what a practitioner actually does on the job. It provides a way to describe the most important functions and responsibilities of the job and what the entry-level practitioner needs to know and be able to do in order to carry out responsibilities and functions. The focus is on acceptable performance, not outstanding performance. (p. 17)

There are a variety of methods available to conduct a job analysis (Burns, 1985; NCHCA, 1980; Shimberg, 1982; Smith, 1986), but the end result is a detailed inventory of the important or critical knowledge, skills, and abilities required to perform the job at a minimal level of competence. It identifies the important and frequently used domains, or content areas, of the job in question. This inventory leads to test specifications or a blueprint. The blueprint must relate the content of the test to the functions of the job. The test blueprint identifies the exact content, the level of knowledge required (refer to Bloom's taxonomy of educational objectives), the number of items per domain or task, and the level of difficulty of each item. The question is one of content validity, whether the test specifications are appropriate to and representative of the domains of practice to be tested (American Psychological Association [APA], 1974; Gronlund, 1981; Kerlinger, 1973; Lennon, 1955). The job analysis and test blueprint are key factors in increasing job relatedness. (A related example would be a blueprint of a classroom test where items of the exam must be representative of the content and the level of difficulty of instruction. Every student knows when these properties have not been adhered to.)

Types of tests

Generally there are two types of tests: written and performance. Written tests usually employ paper-and-pencil or computerized formats and are appropriate for any profession for which a job analysis has revealed that specified knowledge or application is related to practice.

In addition, some professions include performance tests, such as simulations or demonstrations, where execution of certain procedures is required on the job, such as nursing and dentistry. The use of either or both types of tests is dependent on the nature of the job and the results of the job analysis.

One type of test is not "better" than the other, because both must relate directly to minimal competence. However, virtually all professions use at least written tests due to their ease of administration and scoring. Critics of written tests argue that they may be better suited to assess knowledge than performance (the issue of which is more appropriate for defining competence). Critics of performance tests point out that sometimes non-essential but easily tested skills are measured and that the use of judges for performance reduces the validity, reliability, and fairness of the test results. Both types have disadvantages; the more defensible one can be determined from the results of the job analysis. Other considerations in selection include cost, time, administration factors (such as number of testing sites, judges, candidates and testing forms), scoring factors (such as machine versus hand scoring of tests), and psychometric properties (Burns, 1985; Shimberg, 1982).

Test security

Since test questions and scores are used to determine competence and whether the candidate receives the credential, security of the test and the process is imperative. Test security is critical at three major points in the testing process: prior to testing, during test administration, and after testing. During test construction, several individuals come in contact with test materials, such as expert panels, practitioner reviewers, and the credentialing body's administrators. It is a common policy that no one individual from the profession has the opportunity to view the test(s) in its entirety. During test administration, security may be enhanced by requiring candidates to show proof of identification at entrance, reducing opportunities for copying, and by screening and training test proctors. After test administration, care must be taken to reduce cheating through discouraging test-takers from "spreading the word" of test questions and through careful handling of test forms (Burns, 1985, p. 33–34). Another aid in test security is the creation of several "equivalent forms" of the test, which is especially helpful for security prior to and during the administration.

An additional outside threat to the integrity of exams is being introduced through legislation. These "truth in testing" laws first

addressed educational entrance exams but are now entering the credentialing arena in the "public's interest" and are intended "to allow people
taking licensing exams to review actual past test questions, to allow test
takers to learn from past examinations' subject areas and to permit independent researchers to review these tests for validity and fairness"
(Shimberg, 1987a, p. 1). To accomplish this, "copies of all questions
used in determining the passing grade, corresponding acceptable answers, and all rules for determining passing grades would become
public record" (Shimberg, p. 1). Thus, test-takers, especially those who
do not pass the exam, would have unprecedented access to testing
materials. It is not difficult to see that while the intent of providing test-
takers with information on their scores is appropriate, test security
would be greatly diminished and test costs significantly increased if this
type of legislation would pass for credentialing groups (Burns, 1985;
Shimberg, 1987c).

Interpretation and use of test scores

One interesting issue that gains considerable attention in test
construction and implementation is the setting of the passing, or "cut,"
score. The cut score is the dividing line between those who pass the examination and receive the credential and those who do not. Credentialing examinations are not graded or concerned with a range of scores (as
are educational tests) because the purpose is to distinguish between
competence and noncompetence, not the range of competence. The
focus of credentialing test scores falls on the immediate vicinity of the
passing score. "The concern is not with those who are clearly qualified
(those making high scores) or with those who are clearly not qualified
(those making very low scores). The concern is with those just above
and below the passing point" (Burns, 1985, p. 28). So the issue becomes
one of the reliability, or accuracy and consistency, of test scores. If the
scores are not reliable, two types of wrong decisions may be made about
the candidates: "1. a test-taker who actually belongs in the lower group
can get a score above the passing score; 2. a test-taker who actually
belongs in the higher group can get a score below the passing score"
(Livingston & Zieky, 1982, p. 12). It is easy to understand the
importance of the cut score, both to the candidate and the profession.

Several methods have been developed to determine passing scores
(see Angoff, 1971; Nedelsky, 1954; Rosen, 1987), and there is considerable statistical evidence for encouraging their use. However, two
factors enter into the selection and use of cut score procedures. First is
that the selection of the cut score procedure is a *policy* decision. The

governing body, by policy, not only selects the method but also makes other decisions (such as members of the review panel) in the implementation of the method (Jones, 1987). As each method, like all statistics, has benefits and constraints, the policymakers must weigh these factors and select a procedure (NCHCA, 1980a). Second, all measurement contains some degree of error. "It is important . . . to recognize that wherever the cut or passing score is set and however good the test, score error will exist in the measurement and in scores" (Burns, 1985, p. 28). The aim of commercial testing companies and credentialing organizations is to reduce the likelihood of error as much as is feasible; this may be accomplished through sound measurement practices.

Sound Measurement Practices

Many of the above issues have been addressed through the establishment of professional and legal standards for test construction and administration. These have been introduced by professional measurement organizations, commercial testing companies, individual consumers, and consumer protection groups. Some examples of these standards in published form include the following (Burns, 1985; Shimberg, 1982):

Professional standards
1. Standards for Educational and Psychological Tests (APA, 1974)

2. Joint Technical Standards for Educational and Psychological Testing (APA, American Educational Research Association, and the National Council on Measurement in Education, 1985)

3. Criteria for Approval of Certifying Agencies (NCHCA, 1980b)

4. ETS Standards on Test Quality and Fairness (ETS, 1987)

Related references
5. Passing Scores: A Manual for Setting Standards of Performance on Educational and Occupational Tests (Livingston & Zieky, 1982)

6. ETS Sensitivity and Review Process (ETS, 1986)

Legal standards
7. Federal Uniform Guidelines on Employment Selection Procedures

(Equal Employment Opportunity Commission, 1978).

The importance of these publications is in the establishment of strict measurement criteria for test development and implementation so that groups such as credentialing bodies not only have guidelines to follow but also have increased legal defensibility for their practices and decisions should they be questioned. They also aid the consumer, the test-taker, in being assured that testing practices are as valid, reliable, and fair as is psychometrically possible.

The Therapeutic Recreation Profession

The first credentialing program for therapeutic recreation personnel began in 1956, when the Council for the Advancement of Hospital Recreation (CAHR) created the National Voluntary Registration Plan for Hospital Recreation Personnel (Carter, 1981; Frye & Peters, 1972). In that year CAHR established standards, decided upon the mechanism for implementing the standards, and formed the Board of Registration. Standards for qualification included both education and experience, although educational requirements were sometimes waived for persons considered pioneers in the field (Grubb, 1956).

The initial decisions–of program structure and methods of defining competence–have impact on the credentialing program of today. Although called registration, the program structure better fit under the previously defined term of *certification* because it required some level of competence rather than a simple listing of the candidate's name. In addition, the method chosen to define competence included a review of the candidate's education and experience.

These two structures basically remained the same, with several significant changes in titles and standards for education and experience, until 1980 and 1981. At that time, the Board of Directors of the National Therapeutic Recreation Society (NTRS), which took over administration of the program from CAHR in 1966, created a separate, autonomous body to govern the credentialing program. National legal precedence was being set by requiring that credentialing organizations be independent and autonomous from membership associations (NCHCA, 1980). NTRS followed this lead by creating the National Council for Therapeutic Recreation Certification (NCTRC) in 1981. This nine-member Council is charged with three major responsibilities: setting national evaluative standards for the certification and recertification of therapeutic recreation personnel, granting recognition to those who meet the standards, and monitoring adherence to standards by certified personnel (Carter, 1983).

The recent progress made in the credentialing arena for therapeutic recreation personnel has been substantial. The entry-level standards have been refined into a two-level plan for professionals (Certified Therapeutic Recreation Specialists) and paraprofessionals (Certified Therapeutic Recreation Assistants.) This change has provided consistency with other health related professions and has minimized confusion over qualifications within the field.

Another substantial change in the credentialing program has been the initiation of a testing program for professional level personnel. Although the previous program of reviewing an applicant's education and experience was satisfactory, the move toward a national examination shows some level of discomfort with those standards as the sole definition and measurement of competence. As mentioned previously, not only is the definition important, but likewise the ability to measure competence. And it was felt that validity, reliability, and fairness of the credential would be increased even further through the implementation of an examination procedure.

In 1982, the NCTRC established the Test Development and Research Committee (later renamed the Test Management Committee) to explore the possibilities and problems of test development and administration. The committee has established liaisons with testing companies; has conducted research on entry-level knowledge of professionals (Stumbo, 1985,1986a), paraprofessionals (Stumbo,1986b), and bachelor's degree curricula (Stumbo & Peterson, 1987); and has generally provided the overall direction for test development activities.

A significant milestone occurred in April 1987. After five years in development, the NCTRC Board of Directors voted to approve a contract for a formal job analysis with the Educational Testing Service of Princeton, New Jersey; the contract was signed the same year. The importance of the job analysis was twofold. The results of the job analysis—the delineation of important, critical and frequently used domains in professional level practice—was the first time that a nationally based study was conducted on entry-level professional competence. Although the profession has approved and published several documents, such as standards of practice and accreditation standards, which help define the field, none of these have been based on the type of comprehensive and psychometrically sound research used in the job analysis. It has defined the parameters of the profession and will benefit the credentialing program as well as other professional activities.

A second important milestone occurred in October 1988 when the Board of Directors approved a test development contract with ETS. The results of the job analysis showed that therapeutic recreation has a unique and coherent body of professional knowledge which practitioners use in their employment settings. The job analysis also revealed that there was a high degree of agreement on the job responsibilities and knowledges needed to practice, regardless of setting type. These two factors aid in the feasibility and usefulness of the testing process by drawing on a large , but definable set of competencies for entry-level practice. The test, then, becomes an additional measure to the sitting requirements for defining minimal competence. (A document detailing the results of the national job analysis is available from the NCTRC office.)

The first test administration is slated for the fall of 1990 and will include both incumbents and first-time applicants. By the end of 1995, all actively certified professionals will have passed the sitting requirements and test to become credentialed. At this point in time, the consumer, as the major benefactor of all credentialing programs, will have a greater assurance that certified, practicing professionals are competent to provide quality services.

One decision leads to others, and the approval of a testing program caused many issues to surface rapidly. Among these are the exact nature of sitting requirements, grandparenting, re-certification criteria, cut or passing scores, and relationships with state credentialing programs, as well as logistical concerns of when, how often, and where to administer the exam. These are just a few of the many concerns of test development and administration, but are "well worth the price" as the profession of therapeutic recreation continues to advance in the definition and measurement of minimal professional competence.

For a current update on testing activities, write or call: National Council for Therapeutic Recreation Certification, 49 South Main Street, Suite 005, SpringValley, New York, 10977, (914) 356-9660.

Study Questions

1.   What is your personal definition of professional competence? How would you operationalize this to the field of therapeutic recreation?

2.   How does the structure affect the operation and purpose of the credentialing program? How does this affect the definition and measurement of competence?

3.   What are arguments for and against each method of measuring competence? In terms of validity, reliability and fairness, which are the most appropriate for therapeutic recreation?

4.   What are the advantages and disadvantages of an examination? How would you respond to both proponents and critics?

5.   What are your opinions concerning the current direction and decisions of the NCTRC? What do you think will happen in the next 5 or 10 years?

References

American Psychological Association. (1974). Standards for Educational and Psychological Tests. Washington, DC: Author.

American Psychological Association, American Educational Research Association, & National Council on Measurement in Education (1985). *Joint Technical Standards for Educational and Psychological Testing*. Washington, DC: Authors.

Angoff, W.H. (1971). Scales, Norms and Equivalent Scores. In R.L. Thorndike (Ed.), *Educational Measurement* (2nd ed.). (pp.508-600). Washington, D.C.: American Council on Education.

Bryant, S.K. (1981). Voluntary Certification and the Uniform Guidelines on Selection Procedures: A Potential Problem for Personnel Managers. *Health Policy and Education, 2* 135-182.

Burns, R.L. (1985). Guidelines for Developing and Using Licensure Tests. In C. Fortune and Associates (Eds.), *Understanding Testing in Occupational Licensing* (pp.15–44).San Francisco:Jossey-Bass.

Carter, M.J. (1981). Registration of Therapeutic Recreators: Standards from 1956 to Present. *Therapeutic Recreation Journal, 15* (2), 17-22.

Carter, M.J. (1983). Therapeutic Recreation Credentialing: Its History, Issues and Future. In G. Hitzhusen (Ed.), *Expanding Horizons in Therapeutic Recreation* (Vol. 10, pp. 193-208). Columbia, MO: Curators University of Missouri.

Danish, S.J., & Smyer, M.A. (1981). Unintended Consequences of Requiring a License to Help. *American Psychologist, 36* (1), 13-21.

Educational Testing Service (1986). *ETS Sensitivity Review Process: Guidelines and Procedures*. Princeton, NJ: Author.

Educational Testing Service (1987). *ETS Standards for Quality and Fairness*. Princeton, NJ:Author.

Equal Employment Opportunity Commission. (1978). Federal Uniform Guidelines On Employment Selection Procedures. *Federal Register*, Part I, August, 25, 1978.

Frye, V., & Peters, M. (1972). *Therapeutic Recreation: Its Theory, Philosophy and Practice*. Harrisburg, PA: Stackpole Books.

Grant, W., et al. (1970). The collateral consequences of a criminal conviction. *Vanderbilt Law Review, 23*:(5), 1002, 1010.

Gronlund, N.E. (1981). *Measurement and Evaluation in Teaching* (4th ed.) New York: Macmillan.

Gross, S.J. (1978). The Myth of Professional Licensing. *American Psychologist, 33* (11), 1009-1016.

Grubb, A. (1958). Are You Registered? *Recreation for the Ill and Handicapped, 2* (4), 8-9.

Hogan, D.B. (1979). Is Licensing Public Protection or Professional Protectionism? In P.S. Pottinger & J. Goldsmith (Eds.), *Defining and Measuring Competence*. (pp.13-24). San Francisco: Jossey-Bass.

Jones, J.P. (1987). Handout Accompanying Presentation on Cut Score Procedures. Presented at the conference of the National Clearinghouse on Licensure, Enforcement and Regulation, Kansas, Missouri.

Kerlinger, F.N. (1973). *Foundations of Behavioral Research*, (2nd ed.). New York: Holt, Rinehart and Winston.

Lennon, R.T. (1955). Assumptions Underlying the Use of Content Validity. In *Content Validity of Nonfactual Tests* (pp. 294-304). Symposium Conducted at the American Psychological Association Convention, San Francisco.

Livingston, S.A., & Zieky, M.J. (1982). *Passing Scores: A Manual For Setting Scores On Performance on Educational and Occupational Tests*. Princeton, NJ: Educational Testing Service.

National Commission on Health Certifying Agencies (19780a). *Guidelines for Membership Criteria: Report On Cut-off Scores*. Washington, DC: Author.

National Commission on Health Certifying Agencies. (1980b). *Perspectives on Health Occupational Credentialing*. Washington, DC: US Department of Health and Human Services.

Nedelsky, L. (1954). Absolute Grading Standards For Objective Tests. *Educational and Psychological Measurement, 14*, 13-19.

Olson, P.A., & Freeman, L. (1979). Defining Competence in Teacher Licensing Usage. In P.S. Pottinger & J. Goldsmith (Eds.), *Defining and measuring competence* (pp.1-11). San Francisco: Jossey-Bass.

Pennell, M.Y. (1972). Accreditation, Certification and Licensure. In E.J. McTerma & R.O. Hawkins, Jr. (Eds.)*Educating Personnel For the Allied Health Professions and Services: Administrative Considerations.* St. Louis: C.V. Mosby, 66-84.

Pottinger, P.S. (1979). Competence Assessment: Comments on Current Practices. In P.S. Pottinger & J. Goldsmith (Eds.), *Defining and Measuring Competence (pp.25-39).* San Francisco: Jossey-Bass.

Reynolds, R.P., & O'Morrow, G.S. (1985). *Problems, Issues and Concepts in Therapeutic Recreation.* Englewood Cliffs, NJ: Prentice-Hall.

Rosen, G. (1987). *Advanced Testing Issues - A New Method for Setting Criterion-Referenced Passing Scores.* Paper presented at the meeting of the National Commission for Health Certifying Agencies, Miami, Florida, December.

Schmitt, K.L. (1987). *Licensing and Certification: A Complementary Relationship.* Paper Presented at the meeting of the National Commission for Health Certifying Agencies, Miami, Florida, December.

Scofield, M.E., Berven, N.L., & Harrison, R.P. (1981). Competence, Credentialing and the Future of Rehabilitation. *Journal of Rehabilitation, 47* (1), 31-35.

Shimberg, B. (1981). Testing for Licensure and Certification. *American Psychologist, 36* (10), 1138-1146.

Shimberg, B. (1982). *Occupational Licensing: A Public Perspective.* Princeton, NJ: Educational Testing Service, Center for Occupational and Professional Assessment.

Shimberg, B. (1984). The Relationship Among Accreditation, Certification and Licensure, *Federation Bulletin.* (Federation of State Medical Boards of the United States), April, 99-116.

Shimberg, B. (1987a). Alternatives to Legislative Prescriptions: Truth in Testing for the Professions. *Issues* (National Council of State Boards of Nursing), *8*(4), 1-7.

Shimberg, B. (1987b). Assuring the Continued Competence of Health Professionals. *The Journal,* September/October, 8-14.

Shimberg, B. (1987c). *Emerging Trends in Licensure and Assessment of Continued Competence.* Paper presented at the meeting of the American Occupational Therapy Association, Indianapolis, Indiana.

Smith, G.A. (1986). An Overview of NBRC's Five Step Examination Development Process. *NBRC Newsletter,* September, 3-4.

Stumbo, N.J. (1985). *Content Validation Study of Entry-Level Knowledge Needed by Therapeutic Recreation Specialists.* Unpublished doctoral dissertation, University of Illinois, Urbana-Champaign.

Stumbo, N.J. (1986a). A Definition of Entry-Level Knowledge for Therapeutic Recreation Practice. *Therapeutic Recreation Journal, 20*(4), 15-30.

Stumbo, N.J. (1986b). Preliminary Investigation of Therapeutic Recreation Assistant Knowledge. In R.D. MacNeil (Ed.), *Abstracts From the 1986 Symposium on Leisure Research* (p.43). Alexandria, VA: National Recreation and Park Association.

Stumbo, N.J., & Peterson, C.A. (1987, September). *Therapeutic Recreation Curricula: Professional Preparation and its Relationship to the Knowledge Base.* Paper presented at the Symposium on Leisure Research at the meeting of the National Recreation and Park Association, New Orleans, Louisiana.

Thorndike, R.L., & Hagen, E.P. (1977). *Measurement and Evaluation in Psychology and Education* (4th ed.). New York: John Wiley & Sons.

U.S. Department of Health, Education and Welfare–Public Health Service. (1977). *Credentialing health manpower.* Washington, DC: Author.

PROFESSIONAL RELATIONSHIPS IN CREDENTIALING

Marcia Jean Carter

Introduction

Through a series of formal and informal privileges, a profession gains sanction in specific spheres of competence. This authority is evident when standards are applied to admission into the profession and to practice or delivery of the unique service or function as defined by the profession's body of knowledge. Professional identity is garnered from delineation of a "scope of practice" defined by knowledge, skills, and abilities (KSA) specific to the particular area of expertise. This identity is significant to the members of the profession, to the profession itself, and to the recipients of service because it distinguishes the profession from other bodies.

Professional identity results from display of competencies recognized as the central tenets of the profession. A credential serves to identify persons and programs who have met either certain degrees of competence or standards essential to a unique body of knowledge. Implicit with a credential are professional privileges; also implied are standards of preparation, practice, and training. A credentialing system embodies many of those concepts which are fundamental to a profession, such as standards, autonomy, sanctions, ethics, philosophy, research, and academics. Consequently, those issues apparent in the profession are evident as standards evolve, identifying the professional to the public.

In the first section of this chapter, fundamental components of credentialing are identified, defined, and studied as they interrelate and have impact upon the service provider and the service consumer. The means by which professionals and preparation programs gain a "piece of paper showing their right to a certain position or authority"(Webster's, 1977) are interpreted and considered as singular and as interrelated components. Content of credentialing plans are examined and compared and contrasted among the various processes. Alternative admin-

Figure 1
Credentialing Components

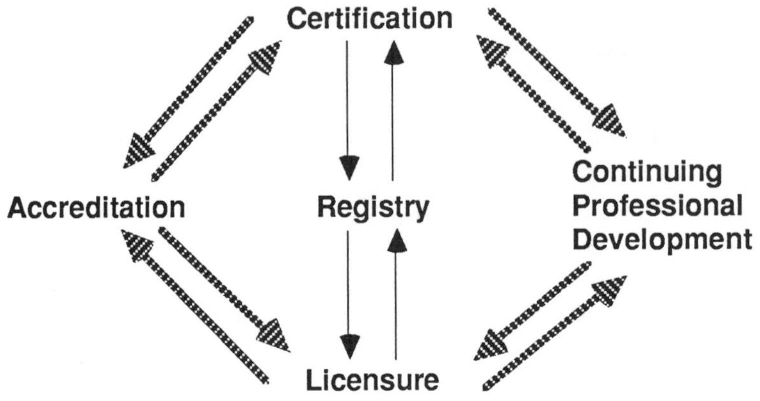

Certification

Accreditation   **Registry**   **Continuing Professional Development**

Licensure

Credentialing   Components

istrative models regulate credentialing procedures. These too are reviewed with respect to existing content and processes. A closing portion of this section requires the reader to explore credentialing from the consumer's perspective.

These issues raised as the tenets of credentialing are scrutinized from the perspective of an evolving profession in the second half of this chapter. A profession is defined by its philosophy, research, standards, code of ethics, autonomy and sanction, and unique service scope. A credentialing system implies relationships among these attributes. As therapeutic recreation evolves, dynamics of professionalization cause political, legal, economic, and technical issues to arise from interactions among the processes that define a profession. A closing portion summarizes the issues evolving as the profession moves toward more sophisticated credentialing relationships.

Credentialing Processes

Persons seeking verification of their competence in a specific area of expertise may select three forms of credentialing: registration, certification, and licensure (Figure 1).

Registration

A registry is the product of a registration process. This list or roster contains names of persons who possess prescribed credentials gained through certification or licensure. Either a governmental or nongovernmental agency retains and updates the document as persons satisfy standards of national-level certification programs sponsored by professional associations or state-level licensure programs managed by state governments.

Certification

Certification is a voluntary national process whereby a governmental or nongovernmental agency or association grants recognition of competence to an individual who has met predetermined qualifications. Certification is sometimes referred to as "title control" because those certified are entitled to use special professional title designations identified by trademarked letters or phrases like "CTRS/CTRA" (Certified Therapeutic Recreation Specialist/Certified Therapeutic Recreation Assistant). This process does not prohibit uncertified persons from practicing their occupation. However, only those persons who have met the standards are permitted to use the title designation. Usual qualifications include graduation from an approved training program, acceptable performance on a qualifying exam, and/or completion of some specified amount or type of work experience.

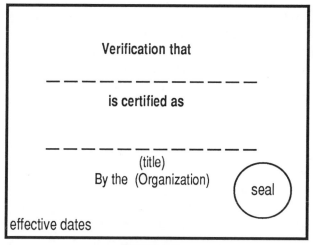

Certificate

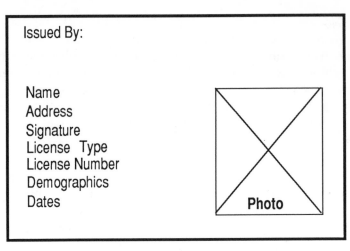

License

Licensure

Licensure is a process by which a governmental agency grants permission to an individual to engage in an occupation upon finding the applicant has attained a degree of competence to ensure protection of public health, welfare, and safety. Licensing laws are sometimes referred to as "practice acts" because they define a scope of practice identifying functions appropriate to the given occupation. Licensing is the most restrictive form of regulation because the power to either grant or withhold a license can be used to deny persons the opportunity to earn a livelihood in their chosen occupations. A license is issued under state law by a government-authorized board and is valid only in that particular state. Under a typical licensing statute, the applicant must satisfy certain education and training requirements, successfully complete an examination, and possess certain personal or demographic prerequisites such as a minimum age, minimum period of state residence, and evidence of good moral character.

Accreditation

Accreditation is a form of credentialing that focuses on the institution or the program (process) rather than the product (student). This occurs when an association or agency grants public recognition to a school, program, or health-care facility which has met certain established standards as determined through initial and periodic evaluations. Accreditation concerns the quality and integrity of the institution.

With some models, institutional accreditation must be achieved prior to review for specialized program accreditation. This is true of the National Recreation and Park Association Council on Accreditation process, for accreditation with one of the regional education associations is a prerequisite to a visit of the National Recreation and Park Association (NRPA) and American Association for Leisure and Recreation (AALR)–sponsored recreation team. Two hospital accreditation programs with which therapeutic recreators come into contact are those of the Joint Commission on Accreditation of Healthcare Organizations (JCAHO) and the Commission on Accreditation of Rehabilitation Facilities (CARF). Their standards set technical criteria for service quality, such as the requirements for assessments and program planning, as well as for types of service providers, occupational therapists, psychiatrists, and activity personnel.

Individual and institutional credentialing processes become intertwined as a profession matures. Incorporation of certification standards and processes into licensing statutes and regulations is common. Successful completion of an accredited program and the possession of a certificate from a professional association are prerequisites to state licensure exams. Likewise, graduation from accredited institutions and programs may be sitting requirements for professional association certification exams which must be passed prior to one's names being placed on a registry. A licensing board may grant reciprocity to someone holding a national-level certificate or allow the out-of-state person to sit for that particular state's licensing exam, waiving residency requirements.

However, confusion and conflict may result with the multiple use of credentialing standards. For instance, Utah may accept a National Council for Therapeutic Recreation Certification (NCTRC)-held certificate carte blanche while Georgia may require NCTRC documentation plus certain additional standards. As another example, NRPA may accept an NCTRC Therapeutic Recreation Specialist (TRS) credential through direct, national-level certification–additionally issuing the Certified Leisure Specialist (CLP)–while Michigan, a state with an NRPA-approved plan, may require yet further casework for CLP with TRS designation. What is called a certification law in one state may in another be referred to as licensure, as is the case with some coaching standards. Another example is an association placing persons' names on the registry only if they pass the exam, with others requiring registration prior to sitting for an exam. Thus, the issue lies with the interpretation of the perceived benefits and privileges assigned respective credentialing forms because the forms are not used consistently among the professional groups.

One approach to resolving concerns caused by multiple credential use is to establish cooperative relationships among the national- and state-level sponsors or bodies of like credentials. This action would support the concept that to be valid an instrument must be appropriate to the job tasks unique to a particular locale or setting. Thus, a state-level certification or licensure exam containing questions on special recreation districts would be appropriate to Illinois but irrelevant in New York. Reciprocity would also be enhanced when each state sets, for instance, as a minimum requirement, certification with NCTRC as a prerequisite to obtaining access to state processes. States might also consider including accreditation from approved professional preparation programs as a minimum prerequisite to their processes, using a vehicle like the *Parks & Recreation* listings of NRPA-AALR accredited schools to verify such training.

Credentialing Content

The intent of the credentialing processes is to verify an applicant's competence to practice a given role. The assumption underlying this belief is that certain knowledge, skills, and abilities (KSAs) are required in this role or area of competence. Therefore, content of credentialing programs is determined by an analysis of the role of the therapeutic recreation specialist. To become credentialed or to enter the practice, an applicant must show evidence of mastery of the KSAs defining the therapeutic recreation specialist. To remain "active" the practitioner should demonstrate continued competence or mastery of the tenets central to Therapeutic Recreation (TR) over an occupational lifetime.

The three E's—education, experience, and evaluation-encompass content essential to ensure quality service delivery. To either gain access to the credential or receive and maintain the credential, persons complete formal requirements verifying their competence with one or a combination of these three indices. Criteria defining these indices are classified as entry, eligibility, and continuing competency criteria or measures.

Entry

Entry criteria consist of seating requirements or prerequisites to access standards. Evidence commonly submitted includes proof of

The Three Es of Credentialing

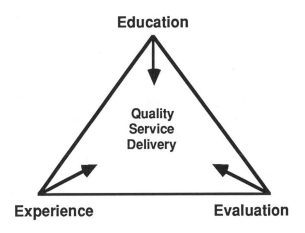

birth or age by a birth certificate or a driver's license, personal identification by a picture or a social security card, documentation of good moral character as validated by absence of incarceration for committed felony, and United States citizenship or particular state residency (Shimberg, 1980). Entry requirements may also include possession of a credential from another state or national association. This might occur when an applicant is requesting an upgrade or level change or is a new state resident. Validation of these criteria may come with notary signature on the application document.

Eligibility

Eligibility requirements define education, experience, and evaluation standards believed essential to the practice of therapeutic recreation. Generally, the higher the credential level requested, the more stringent these criteria become. Documentation of these standards comes from transcripts and certificates, reference letters, official college documents, and registries of approved courses of study. Evidence of education may come with requiring a certain number of years of schooling, degrees, graduation from approved or accredited curriculum, or completion of definitive coursework, and completion of an internship or practicum in the specialty area. Some bodies permit the substitution of greater amounts of work experience or successful completion of training programs in lieu of degree requirements. In addition to a specified training experience, some bodies require experiential requirements beyond education requirements, which may or may not need to be completed under properly qualified practitioners. Traditionally, this requirement was associated with technical fields like that of medical technicians and was believed necessary to fill the didactic void of academic curriculums. Experiential requirements are commonly used to differentiate between various credential levels and to retain "certificates" after a number of years in the field.

The paper-and-pencil exam is the most commonly used form of evaluation and often occurs following successful satisfaction of other forms of entry and eligibility criteria. Such forms of evaluation include simulations, submission of reports on individual projects, development of individual portfolios, site visits, peer reviews or audits, and self-assessment studies. Regardless of form, evaluation outlines must be job-related; measure KSAs essential to safe practice; be secure, valid, reliable, and nondiscriminatory; be weighted properly; and have, as the passing score, "minimal competency levels." Professional testing services are often employed by associations to develop particular evaluation programs because they have the expertise to complete the research and secure and defend the product in a nonbiased manner.

Continuing competency

Regardless of how well prepared a therapeutic recreator is upon entry into the field, the need to continue growth and development becomes greater with the passage of time. Continuing professional development is a lifelong learning process to ensure the delivery of quality services. Until the early 1980s, the continuing education unit (CEU) as defined by the Council on Continuing Education Unit was the accepted measure of renewal mandated following certification or licensure. The usual procedure was to require a certain number of CEUs to be accumulated over a brief time period believed to be equal to the pertinence of KSAs for practicing specific techniques, often a 2- to 5-year period. Associations rescinded mandatory CEUs after establishing that accumulation of a certain number of CEUs does not automatically imply continuing competence. Measures introduced to assure continuing competence have included reexamination, simulation, peer review and audits, and self-assessment practices (Shimberg, 1980).

Which requirements are truly job related, and what constitutes the minimum standard essential for safe and effective performance?

Which of the entry and eligibility requirements denote KSAs needed by TR professionals? What is the half-life of our unique KSAs? There is an absence of research to substantiate current credentialing practices. As with other health-related professions, custom has dictated standards. Our existing system is driven by how we gain our *expertise*-academics, rather than by how we use our *competence*-occupation. Some entry and eligibility requirements appear more valid than others: identification like a picture or a social security card verifies that a credential is awarded to the person so qualified. Review of transcripts does substantiate that coursework from accredited schools has been completed. Reference letters do confirm experiences. Yet after a certain level is achieved, additional degrees, training, and clock hours of adult education do not necessarily ensure that practitioners will provide a higher quality of service. Also, courts of law have questioned the constitutionality of such requirements as residency, citizenship, and "good moral character," citing violations of the Fourteenth Amendment, which assures equal protection for all persons with criminal records (Shimberg, 1980).

Credentialing Procedures

Over 250 associations and societies monitor professional certification programs. Teacher education credentials are jointly administered by state governments and professional preparation institutions. The federal government, through the Department of Justice and the Federal Trade Commission, has become involved in the credentialing arena, with legal mandates resulting from court cases on equal opportunity and fair business practices. At the state level in therapeutic recreation, Georgia, Utah, and North Carolina have developed credentialing programs through cooperative efforts of government and professional associations. A third scenario finds credentialing under the auspices of a contracted, outside service, with both professional association and government cooperation. This model is most evident with the administration of licensure exams prepared and monitored by professional testing companies for state licensure boards comprised of members from the professional organization.

Roles and responsibilities of government, professional associations, and contractors have been influenced by the regulatory decisions of the courts, interpreting the equal employment opportunity (EEO) standards and the antitrust laws. Therapeutic recreation credentialing standards have yet to be tested in a court of law. Are there impending economic, legal, professional, or procedural issues that could bear upon the administrative model finally selected with our standards? Court decisions and legal interpretations in the health care field do influence future organizational patterns and operating procedures.

Who should maintain control over a credential: the federal and/ or state government, the professional association, or a combination of both? Who is more qualified: the government or the professional? The historical argument is that the professional is more qualified to judge whether or not the tenets of therapeutic recreation are being properly practiced. However, with the passage of the Health Training Improvement Act in 1970, the federal government first took note of credentialing personnel in the health-care arena. In 1971 and again in 1973, the Department of Health, Education, and Welfare (HEW; now Health and Human Services, HHS) urged states and associations to adopt a 2-year moratorium on further legislation for practice or employment of health personnel. Two Supreme Court cases, Goldfarb v. Virginia State Bar (1975) and Griggs v. Duke Power Co. (1970), laid to rest any doubt about the existence of professional exemption from either antitrust laws or equal employment opportunities. In the first case, concerning a minimum fee schedule for legal services established by an association of lawyers, the Court held that "learned professions" are subject to review under antitrust laws that originally applied to trade or commerce. A company policy requiring a high school education was found to be in violation of Title VII in the second case. The Court ruled that testing or measuring procedures could not control personnel selection decisions unless it was determined that they were a reasonable measure of job performance.

Why government involvement? Statements printed with the 1971 and 1973 HEW positions indicated a concern for the proper and efficient use of personnel to meet the health care needs of consumers. Court decrees have since shown concern for "professional monopoly" issues, "price fixing," restrictions in consumer choice, and barriers to the right of individuals to select their own vocations. These are some of the more significant reasons for credentialing. Other positive reasons to support government involvement in some form include the ability of the government to withstand legal rigor, the universal development of standards encouraging reciprocity, the government's strong financial base, its political clout, and an unbiased development of standards. With the contracting of services utilizing a professional testing service of note like the Educational Testing Service or the Professional Examination Service (ETS, PES), the credentialing process gains psychometric expertise and legal support as well as a research base to continue development of standards and competency measures. The reasons for professional involvement include access to experts who purport to know the field; self-regulation; assumption of personal investment or commitment to the profession; less red tape; apparent positive relationship between credentialing and other professionalization processes like research, autonomy, and sanctioning; and the desirable link between credentialing elements and the practice of therapeutic recreation where government is not involved.

Numerous variables influence the roles and responsibilities assumed by government, professional groups, and service contractors. Involvement of each can have positive or negative consequences. Therapeutic recreation is identified as an emerging or evolving profession. There does appear to be validity in using both government and paid experts external to our profession. Sanction and definition of scope come with support from legislators. Clout is gained when peers in related disciplines perceive our equal status, gained through the wearing of legally defendable credentials. Both facilitate delineation of service scope and justification of our existence. With the assistance of professional testing experts, we gain a broader research base and valid means to withstand court tests of our content. Cooperative efforts enhance funding bases and assurance of consumer interests.

Credentialing and the Consumer

Is the public well-being protected with issuance of credentials? Who benefits–the consumer, the practitioner, or both? Research in therapeutic recreation has begun to link competence and job tasks. The organizational structure and autonomous nature of NCTRC show an apolitical orientation. The uninterrupted existence of a national plan since 1956 represents our professional commitment to the validity of a credential. Yet can we answer the preceding questions in the affirmative?

Individual and institutional processes are in place; their content lacks data base linkage to practice. Regulation by the government and its branches suggests we have yet to develop valid and reliable tools that ensure quality service delivery upon entry and over the occupational lifetime of the practitioner. If questioned individually, practitioners would profess to be concerned with the quality of their programs and the well-being of their consumers. The wearing of the label "CTRS/CTRA" is no guarantee or assurance of quality or consumer safety.

There remain tasks to be completed during the professionalization process that are essential to credentialing. Impetus to clearly delineate a philosophy, undertake efficacy research, define standards, and gain legitimate sanctions are underway. These are fundamental credentialing prerequisites and will enable resolution of pending economic, legal, professiona,l and procedural issues.

Relationships in the professionalization process

Scope of practice

In our zeal to gain professional identity through credentialing processes, we have neglected the research necessary to establish a sound philosophical base. Identification of functions performed by therapeutic recreators is the initial step in the development of credentialing processes. The urgency to delineate a unique professional motif is attributed to such scientific and social forces as technology and specialization in the health arena, government concern to regulate health manpower, and consumer demands for accountability and cost containment. From research comes our applied body of knowledge—our service motif. The public expects service quality from professionals who possess validated knowledge, skills, and abilities. The public has assumed that the holding of a credential restricts practice to persons who have demonstrated their qualifications in a prescribed set of functions. Those persons not holding credentials are therefore presumed to not be capable of performing certain services in the public interest.

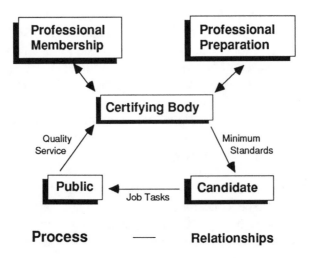

Efficacy research is necessary to justify the hows and whys of therapeutic recreation. Past research has focused on standards and professional preparation essential to professional identity. Empirical research determines, as an example, whether the National Therapeutic Recreation Society (NTRS) Leisurability Philosophy is being actualized. Is there parity between the professed raison d'etre of the field and professional service practices (Halberg and Howe-Murphy, 1985)? A philosophy serves as the foundation of knowledge, skills, and abilities by describing beliefs and principles which set the scope or parameters of therapeutic recreation functions. Implementation of the philosophy comes through practice of a service defined by the purpose, goals, and objectives developed from the philosophy. A competent professional is one who possesses the knowledges, skills, and abilities to apply the knowledge base assumed by the philosophy. A philosophy is formulated on what is and what could be, practice of which may not necessarily be appropriate. Can therapeutic recreators delineate a core of knowledge, skills, and abilities necessary to practice across settings and in concert with our raison d'etre? And is there potential danger if a consumer receives services from a practitioner who does not wear either a CTRS or CTRA name tag?

Are there different competencies implied among the three services delineated along the leisurability continuum of the Gunn and Peterson model (1978) or during the helping relationship described by Carter, Van Andel, and Robb (1985)? Fundamental to therapeutic recreators is the process of assessment, planning, implementation, and evaluation applied to achieve predetermined outcomes influenced by the clients' functioning, significant others, the selected experiences, and the therapeutic environment. The wearing of a credential says one is capable of applying this concept across settings and in a manner supported by the public and the consumer as essential and unique. The distinguishing features of therapeutic recreation as a field are evident regardless of the service delivery setting or the title assigned the leader of the program.

Research enhances the body of knowledge and validates how and why services are delivered. However, our research efforts have been short-sighted (Rickards, 1985). Competency statements have been delineated. Job tasks have been categorized and analyzed. Curriculums reflect listed competency statements and job task descriptions. Our attention has been on professional preparation rather than on practitioner efficacy. To justify our long-term competence, applied and data-based research must explore the intricacies of leadership interaction and client behaviors, before and after therapeutic experiences, and of system attributes causing the therapeutic recreation process to be fluid and dynamic. With a professional credential, the profession, the consumer, and the public believe that the reason for our being and our field practices are one in the same.

Territorial conflicts have arisen between therapeutic recreators and, for instance, social workers and physical and occupational therapists, in part due to our lack of a clearly defined service scope and the pace at which our credentialing mechanisms have evolved. History reveals an earlier entry into the health arena by our peers. Likewise, their credentialing tools resulted from delineation of functions when there were fewer specialists and before the escalation of medical costs. In our case, the urgency to achieve recognition among colleagues fostered growth and development of credentialing tools. Unfortunately, these phenomena occurred without commensurate energy devoted to formulating a viable philosophy and undertaking research necessary to ensure a unique valid service motif.

Standards

Standards establish minimal levels of function, activity, or practice. The boundaries of therapeutic recreation have been established by empirical and normative standards derived from traditional knowledge and field practices. These criteria serve as evaluative indices of the field to colleagues, consumers, accrediting bodies, federal regulating agencies, and the public. Standards currently in place include the academic competencies of the Council on Accreditation, the personnel guidelines of NCTRC, the professional standards of practice of NTRS, and those imposed by either government agencies or private nonprofit accrediting bodies like JCAHO and CARF.

 Standards are put forth by a professional to enable accountability, documentation, and self-regulation. A credential denotes one's right to provide services defined by these standards. In one of the few professional writings on standards, Van Andel (1981) advises professionals to continue to evaluate existing standards to ensure that they are valid, appropriate, and represent all facets of practice. Is further research and development of credentials appropriate when there appears to be minimal recent professional boundary-setting or validation of existing standards? And will individual possession of credentials necessarily enhance the service qualities established in existing standards?

Confusion and concern among professionals has resulted from the existence of several sets of standards and various administrative models. One is confronted with the issue of who should define and evaluate preparation, personnel, and professional standards. For instance, does the presence of reimbursement from either government-regulated or private insurance agencies justify certain credentials, prescribed curriculums, professional protocols or a combination of these components? Within the field, does one set of standards have precedence over others? That is, since preparation chronologically precedes professional practice, should these standards establish boundaries imposed by the professional during service, or vice versa?

A credential is a symbol that certain performance standards have been achieved. The achievement of accreditation with the consequent awarding of either the right to display a seal or be listed in a registry are tokens of the professionalization process. To become a profession, therapeutic recreators must establish boundaries with formal procedures to ensure adherence to fundamental directives. There is a need to investigate the relationship between preparatory curriculum standards and those imposed on personnel; should graduation from an accredited program automatically give access to certification? There is also a need to determine whether compliance with the NTRS Standards of Practice for Therapeutic Recreation Service is dependent upon one's academic preparation and possession of a personal credential. Further, there is a need to determine whether satisfaction of minimal preparation, personnel, and professional standards ensures quality services as defined by government, external accrediting bodies, and third-party reimbursers. With resolution of these issues, therapeutic recreation will move closer to developing a rationale for its existence while maintaining a proper perspective on consumer services.

Autonomy and sanctioning

A primary justification for credentialing standards is the protection of the public through the establishment and enforcement of minimum levels of practitioner competence. A code of ethics, considered one of the requisites of a profession, spells out relationships between the practitioner and the public (Shimberg, 1980). This code of conduct symbolizes the autonomy or "self-growing" powers of a professional body by sanctioning what it is that therapeutic recreators perform or do. Content of ethical codes can be incorporated into the credentialing processes of a professional society or governing board. To illustrate, a portion of the NTRS Code of Ethics (National Therapeutic Recreation Society, 1985a) is presented, followed by the purpose statement from the model Therapeutic Recreation Practice Act (1985b).

II. Above all else, the therapeutic recreation professional is guided by the accepted responsibility of encouraging and providing quality service to the client/consumer. He/she demonstrates respect for the dignity of the client/consumer as an individual human being. He/she makes an honest effort to meet the habilitative, rehabilitative and leisure needs of the client/customer and takes care that the client/consumer is not exploited or otherwise abused. This includes but is not limited to the guarantee of basic human rights under law .(pp. 57-58)

101.1 Title. — This Act shall be known and may be cited as the "Therapeutic Recreation Practice Act." 101.2 Purpose. — In order to (1) safeguard the public health, safety,and welfare, (2) protect the public from being misled by incompetent and unauthorized persons, (3) assure the highest degree of professional conduct on the part of therapeutic recreation specialists and therapeutic recreation assistants, and (4) assure the availability of therapeutic recreation services of high quality to persons in need of such services, it is the purpose of the Therapeutic Recreation Licensing Act to provide for the regulation of Therapeutic Recreation Specialists and Therapeutic Recreation Assistants. (p. 1)

The regulatory nature comes with the acceptance of these positions by the professional members and the public at large as demonstrated by their willingness to either judge their peers or demand quality services. One's credential may be withdrawn as a result of being judged incompetent by one's peer. Another approach to upgrading services is to demand that higher levels of minimal competence be demonstrated prior to the issuance of a credential.

Government intervention has resulted in additional regulation from the Department of Justice and the Federal Trade Commission, and from judicial interpretations of Title VII of the 1964 Civil Rights Act. Regulatory issues to be considered by therapeutic recreators, as the profession strives to become autonomous are summarized with three questions: Are credentialing requirements job related, in the public interest, and nondiscriminatory? Could a monopoly be created which would deny uncredentialed people job opportunities, when in fact they could be useful and effective therapeutic recreators? And will regulation increase service costs?

The possession of either CTRS or CTRA identifies its holder as one who has the minimal competence to practice therapeutic recreation.

The loss of such a credential implies inability to provide quality therapeutic services.   Criteria stated in the model practice act are reasons given for censureship (National Therapeutic Recreation Society, 1985b).

106.1   Revocation, suspension, or denial of license.– The board shall have the power to enforce this Therapeutic Recreation Practice Act and to deny, revoke, or suspend any license as a therapeutic recreation specialist or therapeutic recreation assistant issued by the Board. The board may issue a letter of reprimand, restrict, revoke, or suspend any license issued pursuant to this Article or deny any application for a license if the Board determines that the licensee or the applicant:

1. Has given false information or has withheld material information from the Board in procuring or attempting to procure a license pursuant to this Article;
2. Has been convicted of or plead guilty or nolo contendere to any crime that indicates that the person is unfit or incompetent to practice therapeutic recreation;
3. Has a mental or physical disability or uses any drug to a degree that interferes with his or her ability to practice therapeutic recreation;
4. Engages in conduct that endangers the public health;
5. Is unfit or incompetent to practice therapeutic recreation by reason of deliberate or negligent acts or commissions regardless of whether actual injury to the patient is established;
6. Engages in conduct that deceives, defrauds, or harms the public in the course of providing therapeutic recreation services: or
7. Has willfully violated any provision of this Article or of regulations enacted by the Board. (pp.17-18)

To be effective, a code of ethics must clearly distinguish between incompetent behavior and competent behavior rooted in well-founded knowledge of what constitutes quality therapeutic recreation services. Presently the only system in place to detect incompetence is that which exists with the quality assurance measures within the third-party payment systems.

Autonomy comes from public acknowledgements defining professional competence in therapeutic recreation and professional commitment to enforce those standards of quality. Effective sanctions or enforcement mechanisms must be accepted by the professional community and must have the power to either result in a higher level of professional competence or in removal of the practitioner from the field. Although purported to be in the public interest, behavioral guidelines delineated in the NTRS code of ethics lack both empirical evidence of community support and sanctioning by the professional body.

Decisions of the United States Supreme Court during the 1970s greatly expanded the scope of the antitrust statutes found in the Sherman Antitrust Act of 1888 and Section 5 of the Federal Trade Commission (FTC) Act of 1914 as amended in 1938 (Falk, Weisfeld, & Tochen, 1979). These decisions have limited a professional group's ability to determine its terms of employment and utilization, establish fees, present information to consumers or advertise, and dictate supply of personnel by imposing hiring criteria. Additional restrictions have resulted from court interpretation of the 1964 Civil Rights Act, Title VII, as amended by the Equal Employment Opportunity Act of 1972 (EEO). Employment selection criteria under EEO must consist of empirical data demonstrating correlation between performance on the job and the evaluative criteria, whether that be education, experience, or examination.

We must ascertain whether the present NCTRC standards are job related and nondiscriminatory and whether we create a monopoly on the job market by requiring the attainment of CTRS or CTRA prior to employment. Further, we must determine whether the cost of professional credentials is being passed on to the consumer through higher fees. That is, with increases in recertification fees or test fees, is there a proportionate increase in the hourly therapeutic recreation service fee? With the imposition of an additional credentialing requirement such as successful completion of an exam, will consumers pay more for services rendered by credentialed therapeutic recreators?

To gain autonomy and sanction over therapeutic services, therapeutic recreators must adopt a proactive political posture and display personal and professional commitment to agency regulations and standards of practice. Clarity must be brought to a code of ethics with definition of what constitutes both competent and acceptable behaviors and incompetent or unacceptable practices. Legislators and administrators must be educated to the tenets of consumer services. Within our agencies and professional organizations we must become advocates willing to impose and enforce standards defining quality services through the preparation of documents like "Client Rights and Privileges in Therapeutic Recreation" and "Standards of Professional Performance."

Credentialing and the professional

Does the implementation of a credentialing program necessarily enhance the practice of therapeutic recreation and elevate the status of the profession as an emerging specialty area? Is further role delineation a requisite to both credentialing and professionalization of the field? Therapeutic recreation is in the formative stages of development as a profession. There is a need to delineate our scope of practice better through continuous development of our philosophy and efficacy research. Existing therapeutic recreation standards also enhance our stature as a professional entity. Yet there is a need to investigate the relationships between these criteria and the presence or absence of a credential. Professionals must be able to link their reason for being with their practice. Rudimentary documents and processes support self-regulation. Professionals must develop mechanisms to enforce codes of ethics and standards of practice. Consumers must be willing to sanction therapeutic recreation as an essential unique service area. The possession of a credential denotes a degree of peer and consumer recognition–As professionals, we are obligated to demonstrate the linkage of credentials to services rendered.

Summary

Throughout this chapter, questions on credentialing have been raised. These concerns are similar to those raised by other organizations and are issues that have yet to be resolved with data from basic and applied research. The key questions concern which credentialing process has to do with content and which procedures will best ensure quality consumer services while clearly delineating the professional competencies practiced by therapeutic recreators. The criteria of a competent therapeutic recreation professional must be established. We must determine what kinds of and how much education, training, experience, and evaluation are essential to the properly qualified therapeutic recreator. Job tasks and credentialing criteria must be linked. The unique knowledge, skills, and abilities must be delineated. Therapeutic recreators must justify their unique assets while developing self-governing tools and processes to withstand legal, ethical, political, and social challenges from within and from consumers and the public.

Study Questions

1. Compare and contrast the three forms of credentialing—registration, certification, and licensure. Which of these, in your opinion, is the most desirable for the profession in the future?

2. Accreditation of facilities and programs has become a complex and sometimes disjointed effort. Examine the current status of relationships between various accrediting bodies such as NRPA, JCAHO, CARF, etc.

3. Discuss the role of continuing education in the maintenance of knowledge, skills and abilities in therapeutic recreation. Is the system working? What are the alternatives? How can we make the system work?

4. A national examination to test the competence of aspiring or seated therapeutic recreation professions will soon be a reality. What problems are evident with such an approach? What "power" will the exam have in professional preparation programs (curriculum development) and accreditation of facilities and programs?

5. Examine current standards of practice in therapeutic recreation. Are they clear and precise? Do they adequately meet the needs of the consumer/client?

References

Carter, M.J., Van Andel, G.E., & Robb, G.M. (1985). *Therapeutic Recreation: A Practical Approach.* St. Louis, MO: Times/Mirror/Mosby College Publishing.

Falk, D.S., Weisfeld, N., & Tochen, D. (1979). *Perspectives on Health Occupational Credentialing* (Contract No. 232-78-0187). Washington, DC: U.S. Department of Health and Human Services.

Gunn, S.L., & Peterson, C.A. (1978). *Therapeutic Recreation Program Design: Principles and Procedures.* Englewood Cliffs, NJ: Prentice-Hall.

Halberg, K.J., & Howe-Murphy, R. (1985). The Dilemma of an Unresolved Philosophy in Therapeutic Recreation. *Therapeutic Recreation Journal, 19* (3), 7-16.

National Therapeutic Recreation Society. (1985a). Code of Ethics. *Theapeutic Recreation Journal, 19*, (4) 57-58.

National Therapeutic Recreation Society. (1985b). *Therapeutic Recreation Practice Act.* Alexandria, VA: Author.

Rickards, W.H. (1985). Perspectives on Therapeutic Recreation Research: Opening the Black Box. *Therapeutic Recreation Journal, 19* (2), 15-23.

Shimberg, B. (1980). *Occupational Licensing: A Public Perspective.* Princeton, NJ: Educational Testing Service, Center for Occupational and Professional Assessment.

Van Andel, G.E. (1981). Professional Standards: Improving the Quality of Services. *Therapeutic Recreation Journal, 15* (2), 23-30.

Body of Knowledge Issues

photo courtesy of San Francisco Center for the Handicapped

Through symbiotic relation, science and the humanities, *together*, achieve a better collective response to the problems of freedom, choice, and constraints in therapeutic recreation.

—Kenneth E. Mobily

THE ROLE OF SCIENCE IN
THERAPEUTIC RECREATION

Gary D. Ellis

Abstract

The purpose of this paper is to examine the role of science in therapeutic recreation. Two factors that provide impetus for scientific development within therapeutic recreation are identified. These are the emergence of the age of accountability and the natural process of intellectual development of the field. The possibility that technological development is as critical a need as scientific development is raised. Finally, challenges that must be faced in the scientific development of therapeutic recreation are discussed, with emphasis on recreation and leisure curricula in higher education programs.

Accountability

Two major forces have led to the need for an examination of the role of science in therapeutic recreation. One of these forces is an increasing societal demand for accountability. Litigation during the 1970s and 1980s soared to new heights as citizens challenged one another and providers of goods and services to fulfill promises, obligations, and responsibilities. Tax reform to ensure efficient spending became a key issue in virtually every election. Leaders at the highest levels of government were called upon to provide both legal and moral justification for specific actions. During the 1970s, the country watched in awe as the Watergate conspiracy brought about the undoing of President Nixon, and in the 1980s, leading figures in the Reagan Administration faced weeks of Congressional hearings to determine the appropriateness of their actions during the Iran-Contra affair.

Therapeutic recreation has been greatly affected by this increasing demand for accountability. In its early period of development, therapeutic recreation was accepted by health care professionals on a speculative and intuitive basis. It made sense that people with injuries and disabilities needed recreation for full and complete lives, and the possibility also existed that recreation could have rehabilitative benefits. Nothing was known, and indeed few people cared, about what specific benefits could be realized through therapeutic recreation, what specific clinical-recreational processes would create those benefits, or in what situations such processes would most effectively be applied.

As accountability demands increased, pressures mounted for answers to the difficult questions about the benefits of therapeutic recreation. Clients, third-party payers, and a growing health care industry became acutely aware of the loosely defined benefits and the random hodgepodge of therapeutic recreation interventions. What, specifically, was being purchased with health care dollars spent on therapeutic recreation? What benefits were being obtained, and how efficient was therapeutic recreation as a process for obtaining those benefits? For the first time, the therapeutic recreation profession was required to take a serious look at its process and outcomes. The need for operationalization of benefits, standardization of clinical therapeutic recreation processes, and scientific verification of the effectiveness and efficiency of these processes became evident.

The Natural Process of Intellectual Development of the Discipline

The need for an examination of the status of therapeutic recreation as a science is not only a reactive function of increasing demands for accountability. The second major force is the natural process of intellectual development of the discipline. Based on Iso-Ahola's (1980) application of Hollander (1976), Witt (1987) has outlined the evolution of intellectual development in therapeutic recreation. In the early days of the discipline, speculation, conjecture, and rhetoric were the dominant modes of intellectual activity among its scholars. Debates occurred on such topics as the meanings of terms and the significance of leisure. This period of conceptual debate was followed by preliminary attempts to study therapeutic recreation empirically. Activity checklists were developed and attempts were made to identify recreational preferences, styles, and activity types. This new era of development was significant in that it introduced empirical research into the collective thought of the field. The lack of theory, critical reasoning, and a rigorous philosophical base, however, limited its long-term impact.

Currently, a new era is emerging. This era is marked by the application of rigorous and innovative scientific methodologies (e.g., Dattilo & Barnett, 1985; Wade-Campbell & Anderson, 1987) that are rooted in well-developed theoretical frameworks (e.g., Mckee, 1984; Savell, 1986; Wassman & Iso-Ahola, 1985). Fundamental questions related to the role and significance of leisure in clients' lives are being addressed.

Both the age of accountability and the natural intellectual growth of therapeutic recreation have led us to the threshold of continued development as a science. As we embark on further development, it is perhaps useful to consider the role of science in therapeutic recreation and the consequences of continued growth as a science. Additionally, alternative directions should be explored, and challenges that must be overcome if the field is to indeed develop as a science must be identified.

What is Science?

A useful point of departure in examining the role of science in therapeutic recreation is consideration of the characteristics and the significance of science. As is true of any topic that is worthy of scholarly inquiry, considerable disagreement exists among philosophers concerning the precise meaning of the term *science*. Ziman (1980) noted that the identification of "the special attributes of science . . . would require a history of Western thought" (p. 35). Nevertheless, Ziman was able to identify four major categories into which most definitions of science may be classified:

- Science is the mastery of man's environment.
- Science is the study of the material world.
- Science is the experimental method.
- Science is [that which] arrives at truth by logical inferences from empirical observations. (pp. 36-38).

Although shortcomings are associated with each of these major views of science, the last of these represents the type of definition which is "favored by most serious philosophers" (Ziman, p. 37). Definitions that follow this general format imply that both logical operations and empirical analysis are central to the method of science.

In addition to logic and empiricism, the concept of "truth" is also of major importance in understanding Ziman's (1980) "most favored" definition of science. Truth, in a scientific context, implies the precise specification of the conditions under which certain phenomena will be observed and the developing of an understanding of why the phenomena occurred under those conditions. The relationship between these conditions and the phenomena can be summarized in an "if-then" statement. "If," for example, water at sea level is cooled to a temperature of 32 degrees Fahrenheit, "then" it will change from liquid to solid form. If light passes an object with gravitational force, then the direction and speed of the light will change. But scientific truth also requires the development of a logical, reasoned explanation of why the phenomena may be observed under those conditions. Simply specifying the conditions under which phenomena will be observed is not sufficient for establishing scientific truth.

Therapeutic recreation practitioners would be able to demonstrate accountability if they were able to demonstrate unequivocally the truth of particular if-then statements. If leisure counseling is applied, for example, then clients' perceived freedom in leisure will be enhanced. If clients develop a deep commitment to a leisure activity, then their self-esteem will be enhanced. Such statements as these are often intuitively held to be true by therapeutic recreation practitioners, but accountability cannot be demonstrated nor can therapeutic recreation science advance until scientific and technological processes have been employed to demonstrate the truth of such statements.

The concept of cause is inherent in if-then statements. The examples in the previous paragraph imply, respectively, that leisure counseling (in a precisely defined and appropriately implemented form) causes clients' perceived freedom in leisure to be enhanced and that deep commitment to a leisure activity causes self-esteem to increase.

The concept of cause, however, is not a simple one. Philosophers of science have struggled with it for many centuries. A point of departure for many of these discussions has been Aristotle's classification of causes into four types: formal cause, material cause, efficient cause, and final cause. Losee (1980) has illustrated each of these in terms of the phenomenon of color change among chameleons. One is speaking of an efficient cause when describing the environmental conditions that must be present in order for the color change to be observed. Material cause is being investigated if the chameleon's color change is being described in terms of the substance in the creature's skin which undergoes change. If one explains the phenomenon in terms of the chameleon's transformation from a leaf to a twig and the associated changes in the reflected light from the chameleon, a formal cause is involved. Final cause involves a teleological explanation: the chameleon changes color in order to escape detection by predators.

The efficient cause concept dominates our contemporary view of science and is reflected in the examples of temperature causing water to freeze, gravity causing light to change speed and direction, and therapeutic recreation causing changes in such variables as depression and self-esteem. The other types of cause, however, may also be relevant to scientific inquiry.

In light of this classification, what type of causes should be the focus of inquiry in therapeutic recreation science? Although the efficient cause view is dominant, perhaps other views have greater potential for stimulating positive growth of the discipline (Mobily, Wessinger, & Hunnicutt, 1987).

It is also important to note that the different concepts of cause imply different approaches to scientific inquiry. If (therapeutic) recreation is considered to be an efficient cause of such conditions as teen alcohol abuse (Perdue & Rainwater, 1984) and alleviation of depression (Wassman & Iso-Ahola, 1985), then a traditional view of science that emphasizes objectivity, rigorous operationalization of variables, statistical treatment of quantitative data, and generalizability of results is appropriate. If, on the other hand, the concept of formal cause is accepted, a qualitative approach to science is needed. Rather than emphasizing objectivity, quantitative methods, and isolation of the effects of one tightly defined variable on another, the efficient cause concept implies the need for a holistic view of phenomena. It respects the perspective of the investigator and focuses on the development of insight into total social systems rather than isolated variables (Ellis & Williams,1987; Howe, 1985; Lincoln & Guba, 1985). The formal cause concept allows therapeutic recreation to be viewed both as a cause and an effect and as a part of a large system, exerting definitive but elusive effects upon clients (Mobily, Wessinger, & Hunnicutt, 1987).

Perhaps the concept of final cause is also of considerable importance to therapeutic recreation. Indeed, much of the rhetoric and speculation that emerged during the early stages of intellectual development of the discipline seemed to assume a final cause orientation. Some examples of these include the position that leisure is important "for a full and complete life" and the notion that the healthiness of a society can be judged by observing the behavior of people during their free time. Scholarly pursuits associated with the final cause orientation would seem to require philosophical inquiry and dialogue. Questions such as "Should people be encouraged to participate in certain activities?" and "What gives therapeutic recreation specialists the right to attempt to change people's leisure functioning?" would become of central importance. Dialogue on such topics as these, however, is rarely encountered.

It is tempting to avoid the problem of identifying the types of causes that are most relevant to therapeutic recreation by adopting the position that all are equally relevant. This approach, however, smacks of a proclivity to avoid confrontation with the enormously complex and enigmatic problems which must be encountered if a knowledge base is to be developed. If therapeutic recreation science is to continue to grow, then focused, logical, and reasoned dialogue is needed on the concept of cause as it relates to therapeutic recreation.

The Role of Science in Therapeutic Recreation

A popular model of the role of science in therapeutic recreation is summarized at the top of Figure 1. This diagram implies a direct linear relationship between science, technology, and the quality of the product or service that is being provided. In terms of therapeutic recreation, the assumption is that therapeutic recreation science identifies and validates techniques ("technology") of assessment, leisure counseling, leisure education, and facilitation that practitioners use in applied settings to enhance clients' well-being. According to this model, the technology of therapeutic recreation is totally dependent upon the science that supports it; no technological growth can occur without scientific progress.

Although the first diagram in Figure 1 represents a popular assumption concerning the relationship between science and technology, a more realistic diagram of such relationships is presented in the lower diagram. In that portion of the figure, science and technology are depicted as different types of undertakings, with the aim of science being knowledge generation and the aim of technology being the creation of planned change that people deem desirable (Cantore, 1977, p. 4). The double-headed arrows indicate that technology grows through science and that science grows through technology. More importantly, the model indicates that science is only one of several forces that influence and are influenced by technological growth. In addition

Figure 1

I. Popular model

Science ⟶ Technology ⟶ Planned change

II. Alternative model

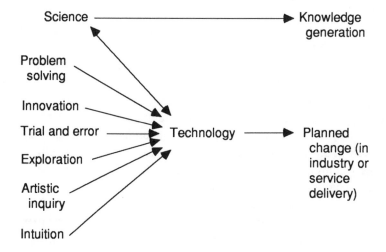

Science ⟶ Knowledge generation

Problem solving

Innovation

Trial and error ⟶ Technology ⟶ Planned change (in industry or service delivery)

Exploration

Artistic inquiry

Intuition

to science, technological growth occurs through such forces as problem solving, trial and error, innovation, exploration, artistic inquiry, and experience. Science is, at best, only one part of the overall process of technological growth.

Although the lower diagram in Figure 1 may seem to be a radical departure from an established view of the relationship between science and technology, a strong historical foundation exists in support of its validity. Prior to and during the Industrial Revolution, it seems that technology progressed quite well without science. Barnes (1985, p.15) has shown that science "had a long way to go before it actually reached the stage of being useful . . . It was not so much that there was a demand from industry that called forth scientists as that scientists arrived on the scene and created a demand for themselves." Indeed, scientific growth has been attributed to technological growth rather than vice versa (Barnes, 1985; Cantore, 1977).

Although few people would deny that science has become a prominent force in modern technology, examples of technological growth outstripping scientific knowledge are abundant. In the area of superconductivity, for example, highly sophisticated technologists are quite successfully identifying superconductive materials by "trying out variations of their newfound recipes, adding different elements, substituting one for another, changing the proportions," while scientists scratch their heads trying to figure out why the new combinations are working (Budiansky, 1987, p.68)

Obviously, the role of therapeutic recreation science cannot be founded solely on the technological needs of practitioners. The technology of therapeutic recreation can and should develop with science serving as only one source of input. Scientists in therapeutic recreation must continue to search for answers to fundamental questions about leisure in the lives of people with illnesses and disabilities. On the front lines, technologists must continue to search for applications of this knowledge, and they must independently develop assessment and intervention techniques that create positive changes in clients' lives. Therapeutic recreation technology cannot afford to continue to wait for therapeutic recreation science to provide practical solutions to problems faced by practitioners.

If therapeutic recreation science can only partially be founded on the technology with which it is associated, what other bases for development of therapeutic recreation science exist? Barnes (1985) has addressed this issue in terms of a distinction between science education and science training. As Barnes points out, "a training transmits instrumental skills of no intrinsic value." Scientific training places science "on a par with dentistry, or cabinetmaking, or even less elevated forms of skilled labor" (p. 17).

Rather than training, science may be placed in an educational context, such as is possible through higher education programs in therapeutic recreation. As part of an educational process, science acquires intrinsic value and "produces inherently desirable changes in those undergoing it, improved powers of inference, for example, or heightened sensibility" (Barnes, 1985, p. 17). These changes produce individuals who are capable of contributing more fully not only to their professions and vocations but, perhaps more importantly, to the democratic process as well. Thus, scientifically well-trained people"may do valuable service in a good society [while] scientifically well-educated people may 'be' a good society" (Barnes, p. 17).

In addition to its role of influencing technology, therefore, science is an important part of the overall educational process. Higher education programs in therapeutic recreation have a responsibility to their students, the discipline, and the democracy to integrate a scientific perspective in their curriculum and instruction approaches. Increasingly powerful accreditation and credentialing movements, driven by the fledgling technology of therapeutic recreation, are emphasizing the need for a training orientation for therapeutic recreation education. Therapeutic recreation educators, however, must recognize their broader educational mission. They must strive to design and establish educational experiences that legitimize the "science" component of the bachelor of science and master of science degrees that are earned by their students.

Higher Education Reform and Scientific Development in Therapeutic Recreation

A variety of challenges to scientific development in therapeutic recreation have been delineated in this paper and elsewhere (Austin, 1982; Compton, 1984; Witt, 1987). Among these are the need for a clear distinction between the roles of therapeutic recreation science and technology; cumulative research programs leading to theory development (Austin, 1982); more intensive research methodology preparation (Iso-Ahola, 1986; Witt, 1987); increased numbers of potential funding sources for leisure research (Compton, 1984); and the need for postdoctoral employment opportunities in ongoing research programs (Witt, 1987).

Overcoming many of these challenges will require large-scale social action. In order to establish funding sources, for example, potential donors and taxpayers (if the sources are to be governmental) must be convinced that a need exists for therapeutic recreation research. A unified effort among recreation and leisure professionals is needed to establish and demonstrate this need. Unfortunately, large numbers of professionals seem to be themselves unconvinced and uncommitted. Although practitioners seem particularly eager to accept research that will document the effectiveness of their interventions, many exhibit little understanding or appreciation for the need of basic research and science. To many practitioners, the sole mission of research is to prove that their interventions are successful. Technology is confused with science.

At the root of this failure to establish appreciation of the need for basic research and scienc‚e are higher education programs in therapeutic recreation. Problems are evident in all phases of those programs, from recruitment to curriculum and instruction of both graduate and undergraduate students.

In terms of recruitment of students, higher education programs seem to attract far too many people who are seeking advanced degrees without having sufficient interest in the fundamental questions at the "cutting edge." A large number of graduate students remain primarily concerned about the job market, with higher education serving only as a means to an end.

Curriculum revision is also an enormous need. Although many people believe that the heart of the curriculum problem is the dearth of research methodology classes at the graduate level, it is likely that the problem is much deeper, beginning at the first course in our undergraduate programs. In many other disciplines, theory, uncertainty, debate, and the intriguing complexity of the relevant knowledge is introduced early in the program of study of new majors. Introductory psychology students, for example, quickly become involved in contrasting views of human behavior. The dynamic theories are contrasted with behaviorist approaches. Physiological approaches are contrasted with cognitive approaches. The complexity of studying psychological variables is pointed out. An air of uncertainty prevails.

Compare such introductory psychology courses to the courses that are typically required for therapeutic recreation majors. While psychology majors are struggling with issues that will help them become scientists, therapeutic recreation students are memorizing trivial facts about where park and recreation personnel work, what they do on their jobs, and how to prepare for careers in parks and recreation. This leads to the false belief that science is, at best, a tangential need in our field because the most important knowledge in our field is already known. More importantly, it relegates our (token) courses on leisure science to the position of being unfortunate distractions to the serious thrust of the field: how to work in parks and recreation. Courses dealing with uncertainty, are in students' eyes necessary evils that must be "gotten out of the way" so the serious business of "how to" can be continued.

As a result, therapeutic recreation graduate students begin at a level that is somewhat comparable to the beginning point of the psychology undergraduate. In order for graduate education with these individuals to proceed, considerable effort must be made to help them begin to see the mysteries and uncertainties associated with leisure and to understand such fundamental concepts as measurement, variables, covariation, and hypothesis testing, (which students in more established disciplines first encountered as sophomores). Through increased emphasis on the mysteries and uncertainties, students must be made uncomfortable with a system into which they have been socialized to unquestioningly accept and dogmatically defend. For many, this is an agonizing process.

True scientific growth in therapeutic recreation must begin with curriculum and instruction revision. Scholars must be attracted to studies in therapeutic recreation, and educational experiences must be designed to emphasize the mystery and complexity of leisure phenomena. The old mainstays in the curriculum must be reviewed. Is "programming" basically the same thing as "marketing"? If so, why not develop an appreciation for fundamental questions in marketing of leisure services rather than continuing our how-to approach and old programming rhetoric? If recreation leadership is so important why has a body of theory, research, and science not grown around that topic to support its continued prominence in our academic programs? If a true scientific orientation to therapeutic recreation and leisure is to be established, even the most deeply rooted of our courses must be scrutinized.

Summary and Discussion

In this chapter, we have explored selected issues in the development of therapeutic recreation as a science. The nature of science and the potential role of science in establishing accountability were pointed out. The link between science and technology was explored, and the position was taken that technology, such as therapeutic recreation practice, has the potential to make great strides forward virtually independently of scientific progress. The central role of higher education in the future scientific development of therapeutic recreation was discussed, with emphasis on recruitment, curriculum, and instructional change.

The intent of this chapter has been to raise questions and issues to be considered as scientific growth continues. What, for example, is the status of therapeutic recreation technology, and in what way should it be related to therapeutic recreation science? In what way does the concept of cause relate to therapeutic recreation science? Would curriculum revision to facilitate scientific growth undermine technological development in therapeutic recreation? These, and numerous other questions that are raised in the chapter warrant further inquiry.

Finally, it is interesting to consider Will Durant's (1961) comments on the limitations and dangers which are inherent in scientific development.

> Science wishes to resolve the whole into parts, the organism into organs, the obscure into the known. It does not inquire into the values and ideal possibilities of things, nor into their total and final significance; it is content to show their present actuality and operation, it narrows its gaze resolutely to the nature and process of things as they are. Science tells us how to heal and how to kill; it reduces the death rate in retail and then kills wholesale in war . . . Only wisdom can tell us when to heal and when to kill. (p. xxvii).

As therapeutic recreation continues to develop as a science, individuals in this field must keep in mind that science is only a tool which provides one way of knowing. If the true significance of therapeutic recreation in modern society is to be identified, it is likely that wisdom, rather than science, will be at the heart of the movement.

Study Questions

1. The chapter distinguishes between science and technology. What specific examples can you identify of science and technology in operation in therapeutic recreation?

2. What barriers to science and technological development in therapeutic recreation exist?

3. Part of the chapter is based on the assumption that therapeutic recreation development parallels the development of modern in-

dustry. This implies that the science-technology relationship in modern industry is directly analagous to that of therapeutic recreation. To what extent is this a valid analogy?

4. The chapter assumes that the development of therapeutic recreation science can be facilitated through curriculum revision in higher education. Rather than focusing on facts about jobs in recreation and leisure, this approach implies a more fundamental view that addresses unknowns about the leisure phenomenon. Do you agree that this need exists? If so, what specific changes would you recommend?

5. The chapter concludes with a quote from Will Durant that points out that science cannot effectively address the issues of "should." That is, "science tells us how to kill [but it cannot tell us] when to heal and when to kill"(1961, p.xxvii). Thus, science can be a threat to modern society. In what ways (if any) can therapeutic recreation science be considered a potential threat?

6. Science is described in terms of if-then statements. What are some of the most important if-then statements that you believe therapeutic recreation science should be working to develop?

7. What view of the cause concept is most important for the development of a knowledge base in therapeutic recreation?

8. Do you believe that therapeutic recreation science can establish accountability for practitioners? Can therapeutic recreation technology establish accountability?

References

Austin, D.R. (1982). Therapeutic Recreation Research: An Overview. *Abstracts from the 1982 Symposium on Leisure Research*. Alexandria, VA: National Recreation and Park Association, 125.

Barnes, B. (1985). *About Science*. New York: Basil Blackwell.

Budiansky, S. (1987, May 11). Why Does a Conductor Turn Super? *U.S. News and World Report*, pp. 68-69.

Cantore, E. (1977). *Scientific Man: The Humanistic Significance of Science*. New York: ISH Publications.

Compton, D.M. (1984). Research Priorities in Recreation for Special Populations. *Therapeutic Recreation Journal, 18,* 9-17.

Dattilo, J., & Barnett, L. (1985). Therapeutic Recreation for Individuals with Severe Handicaps: An Analysis of the Relationship Between Choice and Pleasure. *Therapeutic Recreation Journal, 19,* 79-91.

Durant, W. (1926). *The Story of Philosophy.* New York: Simon and Schuster.

Ellis, G., & Williams, D. (1987). The Impending Renaissance in Leisure Service Evaluation. *Journal of Park and Recreation Administration, 5,* 17-29.

Hollander, E.P. (1976). *Principles and Methods of Social Psychology* (2nd ed.). New York: Oxford University Press.

Howe, C.Z. (1985). Possibilities for Using a Qualitative Research Approach in the Sociological Study of Leisure. *Journal of Leisure Research, 17,* 212-224.

Iso-Ahola, S.E. (1980). *The Social Psychology of Leisure and Recreation.* Dubuque, IA: William C. Brown.

Iso-Ahola, S.E. (1986). Editor's notes: Concerns and Thoughts About Leisure Research. *Journal of Leisure Research, 18,* iv-x.

Lewko, J., & Crandall, R. (1980). Research Trends in Leisure and Special Populations. *Journal of Leisure Research, 12,* 69-79.

Lincoln, Y.S., & Guba, E.G. (1985). *Naturalistic Inquiry.* Beverly Hills, CA: Sage.

Losee, J. (1980). *A Historical Introduction to the Philosophy of Science.* New York: Oxford.

Mckee, P. (1984). Effects of Using Enjoyable Imagery with Biofeedback-Induced Relaxation for Chronic Pain Patients. *Therapeutic Recreation Journal, 18,* 50-61.

Mobily, K.E., Wessinger, E., & Hunnicutt, B.K. (1987). The Means/Ends Controversy: A Framework for Understanding the Value Potential of TR. *Therapeutic Recreation Journal, 21,* 7-13.

Perdue, R.R., & Rainwater, A. (1984). Adolescent Recreation and Alcohol Consumption. *Therapeutic Recreation Journal, 18,* 41-51.

Savell, K. (1986). Leisure Efficacy: Theory and Therapy Implications for Therapeutic Recreation Programming. *Therapeutic Recreation Journal, 20,* 43-52.

Wade-Campbell, K.N., & Anderson, S. (1987). Perceived Levels of Burnout of Veteran's Administration Therapeutic Recreation

Personnel. *Therapeutic Recreation Journal, 21*, 52-63.

Wassman, K.B., & Iso-Ahola, S.E. (1985). The Relationship Between Recreation Participation and Depression in Psychiatric Patients. *Therapeutic Recreation Journal, 19*, 63-70.

Witt, P.A. (1987). *Therapeutic Recreation Research: Past, Present, Future.* Paper presented at the National Recreation and Park Association/Society of Park and Recreation Educators Research Symposium, New Orleans, Louisiana.

Ziman, J. (1980). What is Science? In E.D. Klemke, R. Hollinger, & A.D. Kline (Eds.), *Introductory Readings in the Philosophy of Science* (pp. 35-54). Buffalo, NY: Prometheus.

OTHER WAYS OF KNOWING [1]

Kenneth E. Mobily

Introduction

One morning not long ago, I was sitting on the couch in our living room. Having woken before the rest of my family, I was reading. As it so happens, when the shades are open and the morning is clear, the sun shines in the window behind the couch I was on. As it turned out, the sun was quite hot that day. On reflection, I recall having thoughts about moving, unconsciously analyzing the situation: Would it be worth the effort to relocate? What would be the consequences of staying? What would be the optimal locations? and so on—an objective and logical appraisal of the situation. Before reaching the conclusion of my "data gathering" and deliberation, my 6-year-old strode in after just waking up. After exchanging greetings, she noticed the very sunbeam that was provoking my musings. Quickly appraising the situation from her perspective, she immediately concluded that the only thing to do about this "problem" was to play with it. Because of the pattern on our windows, the sunbeam had made a design on the floor similar to the hopscotch pattern that children draw on sidewalks. Without much hesitation, my daughter proceeded to play hopscotch on the sunbeam. Hence, we both knew about the sunbeam that day—but in retrospect, I believe my daughter knew it better.

By way of analogy, I would like to argue that the situation in therapeutic recreation (TR) is similar to the sunbeam my daughter and I evaluated in the preceding story. Most of us try to know the sunbeam in a rather scientific way, breaking it into its component parts (e.g., the discomfort I experienced being caused by its temperature properties). But there is another way to know the sunbeam, and also TR. This second way of knowing is not entirely independent from the more familiar method of knowing: science and the humanities are partners in the search for knowledge. Though the former is concerned with empirical evidence and the latter with values, scientists cannot ignore values any more than philosophers can ignore facts.

Furthermore, there are times when science takes up the search for knowledge where the humanities leave off. Likewise, science sometimes reaches impasses, points at which it can go no further, points at which it can offer no added clarification of an issue at hand. Assuming that most readers are convinced of the value of a scientific approach to knowing TR, I intend to build a case for the converse: that often the scholar must look for another point of departure in order to circumvent impasses obstructing the scientific method.

To illustrate the limits of an exclusively scientific approach to TR and how the humanities can offer further understanding of TR, I shall turn repeatedly to the interrelated problems of freedom, choice, and control in TR. The basic problem is this:

A.   We can be pretty certain that freedom and choice are good (therapeutic) for people, especially when they are "sick";

B.   We can be fairly certain that recreation is an excellent medium for the expression of freedom and exercise of choice; and

C.   We can be fairly certain that some patients will refuse to participate in recreation programs we offer.[2]

Said differently, if we know recreation is good for people when they are sick and they still refuse to participate, then what should the TR practitioner do?

One response to this problem has been to demonstrate that patient participation can be increased (e.g., Gillespie, McLellan, & McGuire, 1984; McClanahan & Risley, 1975; Quilitch, 1974) when behavioral technology and operant conditioning are used as methods—scientific methods. But have freedom and choice been compromised in order to increase participation? On the other hand, we know (scientifically) that if we do not intervene as practitioners, then it is likely that some patients will continue their inertia.

In the discourse that follows, I begin with a rationale for this second way of knowing, which for lack of a better term can be referred to as "the humanistic method." After enumerating some potential topics addressed better through the humanities than through science, I shall return to the problems of freedom, choice, and control using two examples from the humanities as points of departure. The section ends by expanding on the notion that some of TR's body of knowledge is not only embedded in the humanities but also created by humanistic methods (e.g., analogy, metaphor, "if-then" reasoning, and using different filters). The chapter moves toward closure by describing the conceptual ground shared by both science and the humanities, that is, the components of systematic thinking that are common to both (i.e., rigor, complexity, imagination, and free-minded thinking.)

Rationale

Without question, I do *not* advocate that the humanities replace science. Instead, I argue for the inclusion of both in the delimitation and study of TR's body of knowledge. Perhaps a second approach is needed simply because of the strong grasp that scientific thinking has on leisure studies in general and TR in particular (e.g., the recent calls for efficacy research in TR). Certainly this concern has been evident in the literature and in research presentations at conferences over the last several years (Hemingway, 1986; Hunnicutt, 1984; Mobily, 1984, 1985c; Robertson, 1983; Stormann, 1983). Further, still others who advocate the scientific method argue that it has been incorrectly or incompletely applied in leisure studies and TR (Mannell, 1983; Witt, 1983, 1984), and some even urge the use of more qualitative methods (Bullock, 1983; Riddick, De Schriver, & Weissinger, 1984).

Besides the obvious concern over the unsatisfactory application of the scientific method in TR research, I believe there are two other reasons for all the skepticism over the scientific research in TR. The scientific method is not inherently weak, but we have overlooked its limitations. First of all, science assumes determinism when it comes to human behavior (Babbie, 1986). Determinism simply means that we start from the assumption that all behavior is caused by something else, such as someone else's behavior or other external events. Scientists must make this assumption because science seeks to explain causal relationships.

At first glance, determinism may not present us with much conceptual difficulty. But on closer inspection, making deterministic assumptions in scientific inquiries has major implications for problems such as freedom, choice, and constraint in TR. The scientist, for example, might find that certain environmental conditions can be manipulated so that clients "choose" to attend TR more often. Hours of operation could be increased or recreation programs could be made available on each ward, thus increasing attendance. Through such manipulations the client's behavior has been "determined." Hence, a scientific explanation can be proposed. Increasing hours of operation or offering ward programs causes patients to perceive more choices; given more perceived choices, they choose to attend more often. Short of other manipulations or efforts to uncover the psychological processes which mediate perceived freedom, the scientist has reached an impasse.

Conversely, the philosopher may take these findings and elaborate and extend the understanding of freedom, choice, and constraint in TR. For instance, the philosopher might question whether environmental manipulation can possibly lead to more freedom in the strict sense because, by some definitions, freedom connotes willfullness, and willfullness suggests that a choice is made by the person, not determined by outside forces. Or the philosopher may try to clarify just what sort of freedom is being enhanced through environmental manipulations. For instance, the enhancement of freedom through removal of some previous constraints (e.g., extended hours present patients involved in other therapies all day with their first real opportunity to attend TR) is different from the kind of freedom that results when extra opportunity is present (e.g., the clients are taught a new leisure activity that adds to the diversity of choices).

This brief example underscores a point I made earlier, one that is worth repeating—science and the humanities, fact and value, are not independent of one another. The scientist investigating TR recognized the value of choice, the therapeutic value of empowering the client. Likewise, the philosopher acknowledged the fact that patient choices are susceptible to outside influences and manipulations. Explanations are not offered in a vacuum. Through symbiotic relation, science and the humanities together achieve a better collective response to the problems of freedom, choice, and constraint in TR.

A second limitation of the scientific method is related to the topics it can legitimately address. When it comes to problems of cause and effect, such as, what are the effects of client choice on perception of well-being, science is at home. At the same time, science has difficulty handling moral and ethical problems, though such problems may resemble problems of cause and effect, such as what is the value of perceived well-being in the first place? Hemingway (1986) has recently elaborated on science's difficulty in coming to terms with such moral questions in TR, arguing that therapy is aimed at things valued and, hence, should be concerned with societal and individual valuing. What is the essence of the thing valued that the therapy is aimed at?

Once the limits of science are appreciated, other potential topics are present as candidates to add to the list of subjects appropriately addressed by the humanities. Though ethics and morals have probably been the most frequently explored topics to date (e.g., see the entire issue of *Therapeutic Recreation Journal,* 1985, 4th quarter), much more attention should be focused on freedom, choice, and constraint. Several other topics that science has difficulty handling represent worthwhile areas for investigation by scholars using humanistic methods.

For instance, philosophical methods could be applied to help define and discriminate key terms in TR. Under what conditions and in what contexts do terms like *therapy, prescriptive, recreation, leisure* and *play* (and interrelations among these) acquire particular kinds of meanings? Clearly, this sort of theorizing goes beyond the operationalization of these terms for use as variables in scientific research.

The term *hermeneutics* has been often associated with the kind of thinking advocated here. Hermeneutics is the interpretation of relevant literature on a specific topic to attain a more elaborate understanding of the topic. Hermeneutics is said to be a self-involving (objective), scientific interpretation (explanation).[3]

Another potential way for humanities to contribute to TR is in the sketching of archetypes or models. Currently, there exist few models of what TR ought to be. What is the best model for implementing TR? By answering value-laden questions, we begin to frame such archetypes. Further, framing of archetypes is valid if and only if several scenarios are developed within differing contexts. The resulting dissonance between models would initiate dialogue and conversation, which are the hallmarks of a healthy, vital body of knowledge. (If there is nothing to disagree about, can anything more than the self-evident be known?)

Discovery and Creation

These and other potential contributions to the body of knowledge of TR can be approached in two ways through the humanities—either through knowledge discovery or knowledge creation. In this section, discovery and creation of knowledge are defined and examples of each are applied to TR.

I began with the assertion that science operates on the assumption of determinism—that a person's behavior has a cause outside of the person's control. This assumption further implies that causes are "out there," all around, waiting to be discovered. All the scientist needs to do is to discover them; the resulting discoveries qualifying as scientific knowledge.

Likewise, discovery is a common method of knowledge acquisition used in the humanities. Although the humanities do not assume a deterministic perspective and do not collect objective data, embedded within the humanities is a wealth of knowledge pertinent to TR. The discovery of this knowledge is different from its discovery in science but nonetheless vital to the advancement of TR's body of knowledge.

Discovery

One example of this "digging out" of knowledge embedded in literature involves Dostoevsky's famous chapter entitled "The Grand Inquisitor" in his novel *The Brothers Karamazov*. One character tells the story of the Grand Inquisitor to his brother. The Grand Inquisitor, who convicts people to death for heresy during the Spanish Inquisition, has captured Jesus on a visit to His earthly community. The Grand Inquisitor proceeds to prosecute Jesus for dealing humanity a terrible injustice by granting people free will. He traces several problems and general miseries of humanity to the fact that humans are free to choose. Instead, the Grand Inquisitor would have an exclusive, select minority make decisions for the people because most people do not have the ability to make wise choices and are miserable with the anxiety induced by the responsibility of having to choose in the face of uncertainty (existential anxiety).

The implications are many for TR, but the main one has to do with prescriptive intervention. What are the limits of TR intervention? When is the practitioner obligated to intervene on behalf of clients for their own good? Or are clients better off (psychologically) for making their own leisure choices, even if they make normatively incorrect ones? (And can this be called therapeutic?) By the time readers complete Dostoevsky's chapter, they are left pondering the limits of prescriptive intervention. Correlating the "data" with the importance of freedom to both leisure and therapeutic experiences, we can begin to see the dilemmas, conundrums, and paradoxes raised for TR.

For my second example of discovering knowledge I will rely upon B.F. Skinner's (1962) *Walden Two*. In *Walden Two*, Skinner gives a fictionalized account of a modern-day utopia based on behavioral engineering. That is, virtually every aspect of the lives of the residents of Walden Two is organized so that maximum efficiency is attained. Skinner's lead character, Frazier, has created a society based on the principles of operant learning. Into this utopia enter several "outsiders," visiting Walden Two for various reasons. Through their eyes the reader is given a tour, both geographical and psychological, of Walden Two.

Specialists are in charge of program areas such as food and health—and play. Workers in Walden Two are "paid" in labor-credits which are entered into a ledger. Four labor-credits (one per hour of labor on the average) each workday are required.

A "life of leisure" is a real possibility in Walden Two because of the reduced workday. Skinner allows for several protracted discussions between his characters with regard to how people in Walden Two spend all the free time resulting from the application of behavioral engineering principles. In fact, through Frazier, Skinner suggests that Walden Two will construct a modern-day Golden Age—leisure in the absence of enforced labor.

Skinner's work is at once exciting and disconcerting to read. It is worthwhile to read *Walden Two* in conjunction with Dostoevsky's "The Grand Inquisitor" and perhaps also an anti-utopian novel, such as Orwell's *1984* or Huxley's *Brave New World* . In any event, *Walden Two* lends considerable insight into the topics of freedom, choice, and constraint, especially in light of the promise that behavioral engineering holds for TR research and practice (Dattilo, 1986).

Several studies (e.g., Gillespie, McLellan, & McGuire, 1984; McClanahan & Risley, 1975; Quilitch, 1974) have demonstrated the potent effect reward structures can have on leisure participation among disabled populations. The question is, do the ends justify the means? Further, if freedom is an important component to the perception of leisure, as considerable research suggests, then can conditioned participation in activities be leisure? Clearly, science has demonstrated that we can orchestrate, condition, and influence many kinds of behavior. Only serious reflection about whether therapeutic recreators should do this will help the practitioner decide whether behavioral engineering techniques are warranted and justifiable.

When *Walden Two* is considered in conjunction with "The Grand Inquisitor," the student will likely be left with a certain, but not complete, uneasiness about how much intervention and engineering is justifiable. To be sure, there are a few who seem to suggest clearcut answers, either on the side of entirely prescriptive intervention with the purpose of creating an illusion of choice (Shivers, 1977) or on the side of complete nonintervention (Atchley, 1977). The downside of each of these simple solutions is either coercion of patients (in the case of the prescription-only approach) or apathetic, acquiescent patients (in the case of complete nonintervention).

Indeed, it is tempting to embrace one of these quick-fix solutions, but to do so would suggest that right action is black and white. I want to emphasize that ethical decisions are almost never so clear cut. And I think in the case of freedom, choice, and constraint in TR environments, one must consider the context within which decisions about behavioral engineering are to be made.

At present, it appears as though such techniques could be justifiably used with severely disabled persons (e.g., those showing severe developmental disabilities, senile dementia, or self-abuse). Likewise, it is probably less advisable to employ operant paradigms with the mildly disabled (e.g., those showing mild mental retardation or who are physically disabled without cognitive or emotional involvement). But the real problem has to do with those disabilities that are not clearly mild or severe. In these cases, the amounts and types of intervention to employ and the type of reinforcement schedules to use are much more equivocal.

Readings such as *Walden Two* and "The Grand Inquisitor" should help the student or practitioner come to terms with the need to consider each case on an individual basis and to avoid positions which give only one-sided solutions.

Creation

Turning to creation of knowledge does not require a complete change of gears; it may require only a subtle shift in emphasis. Creation of knowledge is not distinct from discovery of knowledge. For example, teachers are encouraged to use the Socratic method of instruction, based on the notion that learning is more meaningful if the student has to "re-invent" solutions. Whether this re-invention is a discovery or a creation is admittedly debatable. I could maintain that re-invention is rarely identical to the original, so in this light re-invention is a creative process. On the other hand, students are discovering only what is already fact. Nevertheless, because it is not my point to embark on some tirade over what constitutes discovery versus what constitutes creation, I shall just mention the potential for conflict and pass it by as a topic for future dialogue.

In my view, creation of TR's body of knowledge through the humanities could materialize on several possible fronts, including analogy, metaphor, "if-then" reasoning, and alternative "filters." Each of these likely occurs in conjunction with at least one other, but I will try to illustrate each in isolation so that the examples are relatively apparent.

An analogy is a parallel relationship in two topics. For example, I could argue that some of the visitors to Walden Two are analogous to severely handicapped persons whose lives are in chaos, who are made inert by their disabilities. I might then maintain that the residents of Walden Two are analogous to mildly disabled persons whose lives are only somewhat affected by their disability but are, by and large, better off left to their own devices when it comes to leisure choices. In both cases, the analogies drawn can be brought to bear on decisions regarding the use of or abstention from behavioral engineering techniques.

The use of metaphor is a quite common avenue to creative thinking. For example, Dostoevsky uses bread as a symbol for freedom in his story about the Grand Inquisitor. As pointed out earlier, the Grand Inquisitor argues that the ruling class will make decisions for the masses. But to keep the masses pacified, they will be given the illusion of freedom by returning some of their bread (choice), which they produced in the first place. Likewise, in TR the therapist might argue that choice is therapeutic and give clients their choice from among three activities when clients attend their required TR. Using the bread metaphor, we can see that the clients were only given the illusion of choice; they were never given the choice of attending TR in the first place.

"If-then" methodology is a label I have adopted to designate the process of applying a specific type of thinking to TR. It involves assuming a particular philosophy to be true and deducing from its principles what should be true of TR. Such a method addresses questions like "given existential assumptions about the human condition, how should the practitioner intervene with the client?" Other familiar philosophies that are good candidates for if-then reasoning include pragmatism, logical positivism, and behaviorism, to name just a few.

Lastly, by using alternative "filters," taking different perspectives or points of view on reality and experience, we may arrive at a more complex body of knowledge, one that is rich in potential, rich enough to explain both objective and subjective aspects of recreation as therapy. To be sure, science is an important perspective, but other important lenses should be affixed to our viewer. As Meyers (1986) so concisely put it, "each academic discipline offers its own unique window on reality" (p.117). If science is our only filter, we lose at least the ability to place the findings of science in context with the perspectives of history, philosophy, religion, and literature. Anything short of this sort of holistic perspective on TR, and the body of knowledge will wane in credibility as time passes, becoming stagnant, inert, and impoverished for lack of vision.

In sum, the humanities present abundant opportunities for discovery and creation of knowledge pertinent to TR. In our search for ideas worth learning, we should not overlook any concepts which promote a richer body of knowledge.

Thought Processes

Science and the humanities share similar thought processes. I will now touch upon four areas of correlation between science and the humanities: rigor, complexity, imagination, and free-minded thinking.

When I say that science and humanities share common ground when it comes to rigor, I mean that both can present findings which have a "compelling presence," evidence so powerful that we cannot ignore it or discount it. Certainly, good scientific methodology and a well-executed study deserve to be labeled rigorous. But what conditions constitute rigor in the humanities? Well, it is more difficult to say, but I feel certain that most readers could tell if they saw it. Rigor in the humanities means that a work makes sense when taken on its own terms. Therefore, it is unfair to impose the criteria for rigor in science on the humanities and vice versa.

Perhaps an example of compelling presence in the humanities that has bearing on TR will illustrate my point. Fink (1974) applied existentialism to his understanding of play. Just as the existentialist would argue that existence precedes essence, Fink argues that playing precedes understanding of play. This means that for TR's purposes it may be possible for play to possess somewhat disparate purposes, depending on one's perspective. For clients experiencing and playing, there is no idea of therapy as it is traditionally conceived. They are in play's place, in the "playground." Yet, therapists may simultaneously assess and evaluate play behavior in order to measure progress. Therapists perceive the client's playing from the everyday, real world. Hence, it may be possible for play to be a means and an end at the same time. It is this kind of clarification that rigor in the humanities leads to—the experiencing of play being reconciled with its therapeutic potential.

But rigor alone is not enough; it must be accompanied by complex thinking, that is, thinking which allows concepts like leisure, play, and recreation to interact with other symbols like therapy, reality, freedom, and happiness. Complexity in science is, like rigor, fairly easy to recognize, for if a scientific theory offers substantial explanation of a behavioral pattern, then it is complex enough. Again, the criteria for complexity in the humanities are not as clear. But I am prone to invoke James's (1963) plea, "Vote always for a richer universe, for the good which seems most organizable, most fit to enter into complex combinations, most apt to be a member of a more inclusive whole" (p. 232).

The topics of freedom, choice, and constraint present TR with areas in which complexity seems warranted. Both conceptual and empirical literature suggest that these are inextricably linked to the perception of leisure. Thus, it makes little sense to talk about being therapeutic without appropriate consideration of freedom and its subtle variations. If we think in a complex fashion about this, then we should talk of a unified therapy-freedom idea, not of each part in isolation from the other.

The third thought process which sustains both science and the humanities is imagination. By imagination I mean the capability (and willingness) to contemplate multiple possibilities. Dewey (1933, p.150) was noted for his "end in view" approach to learning, encouraging the ability to look to the "horizons" beyond one's egocentric point of view. Though we never fully reach that goal, it guides our inquiries and learning.

For instance, testing the worth of an idea might involve assuming it to be true and then determining whether it makes the greater scheme of things any clearer. This kind of thinking takes imagination, reaching beyond the current experiential world, using ideas to project possibilities, "acting" without acting (Dewey, 1929).

It is essential for both the scientist and the humanist to use imagination. For the humanist, we have maintained that imagination is necessary for contemplating possibilities. For the scientist, imagination is essential to theory development and testing. Good theories require the individual to reach at least one step beyond what is known. Imagination is not idle speculation, but it does require a partial letting go of things we are comfortable with, a willingness to take ideational risks.

The last of the thought processes I wish to comment on is free-minded thinking (as opposed to closed-minded thinking). In fact, it may help to view this thought process more as an attitude. It entails a willingness to suspend judgment (Dewey, 1982) and to guard against premature closure (Babbie, 1986). Clearly, both scientist and philosopher need to assume this attitude. The scientist would be ill-advised to argue that one correlational study yields a causal explanation. Similarly, methods used in the humanities, such as hermeneutics, rely largely on the notion that investigation will lead to greater understanding but not closure of inquiry.

As such, free-minded thinking is often in conflict with things that are standardized. Often, practitioners have difficulty with this sentiment; they want ideas and methods that represent the unvarying tools needed to be successful therapists. It is natural to want this, but it will probably never be the case that any idea or method will be successful all the time, especially when it comes to such volatile phenomena as human behavior.

Therefore, a constant amount of change is necessary to a mature (and maturing) body of knowledge. In addition, we ought to approach cautiously anything that has the look of regimentation, for such close-minded thinking will handicap TR, perhaps beyond recovery. Chances are that TR will be very different in the year 2000 from what it is today. I for one do not want to pass along a legacy of over regulation that might prove to limit opportunities for TR in the future.

We must in fact cultivate a spirit of criticism. Lest this be interpreted as a call for internal strife, let me point out that it is far better for an idea to run the gauntlet of criticism within the field than to have external critics point out embarrassing and glaring weaknesses. We do each other no favors in remaining silent when we see something that should be criticized.

If we assume a less tolerant attitude toward what constitutes knowledge, we substantially reduce the risk of fulfilling Godbey's (1985) prediction that a schism will emerge, severing the field into two camps—those with all the answers versus those with all the questions. Additionally, we must be aware of the insidious nature of close-minded thinking.

> Most fields grow somewhat conservative as they seek recognition: the process of institutionalization is, evidently, one that rewards caution if not conformity. It is this process that leads towards . . . narrow research questions pursued along accepted epistemological and methodological paths. (Hemingway, 1987, p. 7)

Conclusion

I submit that the separation between science and the humanities in TR (and elsewhere) is artificial and that, in fact, objective data and subjective data lie along the same continuum. All data represent information that can be used to pose answers and questions and to further develop TR's body of knowledge. Together science and the humanities can elaborate the body of knowledge that is TR. It is high time that the estrangement between ways of thinking ceases. We are inclined, all too often, to allow some of our "truths" to outlive their usefulness, to allow them to inhibit the development of new truths to fit the ever-changing nature and context of TR (James, 1978, p. 306).

Notes

[1] I am indebted to Professors John L. Hemingway (Old Dominion University) and Richard D. MacNeil (The University of Iowa) for their critical and constructive reviews of an earlier version of this chapter.

[2] Citations to support these points are common knowledge. Those wishing further support should consult Mobily, 1985a and 1985b.

[3] Hermeneutics begins by giving the investigator credit for personal knowledge (Polanyi, 1962), something the scientist has difficulty taking into consideration because it is not scientific to legitimize personal knowledge. The trouble the scientist has with personal knowledge relates to the negative connotations associated with subjective information. There are two senses of the word *subjective*, idle speculation, and personal knowledge acquired through systematic thinking about a topic. The former deserves to be disparaged; the latter is, in part, the method of hermeneutics.

Study Questions

1. In your own words, summarize the similarities and differences between science and the humanities as ways of knowing (epistemology). Make sure to include the basis that each uses to establish certainty and confidence in the respective type of knowledge developed.

2. This question asks you to consider two definitions of TR and analyze these competing definitions. Your task is then to compare and contrast these differing points of view and assess the "truth value" of each. Lastly, you are to employ if-then reasoning using one of these views.

Background information: Recently a significant debate over TR has been evident in the literature (particularly in *Therapeutic Recreation Journal*). Much of the debate focuses on how TR should be defined. Specifically, the meaning of words such as *therapeutic* and *recreation* are pivotal aspects of the entire debate.

Read the NTRS Philosophical Position Statement (1982) and John Hemingway's article on alternative perspectives on TR (1986). Then prepare a four-to-six page paper that includes

a. a one- to two-page summary of both the NTRS definition of recreation as therapy and Hemingway's definition of the same,

b. two pages contrasting Hemingway's definition of TR with the more traditional view represented in the NTRS statement, and

c. one to two pages suggesting what areas of the recreation profession might legitimately be labeled as TR if Hemingway's version of TR is assumed to be true.

3. Many points of departure for dialogue about TR can be found in *Walden Two*. One has to do with the use of behavioral engineering as a means to better leisure. Skinner's (1962) attitude, portrayed through his characters, reflects a confidence in making conditions right (p. 92) that is, being able to arrange the environment and, reinforcements in such a way as to produce desired responses. Suppose, like Walden Two, you can arrange your TR environment and establish reinforcement schedules so that "right conditions" exist. Patients under this scenario, use their free time wisely, almost always involved in meaningful leisure activities and never bored. Given that the (behavioral) technology exists to help you as a TR practitioner accomplish this, assume you institute such a program. What then is the implication of initiating this program? In your answer, describe:

a. the types of patients you would involve in such a program,

b. the types of freedom available to clients in this situation, and

c. how you would respond to criticism that such a program gives patients only the illusion of choice.

4. This question asks you to gain an understanding of the transcendent perspective on play by summarizing the point of view of Huizinga, Fink, or Berger. Next you are asked to take the transcendental perspective as a point of departure for definition of the therapeutic quality of play. Finally, you need to come to terms with this humanistic perspective on play in concert with the more popular philosophical approach to TR.

Background information: Several writers have discussed play from the point of view that it establishes a "special place," a "playground," or a gaming arena for the player. (For examples of this perspective on play, see chapter 1 in Huizinga's *Homo Ludens;* Fink's article "The Ontology of Play" in *Philosophy Today*; or Berger's third chapter, entitled "Theological Possibilities: Starting with Man" in *A Rumor of Angels*). This version of play maintains that play is a transcendental type of experience, one that lifts players out of everyday experience and "magically transports" them to a place out of the ordinary. This feature of play, it is argued, is play's very essence, its uniqueness.

Read one of the three selections suggested above, then write a four-to-six page dialogue that includes

a. a one-to-two page summary of the selected writer's interpretation of play;
b. two pages of discussion on what constitutes the therapeutic quality of play, assuming the writer's transcendental view of play is valid; and
c. one to two pages discussing how a transcendental perspective on play does or does not reconcile with the 1982 NTRS Philosophical Position Statement.

5. Imagine that you are a recreational therapist at a psychiatric facility. One day you and a group of patients are discussing meaningful and worthwhile uses of free time. Throughout your discussion you have emphasized the importance of choice and freedom in pursuing "true leisure." The patients are in agreement with your point of view and have come to a greater appreciation of the control they have over their leisure pursuits because of free choice. However, one of the patients argues that this idea of freedom is fine, but what

happens in the practical case of substance abuse? Specifically, how do you respond to the person who freely chooses to abuse substances as a free-time pursuit?

In two to four pages, make a case against substance abuse as a leisure pursuit. At the same time, do not abandon your position on freedom—that free choice is a vital aspect of "true leisure." Make your argument convincing by including references to outside sources.

6. Professionalism of TR has been and continues to be a topic warranting serious conversation. For most of us, professionalism connotes positive things happening to and within one's chosen vocation. Nevertheless, some suggest that we proceed cautiously and that we thoroughly assess all of the consequences of professionalism in order to avoid some of the dangers inherent in the process.

Read Kestenbaum's (1986) article and respond to the question that he poses to the reader: "What effect does professionalism's need to be of one mind have on [the profession's] moral reasoning and imagination?" (p. 44). Also respond to his further remarks on page 46: "is unity or the idea of unity a proper basis for an ethical outlook?" Finally, consider how professional unity and professional integrity (ethics) might be reconciled with one another.

References

Atchley, R.C. (1977). *The Social Forces of Later Life* (2nd ed.). Belmont, CA: Wadsworth.

Babbie, E.(1986). *The Practice of Social Research* (4th ed.). Belmont, CA: Wadsworth.

Berger, P.L. (1969). *A Rumor of Angels*. Garden City, NY: Anchor.

Bullock, C.C. (1983). Qualitative Research in Therapeutic Recreation. *Therapeutic Recreation Journal, 17*(4), 36-43.

Conant, J.B. (1952). *Modern Science and Modern Man*. New York: Columbia University Press.

Dattilo, J.(1986). Single-subject Research in Therapeutic Recreation: Applications to Individuals with Disabilities. *Therapeutic Recreation Journal, 20*(4), 76-87.

Dewey, J. (1929). *The Quest for Certainty*. New York: Putnam.

Dewey, J. (1933). *How We Think*. Lexington, MA: Heath.

Dostoevsky, F. (1957). *The Brothers' Karamazov.* New York: Signet. (Original work published, 1880).

Fink, E. (1974). The Ontology of Play. *Philosophy Today, 18,* 147-161.

Gillespie, K., McLellan, R.N., & McGuire, F.H. (1984). The Effect of Refreshment on Attendance at Recreation Activities for Nursing Home Residents. *Therapeutic Recreation Journal, 18*(3), 25-29.

Godbey, G. (1985). The Coming of Cross-Pollination of Leisure Studies and Recreation and Park Education: A Response. *Journal of Leisure Research, 17,* 142-148.

Hemingway, J.L. (1986). The Therapeutic in Recreation: An Alternative Perspective. *Therapeutic Recreation Journal, 20*(2), 59-68.

Hemingway, J.L. (1987). Leisure studies in the university: An interdisciplinary approach. In W.R. McKinney & R. Russel (Eds.), *SPRE Annual for Education* (Vol. 2), pp. 1-29. Alexandria, VA: National Recreation and Parks Association.

Huizinga, J. (1950). *Homoludens.* Boston, MA: Beacon.

Hunnicutt, B.K. (1984). The Rhetoric of Leisure Study. *Kentucky Recreation and Parks, 33*(1), 6-7.

James, W. (1963). *Pragmatism and Other Essays.* New York: Pocket Books.

James, W. (1978). How Is Truth Established? On Pragmatic Grounds. In J.A. Gould (Ed.), *Classic Philosophical Questions,* pp. 298-306. Columbus, OH: Merrill.

Kestenbaum, V. (1985). Professions, Ethics and Unity. *Therapeutic Recreation Journal, 19*(4), 41-50.

Mannell, R.C.(1983). Research Methodology in Therapeutic Recreation. *Therapeutic Recreation Journal, 17*(4), 9-16.

McClanahan, L.E., & Risley, T.R. (1975). Activities and Materials for Severely Disabled Geriatric Patients. *Nursing Homes, 24,* 10-13.

Meyers, C.(1986). *Teaching Students to Think Critically.* San Francisco: Jossey-Bass.

Mobily, K.E. (1984). The State of Leisure Research: Ten Miles From Nowhere. *Leisure Commentary and Practice, 3*(5), 1-3.

Mobily, K.E. (1985a). The Ethical Dilemma of Freedom in Therapeutic Recreation. *Therapeutic Recreation Journal, 19*(4), 22-30.

Mobily, K.E. (1985b). A Philosophical Analysis of Therapeutic Recreation: What Does it Mean to Say "We Can Be Therapeutic?" Part I. *Therapeutic Recreation Journal, 19*(1), 14-26.

Mobily, K.E. (1985c, October). *Thoughts on a Reconstruction of Leisure Research.* A Keynote address at the Leisure Research Symposium conducted at the National Recreation and Parks Association Congress, Dallas, TX.

National Therapeutic Recreation Society (1982). *Philosophical Position Statement of the National Therapeutic Recreation Society.* Alexandria, VA:NRPA.

Polanyi, M. (1962) *Personal Knowledge.* Chicago: University of Chicago Press.

Quilitch, M.R. (1974). Purposeful Activity Increase on a Geriatric Ward Through Programmed Recreation. *Journal of the American Geriatrics Society, 22,* 226-229.

Ricoeur, P. (1981). *Hermeneutics and the Human Sciences.* (Ed. and Trans.) J.B. Thompson, Cambridge, England: Cambridge University Press.

Riddick, C.C., De Schriver, M., Weissinger, E. (1984). A Methodological Review of Research in the Journal of Leisure Research from 1978 to 1982. *Journal of Leisure Research, 16,* 311-321.

Robertson, R.D. (1983, October). *Leisure Research and Education or Trading Awareness for Things of Lesser Worth?* Paper presented at the Leisure Research Symposium conducted at the National Recreation and Parks Association Congress, Kansas City, MO.

Shivers, J. (1977). Why not recreational therapy? *Journal of Leisureability, 4*(4), 4-10.

Skinner, B.F. (1962). *Walden Two.* New York: MacMillan.

Stormann, W.F. (1983). The Costs of Professional Recognition. *Leisure Commentary and Practice, 2*(3), 1-3.

Witt, P.A. (1983). The Ever Present Researcher-Practitioner Gap. *Leisure Commentary and Practice, 2*(1), 1-3.

Witt, P.A. (1984). Research in Transition. *Parks and Recreation, 19*(5), 60-63.

Continuing and Higher Education Issues

photo courtesy of San Francisco Recreation Center for the Handicapped

What we do during our working hours determines what we have; what we do in our leisure hours determines what we are.

—George Eastman

THERAPEUTIC RECREATION EDUCATION:
A Call for Reform

David R. Austin

Issues related to curriculum in therapeutic recreation (TR) abound today. Is TR preparation distinct enough to certify that graduates have mastered the unique knowledge and skills needed to practice as health care professionals? Are consumers assured of the professional competence of graduates of TR curricula? Can TR graduates compete in the marketplace when faced with concerns for third-party payments and licensure? Should those with no more than a superficial understanding of TR be making curricular decisions in universities and setting standards for TR?

A beginning place in seeking answers to these and other questions on TR curriculum is to identify assumptions that form the basis for our curricula. Underlying every set of education experiences we define as a curriculum is a set of assumptions. These assumptions need to be made clear and explicit. What assumptions underlie TR curricula? Have they been made explicit? The problems we are facing today in TR education exist because we have not resolved these questions.

This dilemma has not occurred because of a lack of effort. Educators have debated asumptions underlying TR curriculum for years, with particular attention being given to establishing boundaries for TR practice. Bradford Woods and Oglebay Park were sites of lengthy discussions by TR educators to resolve curricular issues during a series of postdoctoral institutes held by Indiana University and the University of Maryland from 1980 through 1985. Yet these efforts have not led to any resolution.

As a consequence, TR has remained very broadly defined, with the result that therapeutic recreation has been perceived as the provision of any recreation services for persons who are disabled. The assumption underlying curriculum has been that all persons, including persons with disabilities, should have opportunities for leisure experiences and that the provision of such services shall be termed *therapeutic recrea-*

tion. Based on this assumption, it is further assumed that TR is a "specialization" within parks and recreation. Therefore it is taken for granted that a TR specialist is a parks and recreation professional who specializes in serving people with disabilities and, as such, needs the basic curriculum all parks and recreation students need, plus some additional training in knowing about disabilities, and perhaps some clinical skills.

Carrying these assumptions further, faculty from all aspects of parks and recreation have the core knowledge of TR and are curriculum experts who can dictate curriculum content for TR. Is this not the very situation we have now as the Council of Accreditation deliberates whether to accredit TR? How many Council members are trained in TR? Some might say, "all of them" because assumably they know parks and recreation, supposedly the core of TR. Others might claim that none of them are expert in TR because they have not been trained in TR and know little or nothing about clinical practice. Whichever view one takes, it is clear that to the Council on Accreditation, TR is simply a "specialization" under parks and recreation like any other specialization, such as recreation program and leadership or recreation and park management.

Is this "right?" Of course it is, once we assume that TR is simply defined as the provision of recreation services for persons with disabilities and that its goal is "improved leisure life style," as claimed by the National Therapeutic Recreation Society (NTRS).

Historical Perspective

Historically, TR has grown from two streams of thought. One might be termed the "recreation for all perspective." Those with this point of view hold that recreation is inherently beneficial and should be available to all, including those in institutions and those who are disabled. This view was that of the old Hospital Recreation Section of the American Recreation Society back in the 1940s. Today it might be termed the "civil rights perspective" in that no one should be excluded from the civil right of recreation participation.

The other major perspective is that of recreation as therapy. TR is seen as a means to ameliorate, improve, or correct conditions in order to prevent illness and to promote health. TR is a means of treatment that involves purposeful intervention to bring about expected outcomes. This was the position of the old National Association of Recreation Therapists (NART) in the 1950s.

ARS and NART championed these two positions until the groups merged into NTRS in 1966. At that time, *therapeutic recreation* was adopted as a broad umbrella term to describe both recreation for special populations (the ARS position) and recreation therapy (the NART position). Since then the NTRS has tried to maintain both positions by adopting a broad view of TR that attempts to encompass both special recreation and recreation therapy. The NTRS position does, however, differ significantly from the old NART perspective in that NTRS has identified "leisure ability" as the ultimate goal for TR, rather than health restoration. A number of authors (e.g., Austin, 1986b; Carter, VanAndel, & Robb, 1985; Meyer, 1980) have objected to the NTRS position, having observed that its all-encompassing approach is too broad and lacks the focus needed to direct a profession.

Implications for Curriculum

It may be suggested that the broad interpretation of TR may also lead to problems in curriculum development. Because of the expansive approach, TR is not seen as a profession with defined boundaries but is simply a specialty area within parks and recreation, directed as full leisure participation by those who are disabled or institutionalized.

Would clear lines of demarcation between special recreation (recreation for special populations) and therapeutic recreation (the use of interventions for health promotion) be beneficial to curriculum development? A case may be made that a definitive separation of special recreation from TR could enhance both. Special recreation would be seen clearly as part of the leisure service delivery system. The assumption would be that the core of the curriculum for preparation would be the provision of recreation and leisure services—the traditional parks and recreation curriculum. The responsibility for training personnel for the provision of services for persons with disabilities would be that of parks and recreation curricula. Therapeutic recreation would be perceived as a segment of the health care system. The assumption would be that the core of the curriculum would be health promotion and intervention strategies dealing with assessment, planning, treatment, and evaluation. As such, the responsibility for the preparation of TR personnel would fall within academic units such as applied health science or allied health.

Are we likely to experience revolutionary changes in TR education? Will TR curricula redefine themselves and move from parks and recreation to allied health?

The answer is "probably not." There is a very practical problem that stands as a barrier to such realignment. In many university departments today, one third to two thirds of the students are in TR. Without TR, these departments might not continue to exist. It is not likely that these departments will be willing to give up TR under such circumstances. Assuming a change is necessary, a more likely scenario would be some type of compromise being effected to give TR more autonomy within university park and recreation departments. TR might be expected to remain in university parks and recreation departments as a distinct curriculum. Perhaps even a distinctive degree in TR will eventually evolve.

At the present time, therapeutic recreation will probably remain in parks and recreation. But it is perhaps time that two areas of curriculum are identified within parks and recreation—one for general parks and recreation and a second for therapeutic recreation. Such an arrangement would properly distinguish therapeutic recreation from the general field of parks and recreation. This will allow therapeutic recreation the following;

1. *Be able to better interpret TR to others.* Today we are competing for our very existence within the marketplace. We must be able to interpret and sell ourselves to health care administrators as professionals grounded in clinical skills, not as "good guys" who offer recreation opportunities. Clear, concise boundaries make this job much easier. In a health care industry faced with financial concerns, accountability, and more sophisticated requirements, we need to be able to clearly describe to others not what we do to enhance "leisure lifestyle" but to improve the client's level of health.

2. *Defining the boundaries of the profession will facilitate the expansion of a documented body of knowledge.* We must show in a precise manner exactly how TR is valuable in treatment and rehabilitation, because nearly all other allied health disciplines have begun efforts to demonstrate the value and worth of their practice. Such empirical evidence can become the basis to teach students the skills and knowledges needed to deliver quality clinical services.

3. *We will be able to better prepare students and provide them with a clear sense of professional identity.* As we become more focused in our curricula, students will develop a clearer sense of mission and purpose. This will allow students to take greater pride in themselves and their profession.

4. *A sharper focus for TR will allow those involved with special recreation to take command of their area.* Those responsible for the

delivery of recreation services, general parks and recreation professionals, can regain the leadership from therapeutic recreation specialists for
the provision of special recreation services. It is time that TR let go of
its role of parenting special recreation and give this mission to those
with whom it belongs—the providers of public parks and recreation.
(Austin, 1986b).

5. *Credentialing of TR professionals will become more
meaningful as TR is separated from general parks and recreation.*
Members of any professional group, such as therapeutic recreation
specialists, must employ a credential that certifies mastery of the unique
knowledge and skills needed in the defined area of clinical practice.
Consumers of services need an identified label that enables them to
differentiate one professional from another and offers some assurance
of professional competence in the services delivered.

Recommendations for Curricular Reform

Once the clinical concerns of therapeutic recreation have been
made explicit, what specific steps need to be taken to reform therapeutic
recreation curricula? This is the question to which this final portion of
the chapter is directed.

Redefine the term "clinical"

The term *clinical* needs to be redefined if it is to be used
effectively to unite TR specialists who employ purposeful interventions to strengthen individuals' coping abilities as well as to modify
those parts of clients' lives and environments that negatively affect their
well-being. The traditional usage of the term *clinical* connotes sickness
or illness, evoking images of medical staff in white garb diagnosing and
treating diseases and disorders through medication or surgery. As
applied in mental health settings, it brings to mind psychiatrists
prescribing psychotropic drugs or conducting insight-oriented
psychotherapy.

Therapeutic recreation clients may find that they need help that
family and friends cannot give, yet they do not have to be sick or
pathological to benefit from therapeutic recreation. TR should not be
narrowly conceived under a traditional medical model. TR does not
have to be done in hospitals and rehabilitation centers. It can be
practiced in any setting where TR specialists use interventions with
therapeutic intent. The systematic process of doing assessment, planning an intervention, implementing the intervention, and evaluating

sought outcomes with individual clients—make therapeutic recreation clinical in nature.

Develop knowledge of research

Both students and practitioners need to be trained to understand the conceptualization and design of research on clinical change. Equally important as training in research methods is developing an appreciation of the necessity to complete field-based research and to utilize findings in clinical practice. Without a commitment to research on the part of practitioners, few studies will be accomplished, because TR specialists must have the desire to initiate research projects or at least cooperate with university faculty and others who wish to conduct studies in the field.

Provide empirical evidence

Closely related to developing research literacy and appreciation is the provision of empirical studies to serve as a body of knowledge for practice. TR specialists need descriptions of effective intervention strategies that work with specific types of clients with specific problems. Systematic scientific studies of effective practice need to be accomplished cooperatively by researchers and practitioners, with the practitioners being highly involved in planning and conducting the research. Practitioners also need to take responsibility for doing descriptive studies to document successful and unsuccessful intervention strategies.

Professional organizations need to take the lead in encouraging research and stimulating financial support for developing the empirical evidence needed as a basis for TR practice. Once empirical research findings are available, both professional organizations and educators have the responsibility to see they are disseminated to students in preservice programs and practitioners in the field.

Responsibility of the profession in professional preparation

Agencies need to assume a larger responsibility in the preparation of future professionals. Colleges and universities can educate students, but the actual training in the techniques of therapeutic recreation practice must be gained in agencies delivering TR services.

Agencies must gear up to provide high-quality clinical supervision for students doing practicum and internship experiences. With clinical supervision being a relatively undeveloped aspect of therapeutic recreation (Austin, 1986a), it behooves agencies to establish formal clinical supervision programs and universities to teach students how to give and receive clinical supervision. Universities also need to prepare future agency supervisors to design and implement the overall field experience (Kunstler, 1985).

Liberal education for undergraduates

Undergraduates "have come to view general education as an irritating interruption—an annoying detour on the way to their degree" (Boyer, 1987, p. 112). This is highly unfortunate because the liberal learning dimension of professional education should deepen students' understandings of themselves and their world. It should contribute to acquaint students with the broader cultural context in which they exist personally and professionally. Liberal education provides students with an appreciation of Western thought and traditions as well as other cultures. Such a perspective enlarges the vision of students, helping them to appreciate differences between people and to build a better world.

The "unhealthy separation of the liberal and useful arts...tends to leave the students poorly served," according to Boyer (1987, p. 112). He suggests that "general and specialized education must be viewed as contributing to common, not competing, needs" (p. 112). In order for TR specialists to have the depth and breadth of education needed to be contributing citizens of the world, they need to become generally educated human beings. Such a background provides a context for professional practice and allows for wider appreciation of the diversity of clients and environments which they encounter.

Knowledge of the biological and social sciences

General education courses that relate to therapeutic recreation can be selected to enable students to establish foundations for professional study. Within the biological sciences, students should study anatomy, physiology, and relationships between biological systems. Social science preparation should include developmental psychology, abnormal psychology, educational psychology, and social psychology, with particular concern for the social psychology of leisure. Sociological concerns such as group dynamics, community organization, and the nature of leisure should form a basis for further study.

TR curriculum developers continually need to weigh the importance of such recreation core courses in the philosophy and history of the recreation movement, area and facility design, recreation and park management, and professional issues in parks and recreation against the necessity for students to gain a sound general, liberal education base along with necessary professional skills in therapeutic recreation.

Revision in core requirements for the therapeutic curriculum

Closely related to the previous recommendation is one to revise the core courses in recreation typically required of therapeutic recreation students. If therapeutic recreation is truly different from general recreation, as suggested previously in the chapter, it follows that therapeutic recreation curricula should not be simply a layering of TR courses on top of recreation courses. Instead, the TR curriculum should reflect those competencies needed by TR specialists to perform as clinicians.

Those in TR certainly need a background from which to understand leisure and leisure behavior. Beyond courses in the social science of leisure, however, there is much room for debate as to the value of therapeutic recreation students' taking some of the courses typically required for general park and recreation students. As with liberal education, curriculum planners need to measure the importance of requirements in the philosophy and history of the recreation movement, area and facility design, recreation and park management, professional issues in parks and recreation, and similar courses, comparing them against educational experiences directly related to clinical applications of therapeutic recreation.

Develop interpersonal relationship skills

According to Kunstler and Austin (1982), "Training in interpersonal skills is imperative for therapeutic recreation specialists" (p. 151). These researchers have found that classroom instruction, with homework assignments, can have a significant impact on the interpersonal relationship skills of TR students. Obtaining skills in attending, clarifying, reflecting, giving and receiving feedback, using silence, reinforcing, summarizing, and nonverbal communication helps assure that TR specialists will be able to establish rapport and maintain therapeutic communications with clients. Highly developed interpersonal relationship skills are at the heart of any clinical program. People possessing such skills will be likely to create an atmosphere in which empathy, genuineness, and respect may be fostered between the helper and the client.

Acquire activity skills

Kunstler (1985) has termed activities as "the primary vehicle for providing therapeutic recreation services" (p. 80). In order to apply activities in a therapeutic manner, it is imperative that TR specialists have a thorough knowledge of various types of activities within fine and applied arts, social recreation, dance, music, physical fitness, sport, and games. In order to have the level of facility needed to use activities to advance treatment and rehabilitation outcomes, it is desirable for students to gain an in-depth experience with at least one specific activity area (e.g., arts and crafts, aquatics, adventure-challenge activities, strength training, drama). Obviously, the more acquaintance a TR specialist has with a particular activity, the more likely it is that he or she may be able to use it in clinical application.

An area in which TR students today often have deficiencies is physical activity. At one time it was common for TR specialists to have a high level of knowledge in this area. Perhaps due to the separation of recreation from physical education curricula, skills in physical activities have largely become a lost art among TR specialists. This is highly unfortunate at a time when activities such as weight training, conditioning, running, walking, and aerobic dance are often used in stress reduction programs.

There currently exists a danger that TR students will not have the opportunity to gain required backgrounds in activities, as curricula are driven by a "recreation model," neglecting courses in activities in favor of those with management concerns. TR faculty and students will be remiss if they allow the omission of opportunities for students to become well grounded in activity skills. Creative approaches to instruction in activities may take the form of permitting students to gain activity skills through general education courses and field experience.

Knowledge of health, medicine, and rehabilitation

To function as clinicians, it is critical that TR specialists be well versed in basic information related to health, medicine, and rehabilitation. Students need to know the etiology, course, and prognosis for various diagnostic categories; disease sequelae; medical terminology; effects of major drugs; health and safety information for working with persons whose physical mobility or ability is reduced due to injury or physical conditions; effects of stress upon individuals; general principles of rehabilitation; and general understanding of wellness.

Therapeutic use of self

Possessing self-awareness, or understanding of self, is a critical part of being a therapist. TR specialists have to know themselves and be reasonably comfortable with themselves in order to be fully effective in helping relationships (Austin, 1982). Having such self-understanding permits TR specialists to respect themselves and to respond to clients with empathy, warmth, and acceptance. Professional helping in fact demands that the helper must ever remain cognizant that the therapeutic use of self requires the professional to keep the primary focus on the *client's* needs, not his or her own.

Use of the TR process

Due to the clinical orientation needed in therapeutic recreation, students must learn how to apply the therapeutic recreation process. Competencies include doing client assessment, formulating treatment and rehabilitation goals, writing behavioral objectives, completing treatment and rehabilitation plans, implementing treatment and rehabilitation approaches, and evaluating outcomes of interventions. Instruction in these skills must not be restricted to the classroom. Proper clinical supervision in agency practice must be provided to assist students to polish their skills in using all parts of the TR process. Such supervision should be given by a certified therapeutic recreation specialist. Current curricula too often give only cursory attention to the TR process, even though it is a critical part of professional preparation.

Specialization at the graduate level

A profession as diverse as therapeutic recreation demands that professionals gain the depth of understanding required to practice with specific types of clients. Undergraduate preparation necessarily has to provide broad-based exposure to a number of different types of clients and settings. Once TR specialists have determined a particular area of practice, however, they should be offered opportunity for specialization. Such specialization is required to advance clinical practice and the profession. Specialization can strengthen the profession because specialized practice is at the cutting edge of the profession. Specialists expedite the production of new knowledge and techniques in their defined areas of practice. They bring about the flow of information from one specialty area to another and to the generic body of knowledge for all of therapeutic recreation.

Summary

Within this chapter a case has been made that all curricula rest on a set of assumptions that need to be made clear and explicit. Assumptions underlying therapeutic recreation curricula have been discussed, and an argument has been put forth that therapeutic recreation should be clearly distinguished from the general field of parks and recreation. Following this, positive ramifications of making TR distinct from other areas of parks and recreation have been outlined. Finally, recommendations for curriculum reform that rest on the previously stipulated assumptions have been presented.

The time has come to make explicit the identifying features that cause TR to be distinct from other areas of parks and recreation, and to call for changes in professional preparation curricula to reflect the distinctiveness of therapeutic recreation. Without such definition, without bringing TR into sharper focus, we will continue to be all things to all people and lack the direction necessary for our profession to survive in the real world of the health care industry.

Study Questions

1. Would clear lines of demarcation between special recreation (recreation for special populations) and therapeutic recreation (the use of interventions for health promotion) be beneficial to curriculum development?

2. Discuss the relationship of "curriculum" to the notion of professional development and identity. What linkages are there? How important is a standardized curriculum?

3. If we are to prepare "clinicians," should this be at the master's degree level? Delineate the differences between associate, bachelor's, master's, and doctoral degree programs.

4. What is the "ideal " therapeutic recreation curriculum? How should it be developed? By whom?

5. Credentialing bodies (state and national) have assumed responsibil-

ity for testing the knowledge and competence of those individuals who desire to practice. Disucss the issues of governance, territory, responsibility, and cooperation between colleges/universities, NCTRC, NRPA's National Certification Board, and the Council on Accreditation.

References

Austin, D.R. (1982). *Therapeutic Recreation Processes and Techniques*. New York: John Wiley & Sons.

Austin, D.R. (1986a). Clinical Supervision in Therapeutic Recreation. *Journal of Expanding Horizons in Therapeutic Recreation. 1,* 7—13.

Austin, D.R. (1986b). The Helping Professional: You Do Make a Difference. In A. James & F. McGuire (Eds.) *A Helping Profession: Selected Papers from the 1985 Southeast Therapeutic Recreation Symposium(pp. 7--32).* Clemson, SC: Clemson University Extension Service.

Boyer, E.L. (1987). *College: The Undergraduate Experience in America.* New York: Harper & Row.

Carter, M.J., VanAndel, G.E., & Robb, G.M. (1985). *Therapeutic Recreation: A Practical Approach.* St. Louis: Times Mirror/ Mosby College Publishing.

Kunstler, R. (1985). Emerging Special Populations and How They Can Be Helped. *Adapted Physical Activity Quarterly, 2,* 177—181.

Kunstler, R., & Austin, D.R. (1982). Instruction in Interpersonal Relationship Skills: An Evaluative Research Study. In L.L. Neal, & C.R. Edginton, (Eds.) *Extra Perspectives: Concepts in Therapeutic Recreation,*(pp. 145—153). Eugene, OR: University of Oregon.

Meyer, L. (1980). Three Philosophical Positions of Therapeutic Recreation and Their Implications for Professionalization and NTRS. *Proceedings of the First Annual Post-Doctoral Institute* (pp. 28--42). Bloomington, IN: Department of Recreation and Park Administration, Indiana University.

THE DISCONTINUITY OF CONTINUING EDUCATION

Richard D. MacNeil
Michael L. Teague
Robert E. Cipriano

Introduction

The issue of professional competence must be of crucial concern in all human service professions. Therapeutic recreation (TR) is no exception. Professional competence is considered to be the integration of three elements: knowledge, skill, and performance. The ability to transform learning into effective and appropriate action is evidence of this competence.

For health professions the competence required for initial employment is usually a product of a postsecondary educational experience. In most health care fields, however, initial competence may be eroded quickly. This is especially true in an environment marked by rapid change, such as exists today. Technological advances and social concerns in the past few decades have required health care providers to make frequent adjustments in professional theory, knowledge, and practice. Since 1980, for instance, many therapeutic recreation professionals have had to respond to "new" issues such as third-party reimbursements, diagnostic-related groups (DRGs), and liability as well as having to deal with "new" groups of service recipients, such as individuals with eating disorders, developmentally disabled aged, and more recently, acquired immune deficiency syndrome (AIDS) patients. The point is that professional competence is not static. Knowledge and skills which may be on the cutting edge of professional practice at one point in time may be obsolete in a few short years. Reflective of this viewpoint, Kempfer has written, "The time has come when if a person does things as he/she did five years ago, that is prima-facie evidence that he/she is obsolete" (1980, p. 4).

The implications of such a scenario point to the need for vigilance in updating one's professional competence through the advancement of

time. A considerable number of different approaches for keeping
current exist. This chapter, however, focuses upon only the most
popular approach, continuing professional education. We begin by
briefly discussing the emergence of the continuing education movement and its presence in health care fields. This is followed by a consideration of TR's experience with continuing education. Next, a
variety of issues related to the application and use of continuing
education are addressed. Potential facilitators and deterrents to professionals' participation in continuing education programs are considered
in the chapter's closing segment.

Development and Use of Continuing Education

Continuing education (CE) may simply be defined as planned
learning occurring after completion of one's formal education, which
is intended to maintain or improve one's professional knowledge and
skills. While such learning experiences may be planned by the
individual for him- or herself, the authors will use the term *CE* to refer
to educational activities which are organized on a profession-wide
level. Structured educational seminars, conferences, classes, and
practicums are the most often used vehicles for providing CE opportunities. State, regional, and national professional associations are the
most likely sponsors of continuing education programs, although
various governmental agencies, educational institutions, and individual health care facilities also often organize CE programs.

In most cases, attendance at sanctioned CE activities results in the
acquisition of a predetermined amount of CE units. Some professions
require that a specified number of CE units be earned for certification,
re-certification, or re-licensure; other professions may simply encourage participation but do not require that a specific quantity of units be
accumulated. When participation in CE is required, a certification of
attendance at educational sessions is the primary mechanism used to
document such participation. Record-keeping procedures vary widely
among different professions. Usually some combination of the individual professional, the CE program's sponsoring organization, and the
professional association share responsibility for documentation. In
situations where CE involvement is required for re-licensure, governmental agencies may also be involved (Boissoneau, 1980).

In contrast to the approaches utilized in training future health care
workers, CE assumes that learners already possess a professional
knowledge base. Thus, instructional strategies employed in CE are

geared toward expanding one's knowledge, skill, and/or performance. Such expansion is usually considered to be synonymous with increasing professional competence. Since improved competence is presumably related to improvement in the quality of patient care, most people would agree that CE for health professionals is desirable and needed. This need is accentuated in a health care environment increasingly sensitive to the demands of public accountability and fiscal austerity.

The American Academy of General Practice (precursor of the American Academy of Physicians) is credited with being the first professional body to use CE units as a means of updating knowledge. In 1947 the organization placed in its constitution a membership requirement of 150 hours of CE participation over a 3-year period (Richards, 1978). Since that time at least seven other medical specialty societies have adopted policies demanding CE of their members. Moreover, between 1950 and 1980 a growing list of states adopted CE requirements for re-licensure of physicians (McCarberg, 1981).

Over the last two decades, numerous other health care professions have adopted policies related to continuing education. Organizations representing such diverse fields as nursing, physical therapy, social work, speech pathology, audiology, and occupational therapy all have chosen to employ CE, in one form or another, as part of professional practice (Boissoneau, 1980, McCarberg, 1981, Vogel, 1979). In some instances, CE units were demanded by states for re-licensure (Watkins, 1982); in other cases, CE was imposed by professional associations for certification/re-certification efforts or simply as a means of updating professional knowledge or skills (McCarberg, 1981).

The perception of CE as the panacea for continued professional competence has been tarnished somewhat in recent years by the lack of evidence supporting claims of increased effectiveness as a result of CE participation (the issue of efficacy will be discussed in more detail later in this chapter). Indeed, some professional groups (e.g., the American Medical Association and the American Hospital Association) as well as some states (e.g., Illinois and Colorado) have reconsidered their endorsement of CE requirements until further proof of the effectiveness of CE training on practice can be established (Carter, 1984). Nonetheless, the acquisition of CE units remains the most popular mechanism for professionals to continually update their knowledge and skills.

Continuing education and therapeutic recreation

As the continuing education movement proliferated during the 1970s, the field of therapeutic recreation gradually made overtures in this direction. Studies published by Unterreiner (1979) and Ray (1980) demonstrated that TR practitioners perceived a need for developing mechanisms to continue to expand their professional knowledge. At the national level, formal recognition of the need to create a vehicle for providing continuing educational opportunities for TR professionals was acknowledged by the National Therapeutic Recreation Society (NTRS) in 1977 with the formation of the NTRS Continuing Professional Development Program (Carter and James, 1979). Subsequently, the Continuing Professional Development Review Board (CPD Review Board) was created and eventually charged with the responsibility

> to revise, update and monitor operational/administrative procedures for continuing professional development; to review applications for endorsement by NTRS; to work in conjunction with the National Council on Therapeutic Recreation Certification. (NTRS, 1983, p.1)

The CPD Review Board directed much of its early efforts to reviewing applications submitted by sponsors of continuing education programs. The purpose of this review was to grant or deny permission for the sponsor to claim NTRS endorsement for their program. Approval allowed CE sponsors to use the phrase "endorsed by the National Therapeutic Recreation Society, a branch of the National Recreation and Park Association." This statement of endorsement, according to Bullock and Carter, "implicitly suggests that only endorsed programs will be recognized at the time when national registration renewal requires a certain number of continuing education units" (1981, p. 47). As of this writing date, the linkage between TR registration renewal and earned continuing education unit (CEU) credits has not been enacted.

The CPD Review Board was also involved in establishing specific evaluation guidelines to be used in the application review process. To this end, "The Continuing Education Unit Criteria and Guidelines," originally developed by the National Task Force on the Continuing Education Unit, was modified by the CPD Review Board to reflect the needs of the TR profession. This document was accepted by the NTRS Board of Directors in 1979, and approval was granted for further study prior to actual implementation.

The profession's efforts to maintain competence was bolstered by the creation of the National Council for Therapeutic Recreation Certification (NCTRC) in 1981. This politically autonomous body was established to oversee credentialing to standards within the profession. Although the CPD Review Board and NCTRC shared a common mission—the continuing maintenance of professional competence—the NCTRC was the body specifically designated to oversee credentialing standards. While the use of CE credit as a standard for initial certification or certification renewal has been discussed by the profession, no firm policy has been established.

The NTRS Board of Directors voted to terminate the CPD Review Board at the 1988 National Recreation and Park Association (NRPA) Congress. This decision left the NTRS's Education and Training Committee and the NCTRC as the primary organizations responsible for addressing the issue of continued assurance of professional competence in the therapeutic recreation field. A significant consideration in the decision to abolish the CPD Review Board was the fact that the procedure of endorsing sponsors for CE programs was recently assumed by the NRPA. Using the basic CEU structure originally formulated by the CPD Board, the NRPA has adopted a CE component to be used in conjunction with their general recreation (i.e., not therapeutic recreation) registration plan (Carter, 1988).

In contrast, the field of therapeutic recreation has not adopted a standardized continuing education plan. Concerns over the identification of the continuing educational needs of TR personnel as well as over the evaluation of CE experiences on TR practice have been cited as reasons for the failure of the profession to adopt a competency maintenance policy (Carter, 1984). In addition, some pragmatic considerations such as procedures for maintaining permanent records of individual participation in CE sessions, verification of attendance, and the financial management of the CE operation have never been resolved (Bullock & Carter, 1981).

In spite of the lack of national CE policy, interest in the development of continuing education does exist. Several organizations, particularly state professional associations, have developed CEU plans. One example of a state-level CEU program, jointly developed by the Connecticut Recreation and Park Association and the Department of Recreation and Leisure Studies at Southern Connecticut State University, is presented in Addendum A on page 175.

Issues Related to Continuing Education

As previous comments indicated, the planned use of opportunities designed to ensure the maintenance of professional competence is widely embraced by health care fields. Earning continuing education units remains the most popular mechanism for the achievement of this goal. This is not to imply, however, that the CE concept is without its critics. In this section we explore three separate but interrelated issues dealing with continuing education.

The efficacy of continuing education

In a 1976 speech, R. Robert Geake, then a member of the Michigan House of Representatives, told conference attendees about his state's recently passed law which required medical doctors to complete 150 hours of continuing education within a 3-year period preceding license renewal. Geake stated that the primary impetus behind the law was to respond to the growing "crisis" in medical malpractice insurance. Many carriers of malpractice insurance were refusing to accept new members. Michigan was facing a situation where many of its physicians would be forced to quit practicing medicine. In response to this crisis, the state legislature enacted legislation requiring mandatory continuing education for its doctors (Geake, 1976). In light of information available at that time, Michigan's response was logical and appropriate.

As we have stated, the basic assumption behind CE is that ongoing educational participation maintains or improves professional competence. Unfortunately, a review of the literature on the efficacy of CE offers few assurances of certainty. Studies conducted to establish the effectiveness of CE have consistently produced conflicting results.

One would intuitively suspect that exposure to educational activities would be effective in increasing professional competence. This assumption is supported by evidence produced in an early study conducted by Rubenstein (1973). This study involved a "back to medical school" experience for practicing physicians and then a postexperience follow-up evaluation. The results suggested that participation in the educational program strongly influenced professional practice. Findings reported by Talley (1978) also support the conclusion that CE can effectively produce changes in the practice of professionals.

In contrast, in one study of medical personnel in California, no correlation was found between perinatal death rates and CE courses in pediatrics and obstetrics (McCarberg, 1981, p.91). The inability of CE to alter the inappropriate practices of physicians was also raised by Miller (1963). Additionally, Shimberg (1982) has raised questions about CE, not so much with respect to its effectiveness but rather with its inability to produce adequate and effective evaluation tools to monitor its impact objectively .

Marcia Jean Carter, an original member of the CPD Review Board and a prominent authority on continued professional competence in

TR, also expressed concern about the efficacy of CEU programs. According to Carter, several professional organizations (e.g., American Medical Association and the American Hospital Association) and states have either rescinded requirements or placed moratoriums on mandatory CE until more substantial evidence of its effectiveness can be garnered (Carter, 1984). In summarizing her position, Carter called for a much more rigorous examination of the relationship of educational competencies to job performance before adopting CE units as a credentialing mechanism.

Almost a decade ago, McCarberg summarized the state of knowledge about the efficacy of CE when she wrote, "Overall the evidence accumulated will partially satisfy all viewpoints: CE participation apparently resulted in improved practitioner performance, competence, or patient health status in approximately 50 percent of the studies reviewed" (1981, p. 92). During the intervening years, researchers have not produced sufficient evidence that would invalidate this statement.

Voluntary versus mandatory continuing education

If the reader will momentarily disregard the doubts as to CE's efficacy and assume that CE can improve professional competence, it follows that efforts to require such experiences of all professionals is justified. This was certainly the rationale behind the movement to require Michigan physicians to complete CEU credits for license renewal (Geake, 1976). Accepting this assumption to be valid, one is free to consider a second basic issue: mandatory versus voluntary continuing education.

A strong push for mandatory continuing education for health care professionals occurred during the 1970s (Moore, 1976). Impetus for this movement was highlighted by a 1976 proposal by the American Public Health Association (APHA) which called for mandatory CE to become part of the re-licensure process for licensed professionals. The APHA endorsed mandatory CE as the preferred method for assuring the public of the competence of health care providers.

Although the specific arguments for requiring CE vary among professional fields, there seem to be several general points upon which all agree. First, if continuing education produces increased professional competence, everyone benefits from required CE. The professionals become more skilled, thus adding credibility to themselves as well as their professions; the needs of patients/clients are better served, thus adding credibility to the employing agency; and in the long term, society is better served through the more efficient utilization of health care resources.

Second, mandatory CE should make planning for continued training easier for both professional and sponsoring agencies. Knowing that one is required to complete a specified number of CE units in a specified time would allow professionals to arrange their schedules to accommodate such training. In like fashion, sponsors could develop a systematic structure for CE training if participation of professionals were ensured.

Third, mandatory CE is nondiscriminatory in nature. Since all professionals would be required to complete a similar amount of training, less skilled individuals would not be singled out the way they might be if, for instance, renewal examinations were used. This also means that the less motivated professional, who might be reluctant to participate in CE if it were voluntary, would be forced to update his or her skills to meet professional standards.

Finally, with required CE training, a vehicle is created for dismissing less competent professionals who may be insulated by existing seniority systems. When continuing education is made mandatory, individuals who fail to satisfy minimum requirements will no longer receive endorsement from professional groups, organizations, or licensing agencies. Without endorsement, the capacity to be employed may be severed or severely impaired.

However, there is no universal acceptance for the idea of mandating continuing education among professionals. While not denying that updating professional skills is important, several critics of mandatory CE have questioned the continuing education process as being the most effective means of insuring continued competence. This skepticism has led to the exploration of other quality assurance alternatives, such as self-assessments, peer review, and reexaminations by some professional associations (Shimberg, 1982).

While the preceding strategies may be alternatives to CE, they still may employ the element of force to accomplish a goal that some suggest should be a matter of personal choice. Voluntary continuing education (VCE) is an approach that expresses this desire for individual choice. VCE would remove the mandate to update one's professional skills, thus putting the burden of updating skills upon the individual.

According to Boissoneau (1980), one major advantage of VCE is that health care workers have the opportunity to select their own mechanisms for updating their professional needs. This may seem like an attractive alternative to a situation where professionals from other health fields or members of the public strongly influence the direction of practice in a profession. It may also be claimed that if continuing education is voluntary, the health professional is allowed maximum flexibility in the pursuit of updated knowledge. Such flexibility, it is reasoned, may enhance the motivation to participate since individuals are allowed to use personal choice in the selection of educational opportunities (Boissoneau, 1980). Another strength of VCE is that since an organized management structure need not be present, it would cost less to operate than would a mandatory plan. Such a savings could, at least theoretically, be passed on to the public in terms of moderated health care costs.

Voluntary CE plans are not without disadvantages. It might be argued that health professionals are dedicated and perceptive enough to realize that if they do not maintain their knowledge and skills, they are ultimately harming themselves. However, the fact of the matter is that "only half of the people in some health professions engage in continuing education at a level that could be called reasonable" (Boissoneau, 1980, p. 150). While data are not available, lack of participation may be particularly problematic in a field such as therapeutic recreation in which salaries tend to be low in comparison to sister professions and in which administrative decisions are most frequently made by individuals with minimal understanding of the TR profession. Moreover, TR's primary quality assurance vehicle is certification, but once the professional is certified, the payment of a fee every 2 years permits certification renewal. Such a situation offers little incentive to "keep current."

Sponsorship and management of continuing education

If one concedes that continuing education is a desirable activity for professionals, another issue is the pragmatic concern over who should organize and manage the CE program. The two groups most often identified with fulfilling this role are governmental bodies and professional associations.

As the previously cited physician re-licensure situation in Michigan demonstrates, governmental units have become involved in the management of CE for some professions. This is particularly true in cases of mandatory CE programs in which a governmental body serves as the mandating agency. Having the government serve as the manager of CE offers certain advantages to health care providers. Perhaps the most important of these include the ability of government units to organize a CE program which can tap a much broader resource base than would be possible by an individual or a professional association. Such a situation would seemingly foster a more diverse and meaningful CE program than would otherwise be affordable. Also, a governmentally managed program would theoretically produce a CE structure which is fair and consistent since it is removed from professional biases and intra-profession "pork-barreling."

On the other hand, a CE program managed by the government results in an educational structure being created and supervised by individuals who may be removed from the profession itself. This situation could be extremely problematic. For instance, what might be the content of CE training sessions for TR personnel if the body organizing the training were nurses? Social workers? Occupational therapists? Additionally, there is the fact that bureaucracy proliferates with government involvement. Given the related perception of government's inability to function effectively, it is unlikely that there would be much popular support for increasing government involvement in managing CE even if mandatory continuing education were required by legislative decree.

In lieu of government involvement, the most reasonable candidates to sponsor and manage a CE program would seem to be professional associations. A primary strength of these associations lies in the fact that their members join by choice; they are not forced to participate. Because their membership is comprised of individuals who have become involved on their own volition, the goals and objectives of professional associations are usually judged to be acceptable to members before they join. The result is the creation of organizations striving for the highest levels of professional effectiveness. As sponsors of CE, professional associations seem well positioned to organize relevant and timely educational experiences for their members. Using associations as managers of CE would, on the one hand, facilitate strong influence on the direction of training by the involved professionals while, on the other hand, theoretically limiting the bureaucracy associated with government involvement.

While professional association sponsorship has many advantages, certain drawbacks to this approach may be noted. The field of therapeutic recreation is a case in point. As was mentioned earlier, the NTRS responded to the issue of continuing education with the creation of the CPD Review Board in 1977. Throughout its 11-year existence, the CPD Review Board diligently studied the issue of continuing professional competence in TR, yet could never thoroughly resolve some of the most basic concerns. According to Carter (1984), the profession has yet to identify the employment performance standards necessary to clarify continuing competencies in TR and lacks effective evaluation tools to measure the impact of continuing professional development activities on professional performance. TR is not alone in its inability to answer these questions (McCarberg, 1981). The problem is exacerbated by the limited resources (e.g., money, personnel) committed to address these issues in the field (Bullock & Carter, 1981; Carter, 1988).

While their voluntary nature is a major strength of professional associations, it may also be considered a liability. Perhaps the single most important negative factor in a professional association's impact on CE is that because it is a voluntary organization, not all the professionals in its particular field are members. While many of its members may be highly motivated to pursue educational experiences on their own, there are at least some professionals who are not motivated to participate in educational activities. Research designed to explore the motivation to participate and the perceived CE needs of therapeutic recreation personnel has been minimal (Coffey, 1986; Ray, 1980; Unterreiner, 1979). As a profession, our knowledge of factors which either motivate or deter CE efforts is extremely limited. How might we begin to resolve this situation?

Potential Facilitators and Deterrents to Professionals' Participation in Continuing Education

Positive reasons and resources that facilitate the participation of professionals in continuing education programs certainly include the high value that professions place on lifelong learning, encouragement and help from university and professional association sponsors, requirements for professional certification and re-certification, and the growing public concern about quality control in health professions. However, two self-evident but often overlooked considerations by program planners for professionals' continuing education are (a) the reasons professionals choose to participate and (b) deterrents to participation. Our intent here is not to look at the specifics behind participation reasons and deterrents but to address the framework by which such concerns can be measured and used by program planners for CE efforts.

Reasons for participation

The reasons professionals participate in CE programs are an important but very underdeveloped area of study. Grotelueschen (1985) noted that the research models for participation have been principally grounded in psychology. Reasons for participation, under a psychology framework, are viewed as antecedent conditions, and actual participation as a behavior or an end. Yet, Grotelueschen criticizes this approach as not necessarily focusing on "either the felt reasons of participants themselves or on the practical implications of research findings for continuing education practice" (p. 34). Houle's (1961) typology of adult learning orientations represents a key exception to psychology-based models. However, Houle's work has also been criticized for not addressing the issue by which knowledge can be used to improve practice. Grotelueschen (1985) adds that the focus on adult education generally has limited applicability since it fails to address highly differentiated subgroups that are a part of professions.

Since the mid-1970s, members of the Office of the Study of Continuing Professional Education at the University of Illinois at Urbana-Champaign have conducted ongoing research on the reasons professionals participate in continuing education. These efforts have been very important since they address professional CE as being separate from adult education theory and efforts. The preliminary results and theoretical design behind this research may have important implications for a wide variety of professions attempting to meet the unique needs and expectations of their professionals for continuing education.

Efforts by the Office of the Study of Continuing Professional Education led to the construction of the Participation Reasons Scale (PRS), developed by Grotelueschen, Harnisch, and Kenny (Grotelueschen, 1985). The PRS is a 30-item self-report instrument that states, in future tense, educational reasons for participation in continuing professional education. A 7-point Likert Scale is used to measure the relative importance assigned to each participation reason. Five basic clusters of reasons are identified: (a) professional improvement and development, (b) professional service, (c) collegial learning and interaction, (d) professional commitment and reflection, and (e) personal benefits and job security.

The PRS has been administered to random samples of professionals in various professions at the local, state, regional, and national levels. A detailed discussion of these findings is beyond the scope of this chapter. However, Grotelueschen (1985) summarizes four general implications based upon this research that have useful application for the designing of therapeutic recreation professional continuing education programs. First, professional improvement and development is the most important but not the only cluster of reasons for professionals to choose to participate in continuing education. Second, the importance assigned to participation reasons varies not only between professions but within profession subgroups. Third, the difference in participation reasons within professions suggests that professionals assume a "developmental evaluation in regard to educational expectations." Fourth, the differences in participation reasons across professions suggest that "educational expectations vary with characteristics specific to individual professions" (p. 42).

The general implications summarized by Grotelueschen may be common sense. However, the salient point is that reasons for participation across and within professions demand that each profession find a method for addressing its own expectations for continuing education. The generic nature of the PRS instrument provides a means by which the therapeutic recreation profession may attain this objective. This instrument affords program planners a simple but effective way to design programs based upon professionals' expectations and to monitor the degree to which these expectations are met. For example, if the cluster of "collegial learning and interaction" reasons were identified as receiving high priority, one can assume that failure to meet these expectations will result in poor future program participation. The conversion of the PRS language to the past tense may then be used as a post-test to provide data for program education and accountability. (Addendum C, page 179 contains an adapted version of the PRS.)

Deterrents to participation

Scanlan and Darkenwald (1984) note that an exclusive orientation to professionals' reasons for participation in continuing education (i.e., motivational orientation factors) "has not proved useful in distinguishing participants from nonparticipants" (p. 155). The research focus should not only be on what impels participation but what deters it. Scanlan and Darkenwald argue, "If it is true that nearly all adults need and want to continue to learn, then the concept of deterrent is obviously crucial to understanding and predicting their involvement in education" (p. 56).

The study of the deterrents of professionals from continuing education involvement remains a weakly developed area. Most efforts have employed descriptive rather than sophisticated measurement designs. Scanlan and Darkenwald's (1984) review of the descriptive efforts, however, reveal the following significant deterrents: "cost, opportunities, job responsibilities, home responsibilities, lack of interest, and lack of confidence." As with the reasons professionals choose to participate in continuing education, these deterrents to participation are likely to differ between and within professions. Thus, program planners for continuing education are challenged to address this issue as it uniquely applies to their own professionals.

Scanlan and Darkenwald (1984) have developed a Deterrents to Participation Scale (DPS) that may be useful for planners of therapeutic recreation professional continuing education programs. The DPS is a 40-item self-report instrument. Based on a factor analysis of the DPS, six deterrent clusters are identified: (a) disengagement, (b) lack of quality, (c) family constraints, (d) cost, (e) lack of benefit, and (f) work constraints. By employing the DPS and the PRS, program planners can address what impels professionals to participate as well as deterrents to participation in continuing education efforts.

Concluding Remarks

The intent of this chapter has been to broadly consider the phenomenon of continuing education and to discuss its implications upon the field of therapeutic recreation. Toward this end we reviewed the historical development of CE and highlighted some of its applications to health care professions, including TR. A second section addressed several major issues of critical concern to continuing education: the efficacy of CE, mandatory versus voluntary CE involvement, and sponsorship and management of CE programs. The discussion closed on the subject of potential motivators and deterrents to professionals' involvement in continuing education.

With the foregoing information in mind, the authors will take this opportunity to present a few closing comments with respect to continuing education and the therapeutic recreation profession. First, to assure the maintenance of competence of TR professionals and to uphold the credibility of the profession as a health care and human service provider, the provision of continuing education opportunities must become a priority issue for the field. A standardized policy on continuing education endorsed by NTRS, the American Therapeutic Recreation Association (ATRA), NCTRC, and other closely affiliated professional associations would be a necessary first step in this direction.

The writers strongly support Carter's assertion that the specific structure of a professional development program must be determined only after a more rigorous investigation of professional standards as they relate to job performance in the TR field (Carter, 1984). Research efforts should also focus upon discovering reasons for participation and nonparticipation of TR professionals in CE activities. Only after we better understand these motivations can we begin to deal with their implications in terms of improving involvement levels in CE activities. Additionally, investigators must address the void Shimberg (1982) noted in evaluation tools that measure the impact of CE involvement upon practice.

The authors also believe that professional associations should remain the focal point of continuing education efforts in TR. Such a belief is based upon two presumptions. First, a continuing education plan which is managed by an outside-the-profession agency would put TR professionals at the mercy of individuals who may have little understanding or appreciation of the field on the one hand, as well as foster the potential for a bureaucratic nightmare on the other. Second, by managing CE through our professional associations, we can take advantage of the collective strengths (e.g., motivation, independence, knowledge) of their members.

In the final analysis, it is evident that the field of therapeutic recreation has come a long way in a short period of time. For the profession to continue to progress as a respected member of our nation's health care team, we must be diligent in efforts to ensure the continued competence of our professionals. The creation of a mechanism to provide for continuing educational needs is not only philosophically desirable, it is a professional necessity.

Study Questions

1. Please make a list of various technological and social forces that you believe might require adjustments in professional theory, knowledge, or practice in therapeutic recreation in the next 10 years. Predict what some of these changes might look like.

2. Debate the following resolution: "The accumulation of continuing education units should be required for re-certification in the field of therapeutic recreation."

3. You have been asked by the president of a national professional organization to develop a draft of a national policy statement on continuing education for the TR profession. Please develop an outline of this policy statement and share it with others in your class.

4. You have just been informed about a forthcoming continuing education workshop which is specifically related to your current position. You are aware that your agency has been reluctant to support CE participation by its TR staff in the past. Please write a letter to your supervisor requesting financial support to cover the costs of your participation in the workshop. Be sure to justify your attendance in terms of long-term benefits to your clients and to the agency as a whole.

5. In a list, identify all of the possible reasons some TR professionals attend continuing education activities. In a second list, identify all of the possible reasons some TR professionals do not attend continuing education activities.

6. Pretend you have been invited to present a CEU workshop on a topic of your choice related to therapeutic recreation. Please outline your talk. Identify three to five objectives that could be used to evaluate the effectiveness of your workshop. Please identify instructional resources you might utilize in presenting your talk.

References

Boissoneau, R. (1980). *Continuing Education in the Health Professions*. Rockville, MD: Aspen Systems.

Bullock, C., & Carter, M.J. (1981). Status Report: Continuing Professional Development Program for Therapeutic Recreators. *Therapeutic Recreation Journal, 15* 2, 46-49.

Carter, M.J. (1984). Issues in Continuing Professional Competence of Therapeutic Recreators. *Therapeutic Recreation Journal, 18,* 3, 7-10.

Carter, M.J. (1988). Telephone conversation, November 28, 1988.

Carter, M.J., & James, A. (1979). Continuing Professional Development Program for Therapeutic Recreators. *Therapeutic Recreation Journal, 13,*3, 12-15.

Geake, R. (1976). Professional Services and Quality: Continuing education as a guarantee. In D. Moore (Ed.), *Mandatory Continuing Education: Prospects and Dilemmas for Professionals* (pp. 13-23). Urbana-Champaign: University of Illinois Office for Continuing Education and Public Service.

Grotelueschen, A.D. (1985). Assessing Professionals' Reasons for Participating in Continuing Education. In R. M. Cervero & C. L. Scanlan (Eds.), *Problems and Prospects in Continuing Professional Education* (pp. 33-46). San Francisco, CA: Jossey-Bass.

Houle, C.O. (1961). *The Inquiring Mind.* Madison, WI: University of Wisconsin Press.

Kempfer, H. (1980). Continuing education in the 1980s: The Growing Edge. *Council for Noncollegiate Continuing Education, 3*, 1-2, 4.

McCarberg, P. (1981). The Efficacy of Continuing Education. In D. Falk, N. Weisfeld, & P. McCarberg (Eds.), *To Assure Continuing Competence* (pp. 89-99). (DHHS Publication No. HRA 81-5). Washington, DC: U.S. Department of Health and Human Services.

Miller, G. (1963). Medical Care: Its Social and Organizational Aspects. *New England Journal of Medicine, 269*, 295-299.

Moore, D. (Ed.). (1976). *Mandatory Continuing Education: Prospects and Dilemmas for Professionals.* Urbana-Champaign: University of Illinois Office for Continuing Education and Public Service.

National Therapeutic Recreation Society (1983, February). NTRS Minutes, Continuing Professional Development Review Board Report, p. 1.

Peterson, C.A., et al. (1977). *A Study of Training Needs of Therapeutic Recreation Personnel in the State of Illinois.* Urbana, IL: University of Illinois Press.

Public Health Association (1976, September). Continuing Education for Licensed Professionals. *Nation's Health*, 10.

Ray, R.O. (1980). Attitudes Toward Continuing Education: A Preliminary Inquiry Into the Professional Development of Therapeutic Recreation Specialists. In G. Hitzhusen (Ed.), Expan*ding Horizons in Therapeutic Recreation VII.*, 171-182. Columbia, MO: University of Missouri.

Richards, R. (1978). *Continuing Medical Education.* New Haven, CT: Yale University Press.

Rubenstein, E. (1973). Continuing Education at Stanford. *Journal of Medical Education, 48*, 911-918.

Scanlan, C.S., & Darkenwald, G.C. (1984,). Identifying Seterrents to Participation in Continuing Education. *Adult Education Quarterly, 34*, 3, 155-165.

Shimberg, B. (1982). *Occupational Licensing: A Public Perspective.*
    Princeton, NJ: Center for Occupational and Professional Assess-
    ment.
Talley, R.C. (1978).   Effect of Continuing Medical Education on
    Practice Patterns. *Journal of Medical Education, 53*, 602-603.
Unterreiner, C.R. (1979). A Study of Continuing Education Needs of
    Personnel Delivering Therapeutic Recreation Services in the
    State of Missouri. *Therapeutic Recreation Journal, 13*, 1, 44-49.
Vogel, B. (1979, September 9). Professional Retraining Influx. NY:
    New York Times, Education section, p.   3.
Watkins, B. T. (1982). Doubt About Wisdom of Requirements Slows
    Continuing Education Movement. *Chronicle of Higher Educa-
    tion, 24*(15), 16.

ADDENDUM A
MODEL CONTINUING EDUCATION UNIT
PROGRAM
Continuing Education Unit Program:
Policies and Procedures

1. *Definition*: One continuing education unit (CEU) is 10 contact hours of participation in an organized continuing education experience under responsible sponsorship, capable direction, and qualified instruction.

2. *Use*: The CEU is used as the basic instrument of measurement for an individual's participation in a sponsoring agency's offering of noncredit classes, courses, and programs.

3. *Registration*: Individuals register for CEU activities on a noncredit activity form.

4. *Categories*: The CEUs will be awarded for noncredit activity programs conducted by sponsoring agencies as either individual or institutional.

   I. Category 1 - individual CEUs
       A. Activities

          1. The noncredit activity is planned in response to an assessment of educational need for a specific target population.
          2. For such a program, there is a recorded statement of objectives, rationale, and purpose prepared prior to the beginning of the activity.
          3. Content is selected and organized in a sequential manner.
          4. There is evidence of preplanning, which should include the opportunity for input by a representative of the target group to be served, the faculty having content expertise, and continuing education personnel.
          5. The activity is of an instructional nature and is sponsored or approved by an academic or adminis-

trative unit of the institution best qualified to effect the quality of the program content and to approve the resource personnel utilized (e.g., state affiliates of NRPA, Connecticut Recreation and Park Association [CRPA]).

6. Participants are registered to provide permanent, individual CEU records and to provide data for reporting.
7. Prior to the beginning of the activity, appropriate evaluation procedures are utilized and criteria established for awarding CEUs to individuals. This may include evaluation of individual performance, instructional procedures, and course effectiveness.
8. A permanent CEU record is maintained for each participant by the sponsoring agency and CRPA.

B. Procedures

1. CPRA should maintain a written description of each non-credit activity (see Appendix B). The description will include the following:

   a. Title
   b. Target audience
   c. Activity objective(s)
   d. Content summary
   e. Evaluation procedure
   f. Name of Instructor(s)
   g. Level
   h. Date of activity
   i. Location
   j. Registration fee
   k. Program number
   l. CEUs
   m. Approvals

2. After the activity has begun, the sponsoring agency will forward the description and registration cards to the designated CEU agency (CRPA).
3. When the activity has ended, the sponsoring agency will obtain instructor-of- record certification of those who met all requirements, and it will inform CRPA, by list, of the participants who are to receive CEUs.
4. Participants will receive a certificate of completion.

II. Category 2 - institutional CEUs

    A.   Activities

        1.   Activities in this category will meet the criteria outlined in Category 1, with the following exceptions:

           a. The noncredit activity may be planned for a more diversified population.

           b. Planning inputs from the target population may not be required.

           c. Individual CEUs are not awarded.

        2.   Individuals who participate in Category 2 activities will register, but no individual record will be maintained and no CEUs will be awarded on an individual basis. Institutional certification of involvement will be made by means of registration data. A file of program materials will be maintained by the designated CEU agency.

    B.   Procedures

        1.   CRPA will maintain a written description of each noncredit activity. The description will be the same as for Category 1 activities, with the exception of having no individual CEUs.

        2.   Individuals who participate in Category 2 activities will register on noncredit activity registration forms, but no other individual records will be maintained.

        3.   Institutional certification of involvement will be made by means of registration data.

        4.   The number of institutional CEUs awarded will appear on the certificate of completion.

ADDENDUM B
NONCREDIT ACTIVITY DESCRIPTION FORM
CEU Noncredit Activity Description

1. Title _____

   _____

2. Target audience _____

   _____

3. Objective of activity _____

   _____

4. Content summary_____

   _____

5. Evaluation _____

   _____

6. Instructor _____

7. Level: General_____   Introductory _____

             Intermediate _____   Advanced _____

             Other _____: _____

8. Dates and times of activity _____

9. Location of activity _____

10. Registration fee_____

11. Program number _____ 12. CEUs _____

                          Aproved _____
                                   Instructor   Date

Approved _____ Approved _____
Conn. Rec. & Park Assn.   School or unit sponsor Date

NOTE: No program may be advertised or promoted until all approvals
have been obtained.

ADDENDUM C
PARTICIPATION REASONS SCALE
PART A: PARTICIPATION REASONS SCALE

DIRECTIONS: There are many reasons for participation in continuing professional education activities. The following list is designed so that you can indicate the relative importance of the general reasons you might have for participating in this specific continuing education activity. For each item, mark the numeral which best represents the degree of importance you attach to each reason.

Professional improvement and development

	Not important	Moderately important	Very important
Reasons			

1. To maintain my current
    professional skills/knowledge   1   2   3   4   5   6   7

2. To gain new skills/knowledge
    needed to advance in my
    profession   1   2   3   4   5   6   7

3. To consider changing the
    emphasis of my present job
    responsibilities   1   2   3   4   5   6   7

4. To help me keep abreast
    of new developments in
    my profession   1   2   3   4   5   6   7

Professional service

5. To maintain my current
    professional skills/knowledge   1   2   3   4   5   6   7

6. To improve my individual service
    to the public as a professional   1   2   3   4   5   6   7

7. To find prospective student
   interns and/or employees to
   fill anticipated positions   1   2   3   4   5   6   7

Collegial learning and interaction

8. To mutually exchange thoughts
    with colleagues   1   2   3   4   5   6   7

9. To learn from the interaction
    with colleagues   1   2   3   4   5   6   7

10. To be challenged by the
    thinking of my colleagues   1   2   3   4   5   6   7

11. To better understand how
    colleagues deal with special
    problems similar to mine   1   2   3   4   5   6   7

12. To renew friendships with
    colleagues   1   2   3   4   5   6   7

13. To develop new collegial
    friendships   1   2   3   4   5   6   7

14. To increase the likelihood
    of personal financial gain   1   2   3   4   5   6   7

15. To increase the likelihood of
    professional advancement   1   2   3   4   5   6   7

16. To enhance my individual
    security in my present position 1   2   3   4   5   6   7

17. To make contacts for future job
    positions   1   2   3   4   5   6   7

18. To decompress from the pres-
    sures associated with my job by
    getting away from workplace   1   2   3   4   5   6   7

19. To meet the continuing education
    unit credits required for
    professional certification   1   2   3   4   5   6   7

20. To enjoy myself by socializing
    with colleagues   1   2   3   4   5   6   7

Professional commitment and reflection

21. To maintain my identity with
    my profession   1   2   3   4   5   6   7

22. To maintain a professional
    commitment to my profession 1   2   3   4   5   6   7

23. To help me develop capabilities
    for leadership positions within
    my professional association   1   2   3   4   5   6   7

24. To gain insight into directions/
    trends associated with my
    profession   1   2   3   4   5   6   7

photo courtesy of Bradford Woods

Leisure is the cardinal point around which everything turns.

—Aristotle

PART II

Professionalization Issues

Summary

To strive for respect, acceptance and dignity among professionals and organizations is a natural phenomenon. In therapeutic recreation this struggle has been best exemplified by the evolution of the credentialling efforts. Norma Stumbo clearly presents the issues facing the profession in testing the professional. Defining and measuring "professional competence" is not only a difficult task for many professions but further confounded when applied to therapeutic recreation. While we are beginning to understand the diversity of job functions, it is inherently problematic to attempt circumscribing the primary job functions common to the profession. Another difficulty is measuring the potential and demonstrated ability of the professional. How do we know that a persons ability to take a test or meet minimum requirements of education, experience, etc., will not result in harm to a client or consumer?

Various forms of credentialling are discussed to delineate between individual and agency forms of credentialling. In addition, various forms of defining professional are discussed. Citizenship, education and experience are discussed as dimensions of most credentialling processes. In addition to the aforementioned, the examination of knowledge is often used as a mechanism for determining competence of the individual. While several professions use this method, therapeutic recreation is just beginning the adoption of the examination as a standard of performance. Insuring that the testing process is compliant with legal, procedural and other requuirements in standardized testing is essential to the credibility of the test as a measure of competence in the discipline. A national testing organization was secured to develop and validate the therapeutic recreation entry level test. One is left with the thought that the "test" is the key to credibility and acceptance. One only need to be reminded of the issues raised by Sylvester and Peterson in Part I, to come to their senses. Is there really a basis for the test? Are we that far along in our philosophical and theoretical knowledge to be ready to test for entry level competence? What are we teaching in the schools? Is there a body of knowledge?

Ellis and Mobily, two of the more profound authors and thinkers in our profession, present sobering realities in the form of our status as a profession. Ellis suggests that we are driven by an era of accountability to justify our existence and ask essential questions about the benefit of therapeutic recreation. Further, he outlines an evolutionary period of intellectual curiosity "marked by the application of rigorous and innovcative scientific methodologies....which are rooted in well developed theoretical frameworks...." Ellis offers hope for the field as a science. He describes science and the quest for truth in a way all should understand and appreciate. He goes on to examine the "cause" issue and lead the reader to the notion of "final cause." Among the more poignant issues addressed by Ellis is the relationship between science and technology. To understand the role of science in therapeutic recreation will require much attention to the penetrating questions of meaning and value, and less attention to the science of training individuals for jobs.

Mobily advances another way of knowing which he terms the humanistic method. The scientific method has been the center of attention for researchers aimed at proving the efficacy of therapeutic recreation for the past several years. Mobily contends that this deterministic approach, which suggests that all behavior is caused by something else, is difficult to apply in cases which do not include the issue of causation. Moral and ethical issues are problematic for the scientific method as they often defy logic or precise categorization. It is suggested that science and humanities offer a symbiotic relationship that can enhance our understandings of the problems of "freedom, choice and constraint in TR." The author suggests several ways in which the humanities can contribute to the emergence of thought, models and knowledge in therapeutic recreation. Using examples from Dostoevsky's *The Brothers Karamazov* and B.F. Skinner's *Walden Two*, Mobily carefully illustrates the relationship of these works to the concepts of leisure. In an intriguing passage the author draws on the Socratic method to illustrate the relationship between creationism and therapeutic recreation. Analogy, metaphor, "if-then" reasoning and alternating "filters" are used to illustrate the opportunities for discovery and creation of knowledge essential to the development of a body of knowledge for therapeutic recreation.

Austin calls for reform in therapeutic recreation education. He asserts that the assumptions underlying therapeutic recreation have not been identified or articulated. The potential split between "special recreation" and therapeutic recreation is discussed and implications for curriculum presented. Austin suggests that for the present time therapeutic recreation will remain in parks and recreation and under the aegis of the recreation and leisure philosophers instead of the medical or rehabilitation types. He does suggest that two distinct areas of curriculum be identified—one for the general parks and recreation type and one for therapeutic recreation. Several advantages of this arrangement are advanced. Curricular reform measures are offered to add clarity and focus to the profession. Changes in terminology, especially the term "clinical," are requested. More emphasis on research and empirical evidence of therapeutic recreation's efficacy is urged.

Changes in the requirements for liberal education, biological and social sciences and core courses are among a host of other recommendations offered by Austin.

MacNeil, Teague and Cipriano examine the continuing education dilemma facing the profession. Rapidly changing knowledge bases and requirements for performance in the job require continual training beyond the baccalaureate degree. Continuing professional education is required by many professions, especially those who comprise the allied health professions. It is clear that the requirement of continuing education as a panacea for upgrading knowledge and skills has been less than effective in proving claims of improved effectiveness and efficiency. Many individuals have expressed concern over the efficacy of continuing education in assuring competence. While these concerns appear valid, a new era may be marshalled in with the advent of a credential testing process which will require frequent updating of one's basic knowledge and skills in order to pass the national competency examination. In the past continuing education was essentially a voluntary effort for most professionals. In the future it may become mandatory. This raises a host of issues and logistical problems. The authors suggest this issue may be one of the more critical areas facing the profession in the future. We must discover why people participate and why they do not. Further, we must begin to understand the professional standards in a manner that allows for linkage to job performance. The bottom line appears to be that continuing professional education and higher education must be examined carefully before a massive testing effort is undertaken. What is to be taught? By whom? What relationship should it have to job performance? Credentialing?

Ethical Issues

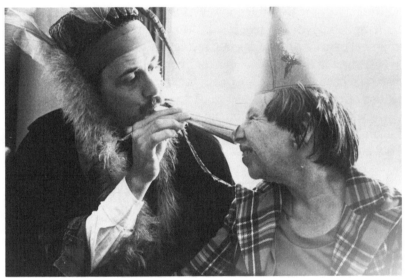

photo courtesy of Bradford Woods

By thinking about context one is better able to appreciate the nature of the action, and demonstrate the belief that an action, in and of itself, was not necessarily "right" or "wrong." Age, as a variable in the consideration of context, tempers our judgment.

—Gerald S. Fain

ETHICS IN THE
THERAPEUTIC RECREATION PROFESSION

Gerald S. Fain

Introduction

The purpose of this chapter is to present a conceptual context that will encourage careful consideration of the moral foundation for therapeutic recreation. Toward this end, the presentation will identify selected ethical challenges that illustrate the tenor and depth of essential dialogue.

All professions have codes of ethics. In the most powerful of professions, practitioners who violate these codes often forfeit their right to practice. Those professions the public perceives as having great potential for doing harm are the ones with the strongest codes and methods for enforcement. Not only is this essential to protect the public against unethical professions, but it is critical to the profession that its members guarantee to the public that they can be trusted. Without this kind of trust, professionals undermine their sanctions to practice.

However, adherence to professional codes is not the only basis for judging the moral character of an individual. In point of fact, it would be a mistake to assume that individuals who are not professionals are morally inferior. Professionals are not morally superior to the non-professional simply because they have codes of ethics.

Scholars across fields tend to agree that moral judgments are enlightened by the degree to which one knows both the context and consequence of the actions in question (Fain, 1984). This is why physicians demand peer review (only a physician can "know" what it is like to make medical judgments) and why it so difficult for moral philosophers to establish moral certitude regarding historical events (MacIntyre, 1981).

The notion of context is fundamental to understanding how one comes to make a moral decision. By thinking about context, one is better able to appreciate the nature of an action and demonstrate the belief that the action in and of itself was not necessarily right or wrong. Without insight as to the nature of the action, one will fail to fully understand it. To illustrate this meaning, one can imagine the act of taking someone else's food. One might say stealing is wrong, and we would agree that honesty is a virtue. However, if the thief is 2 years old, we will come to a different conclusion than if the thief is an adult. So age--as a variable in the consideration of context--tempers our judgement.

To illustrate the meaning of consequence, think about the moral standard that the taking of human life is wrong. Then think about abortion, euthanasia, capital punishment, and war. Is it possible to say with resolve that under *no* circumstance ought human life be taken, even if as a consequence there is greater good?

Because we as a society understand that there is often tension between what we believe and what we do, we may consider that the taking of a human life may, under certain circumstances, be morally acceptable. It is therefore possible to be morally sound while violating the standard. What we know is that adults living in civilized orders hold particular values in common. These values are represented in law and the institutions that serve the society. Schools, religious groups, and political organizations evidence these values, which are representative of majority belief. Individually, people will disagree on the values; knowing that there is disagreement is the basis for moral philosophy. The making of enlightened moral judgments, when there is knowledge of the context and consequence of action, requires experience in debate and a high level of reasoning.

Moral Philosophy

Moral philosophy, as an intellectual and academic field of study, provides the basis for understanding ethics. In moral philosophy one learns the centrality of the moral imperatives discussed by Socrates, Plato, Aristotle, Luther, Spinoza, Kant, Marx, Nietzsche, and Dewey. These questions of "ought" drive this inquiry and, while accessible to contemporary experience, transcend both time and social context.

As explained by Frankena (1973), ethics is a branch of philosophy; it is moral philosophy, concerned with moral problems and judgments. As a field of study, its sturdiness is assessed when it is applied to particular problems or specialized fields of practice. We look to moral philosophy when we question human experience and want to know about "right" and "wrong." Moral philosophy also teaches that virtue, or right action, is elusive, particularized, and debatable. This does not imply a relativistic view of morality, but rather that one understands his own actions, and those of others, as having a wholeness which makes each unique. These judgments are informed by understanding the place in one's own human development, social and cultural heritage, and experience. Children are judged differently from their parents, and the work of a lawyer demands a code of conduct which is differentiated from that of a police officer. Because we know that cultures, schools of philosophic thought, and ideologies differ, we can also understand that questions of virtue are by necessity particularized. Therefore, books of rules and codes diminish in their usefulness when one adopts systems of thought based on the personal integrity of experience. It is only when people organize themselves into groups that there need be agreement on moral concepts. It is when we want to be Americans, or Masons, or therapeutic recreators that we must work to establish a moral basis for our collective action.

Historically, the interest and commitment of Americans toward articulation of such credos was strongest in the late 1800s and early 1900s. The ethical codes compiled by Edgar L. Hermance (1924) and published 64 years ago present a diverse collection of thoughts. He received responses to a questionnaire from more than 700 organizations and published 214 of them in a single volume. Those responding included the American Dental Association, American College of Surgeons, American Seed Trade Association, National Association of Ice Cream Manufacturers, and the United Typothetae of America. It would appear that every organized group of Americans expressed their values in a credo-- not an informal or assumed set of ethical principles, but an explicit, thoughtfully crafted, and publicly available code.

Sloan (1980) reports that by the early 1800s, the teaching of ethics, or moral philosophy, was the central point in the undergraduate college curriculum. He goes on to explain that by 1905 most colleges had moved these courses on moral philosophy from their point of centrality, often taught by the university president, to one of equal status with course offerings across the university. This change was occurring as universities began to expand offerings in specialized departments along with their acceptance of increasing responsibility to prepare a growing number of professionals. During this same period, the recreation movement established its first national organization.

Recreation as Moral Imperative

The Playground Association of America was created in 1906. Born out of the moral imperatives of the melting-pot society that gave rise to the progressive education movement, the leaders in recreation based their work on the values embodied in participatory democracy. They believed that through recreation, children in particular could become morally sound. In 1916 John Dewey wrote,

> Education has no more serious responsibility than making adequate provision for enjoyment of recreative leisure; not only for sake of the immediate health, but still more if possible for the sake of its lasting effect upon the habits of the mind. (1944: 205)

In a direct sense, this commitment to the provision of "recreative leisure" provided the moral imperative for the early recreation movement. Less concerned with sports and games, these practitioners viewed themselves as instrumental in the building of a democratic society.

This founding mission of the recreation movement is today infused into a number of social initiatives and professional roles. Play, recreation, and leisure, understood chiefly within the public domain, has become embodied in numerous unregulated occupations. In general, public recreation has consistently been considered a solution to social problems. Often applied as a means of "keeping children off the streets" or "keeping idle hands out of mischief" the recreation imperative has been to fill free time. Yet, as revealed in the historical record, there appears to be no public need to organize this movement in the way education or other fields are organized. Nor, due to the tremendous diversity within the field, would it seem possible. Recreation is both public and private, for young and old, and takes place in the inner city and wilderness. Universities provide specializations in municipal recreation, tourism, outdoor education, campus recreation, commercial recreation, and therapeutic recreation. Each speciality is assumed to have foundation in some identifiable, discrete, and unique area of public need. And each claims some systemic conceptual and intellectual precepts that are held in common. Using recreation and leisure as the core, these speciality areas, along with possibly others, comprise the basis for the current accreditation program sponsored jointly by the National Recreation and Park Association and the American Association on Leisure and Recreation.

The contemporary meaning of leisure and recreation continues to change. Because of the changes in meaning, it follows that the moral concepts have changed as well--from the Greek ideal of leisure, to the leisure society, to the leisure suit and the leisure village. The moral meaning is affected by the social transformation of the concepts, and the impact to the life of the profession is altered. Struggling to retain the meaning or concepts of the old, with equal interest in maintaining close relationship to social change, the field has sought to interpret classical philosophic thought into the everyday life of contemporary living. Professionals must evolve in order to meet changing imperatives. Of particular interest here is the study of how the recreation movement, over time, responded to the needs of people who were ill, disabled, and on the fringe of society.

As a specialization within the recreation field, therapeutic recreation was formally established in 1949, when the American Recreation Society created the Hospital Recreation Section. Prior to this time therapeutic recreation workers were not easily distinguished within the national movement. However, hospital recreation workers and other recreators employed in medical and rehabilitation centers date back to World War I (Frye & Peters, 1972).

The importance of this action in 1949 was that therapeutic recreation became a speciality within recreation. The recreation profession celebrated the prospects of normalization embodied in the union. Specifically, therapeutic recreators asserted that their mission was to assist disadvantaged people with illness and disability gain the strength and health essential for their re-entry from the specialized setting back into the community. There the community, through the community recreator, would provide normalized recreation experience. In class as a graduate student, I remember Harold Meyer, a guest speaker and president of the American Recreation Society in 1949, saying "First be a recreator, and then be a therapeutic recreator."

This action, creating the Hospital Recreation Section, was a prologue to the consensus building that in 1966 supported the creation of the National Therapeutic Recreation Society, a branch of the National Recreation and Park Association. For the majority of therapeutic recreation workers, the mission was clear and morally sound. In summary, it was based upon the beliefs that recreation had curative qualities and that recreation as experience should be available to all citizens, including those in specialized settings. This moral mission has essentially been sustained to the present.

In review of the work of this professional society, there has been significant emphasis placed on the creation, dissemination, and enforcement of standards. For some, this push toward the building of the group raises important questions. Kestenbaum (1985) addressed the question of unity, explaining that unity of concepts, theories, and practices provides the consistency essential for professions. Without unity there can be no authoritative position on expert knowledge or action. He further explains that ethical reasoning premised on the basis of unity leads to a significant degree of self-deception. Professionals exert a degree of invincibility that fortifies them from outside influence. In a similar way, Hunnicutt (1978:19), in review of the first 12 years of the National Therapeutic Recreation Society, questioned those holding self-congratulatory views of the profession. "Loyalty and commitment are good, but not as final goals. They are functional means to the ultimate end. That ideology is: recreation is an effective therapy and as such should serve people with problems."

Review of the history of therapeutic recreation, with regard to moral imperative, must also include a comment on human rights and community-based services. It is important to note that two early works represented missions that have been abandoned by most in present practice. Nesbitt, Brown, and Murphy (1970) wrote about the culturally and economically disadvantaged, negro-white relations, crowded playgrounds, poverty, and social unrest. Hutchison (1973) wrote about racial discrimination and social violence, strongly making the case that public recreation had a moral responsibility to minority people. (Hutchison was the first president of the National Therapeutic Recreation Society, and Nesbitt assumed the presidency a few years later.)

There can be no serious doubt that those who work in the field of therapeutic recreation are, as a group, morally sound, for it is hard to imagine anyone devoting the days of their lives to this work for other than reasons of virtue. Salaries lag behind most other of the helping professions; there is little public recognition for those in the field of practice; career ladders are typically short, and there is a lack of clarity on the question of role definition. In some agencies, volunteers, along with dance, art, music, and occupational and physical therapists, compete on an equal basis with the therapeutic recreation specialist.

What then is the virtue, or moral foundation, for the field of practice? What is it that attracts people to therapeutic recreation and gives them the commitment to pursue this career? By asking this question and vigorously searching for the answer, for the moral foundation for the field, not only will the student and the practitioner better understand the field and themselves; even more important, the field as a whole, will be better able to define its mission and purpose with respect to the public welfare.

The framework for this inquiry is not entirely philosophic. One cannot simply think about virtue and come to understand its place in the world of human experience. It is essential that the practical, day-to-day work of the practitioner be used as a fundamental source for knowing about this moral foundation. This relationship, between wanting to know what is morally "right" and weighing the experience of human interaction, is the basis for reflective practice. And it is reflective practice that allows one the opportunity to understand virtue.

The National Therapeutic Recreation Society

The National Therapeutic Recreation Society (NTRS), when created in 1966, adopted a "Code of Ethics". The Code, comprised of an introduction followed by a six-point statement, was developed within the conceptual structure of the National Recreation and Park Association (NRPA). At the time, it was the position of the Association that each state branch was to create its own code of ethics that could include provision for areas of specialization, including therapeutic recreation. The plan encouraged state credentialing programs, as opposed to a national program.

The NTRS Code of 1966 gives insight to the moral foundation of therapeutic recreation. The Code is quite clear in stating that the NTRS "affirms its commitment to the goals of the park and recreation movement as represented by the Constitution of the National Recreation and Park Association." This position is analogous to those of specializations in other fields (e.g., pediatricians are first physicians). However, the introduction further declares an a priori adherence to standards and principles embodied in the related health disciplines from which it draws much of its heritage of concern and standards of practice."

The history of codes within the recreation field did not, however, begin in the 1960s. The National Recreation Society adopted the "Credo– Of The Recreation Worker" in 1942 (Nash, 1965). By the late 1940s the New York Association for Health, Physical Education, and Recreation and the District of Columbia Recreation and Park Society had adopted statements. The California Park and Recreation Society in 1953, the Idaho Recreation and Park Society in 1954, and the Virginia

Recreation and Park Society in 1957 established codes (Shapiro, 1970). However, there is no evidence that these statements were more than credos.

In 1973 the NRPA began the development of a model code of ethics. The association had found, as the result of a feasibility study, that most state professional organizations needed a code. The model was completed in 1976 and is comprised of "General Principles" and "Branch Special Principles." The "Branch Special Principles" includes the "Statement of Professional Ethics" by the Society of Park and Recreation Educators, the NTRS Code, and a section called "Students."

When compared to established professional codes of ethics in other fields, the work of the groups in recreation lack several qualities. To begin, the process to establish codes often is based upon cases submitted by practitioners. The cases are then studied, organized into categories, debated, and reviewed by professional membership. Eventually the codes, along with the illustrative cases, are adopted by membership vote. One very impressive example of a professional code and standards for practice was created by the Council for Exceptional Children. Adopted by delegate assembly in April 1983, this volume is explicitly instructive to those who want to know the moral basis for their work. While groups vary on strategies employed to develop codes and cases, involvement by the practitioners is central to the process. Within the recreation field the "Ethical Standards Casebook for Therapeutic Recreators," created by the Illinois Therapeutic Recreation Section in 1978, provides a notable example of this methodology.

Ethics Committee of the
National Therapeutic Recreation Society

The NTRS, as a result of my recommendation as immediate past-president, established an ethics committee in 1980. With the exception of 1981, the committee has continued to the present; I served as chairman until 1987. Several of the committee's accomplishments over this period of time are particularly noteworthy.

- Establishment of the Ethical Practices Committee as a standing committee of the Society (1983)
- Sponsorship of a 1- day seminar on professional ethics at the 1984 NTRS Ethics Institute, National Recreation and Park Associa- tion Congress

- Publication of a special issue of the *Therapeutic Recreation Journal*, devoted to professional ethics (1985)
- Recommendation and support for the creation of the NTRS Philosophical Issues Committee (1985)
- Board approval of the case report form and review procedures. The form, along with a cover letter, was mailed to the entire membership of NTRS (1986)
- Conducting a national study on the status of ethics committees at the state level and initiating a national network (1986)

As a result of these accomplishments, NTRS has distinguished itself within the NRPA. In point of fact, no other group within the recreation field has sustained as active a committee or national profile on the subject of professional ethics.

American Association on Leisure and Recreation

The American Association for Leisure and Recreation (AALR) is part of the American Alliance for Health, Physical Education Recreation and Dance (AAHPERD). AALR established a 3-year Commission on Professional Ethics in 1984; I served as chairman. There had been no such commission or committee in the history of AALR. However, AAHPERD did have a 40-year history of work in ethics within the field of physical education.

The Commission, which was primarily concerned with establishing a framework for professional ethics within AALR, created and disseminated information on ethics and held educational sessions at the AAHPERD national conventions. In April of 1987 the Commission distributed a questionnaire to selected leaders in the field. A total of 32 responses were received from the 63 mailed. In summary, the responses from the questionnaire resulted in the following recommendations:

- *Establishment of a standing committee on professional ethics*
- *Sponsorship of the International Symposium on Leisure and Ethics*

Both recommendations were accepted by the AALR Board of Directors.

Moral Basis for Practice

Despite the work of national organizations, the question of moral basis for practice is still not fully developed. Again, we must ask, "What is the moral foundation for therapeutic recreation?" Is it possible to distinguish therapeutic recreation, on the basis of moral meaning, from the fields of recreation, education, health care, and rehabilitation? What are the replies when one is asked, "Are therapeutic recreators driven by a moral mission that is distinctive from the other helping professions, and can one identify tenets that belong to therapeutic recreation alone?"

These are among the most interesting questions when one studies the life of professionals. The answers have less to do with codes and more to do with human motivation. There must be a reason why people care about practicing therapeutic recreation, and while we do not expect to find agreement across the field, there is the expectation of some agreement--enough agreement to support professional meetings, journals, legislative initiatives, and federal programs.

Review of the profession reveals to me a number of areas I believe illustrate a moral basis for practice. Others could create different lists, and the impressions I have of the profession are no more than a function of my experience. Aside from the present NTRS Code of Ethics and the Philosophical Position Statement of the National Therapeutic Recreation Society (1982), there is little to study. (This is in contrast to medicine, law, psychology, theology, and a host of other fields where texts, debates, and discussions are ongoing.)

Discrimination

Working to eliminate discrimination against people who are ill or disabled, while not unique to therapeutic recreation, does provide an organizing theme for practice. This requires one to know, value, and promote a society that is humane and supportive of individual freedom, as well as to understand the responsibility of the individual's role in protecting the freedoms of others. Much of this work today involves the continuing advocacy for equal participation in community recreation. The deeply rooted discrimination against people who are ill and disabled is profound. Many people still live in worlds designated only by characteristics of disability. Because much of our social policy allows separate but equal programs, fighting discrimination in all of its forms requires continuing social activism.

Health promotion

Contribution to the "cure" and advancement of the health and well-being of the individual in need of medical services is a continuing commitment. This explicitly requires the construction of environments and programs that promote health. Perhaps the most enduring position on the value of recreation in the curative process was written by Dr. Paul Haun between 1952 and 1964 (Haun, 1971). In recent years the proliferation of innovative programs, including the Vinland National Center in Minnesota and numerous outdoor education programs, have based their philosophies on principles of health promotion. For many who work in the field of therapeutic recreation, the opportunity to support health through normalized recreation experience captures the value of their contribution to the healing process. Recreation, as defined in a classical sense, continues to be life giving.

The means, or programs, designed to fight discrimination and promote health through recreation require infinite adaptation and creativity. The particular intervention will always need to be population- and situation-specific. This requires one to understand and practice therapeutic recreation more as an art than a science. As an art, the basis of the practice is dependent upon individual interaction and sustained caring.

Ethical dilemmas

Ethical dilemmas require by definition that a choice be made between two unacceptable alternatives. It may not be possible to make the "right" decision, but it is possible to make an enlightened decision. In the everyday sense, a student may decide to plagiarize the paper of a friend with the hope of getting a better grade. The student knows it is wrong, but when weighing this against the possibility of getting a poor grade in the class, decides to cheat. The student may see this as having to choose between two bad things: getting a bad grade versus getting caught.

This type of dilemma, while in the area of moral character, is a different type of dilemma from the kind associated with professional life. The lives of professionals are characterized by the ethical dilemmas they help people solve. Professionals are intimately involved in helping people decide life choices. Such acts of enlightened decision making, with reference to particular problems, are at the very core of what distinguishes the life of the professional from that of other citizens. It is these acts that require specialized professional knowledge and experience, and it is these acts that characteristically bring the client to a professional.

Responsible Action

The subject of ethics, while of great public interest, has had little explicit place in the professional preparation and formal practice of therapeutic recreation practitioners. This lack of professional rigor in the relationship between the moral philosophic foundation of the field, and the field of practice, has created an intellectual and moral void that characterizes the field today. While there are no substantive claims of unethical practice against those in therapeutic recreation, the same observation could be made of other non-essential public services. For example, the whole of the recreation professions draws little public notice on questions of ethics. We simply do not seem to know whether or not these individuals meet or exceed the moral standards associated with established and publicly respected fields of service.

In contrast, when a physician, a lawyer, or an accountant is found to have violated an important standard of conduct, the profession takes action. The reason is to ensure the public that it will not tolerate unethical practitioners. If the public felt otherwise, it would undermine the entire profession. It is essential to a profession's work that it maintain a profile that demonstrates active vigilance of ethical behavior. It is important to note why the public brings these charges to the profession. It is because they believe they have been mistreated, abused, or taken unfair advantage of. Moreover, they may feel that their health, safety, happiness, or quality of life was impaired because of the action or inaction taken by the practitioner. The individual has assumed that the professional had specialized knowledge and skill that would be used toward the individual's welfare but wasn't.

The assumptions upon which this observation rests serve as the basis for this chapter. Essentially no field of practice can offer transcendence for the practitioner--transcendence from the act of simple labor to that of reflective practice designed to advance the public good scientifically and with rigor--unless there is clear understanding and access to the moral imperatives that drive daily practice. Those who administer this goodness must, out of a sense of moral obligation, be challenged each day to do better, find more "truth," and with the utmost modesty and discipline, share what they have learned with colleagues. These actions will not, however, occur unless the group demands that its members adhere to these standards. Doing what is in the best interest of others, while strenuously protecting the individual against harm, is fundamental to all professional action. The public interest must be held in the highest regard. It is the health and well-being of the individual citizen that is paramount when a group of people come together to form a union, guild, or profession. It is not the protection of the worker, nor the protection of the profession, but first and ultimately the public that must be served. This is the quintessential criteria by which those in therapeutic recreation can judge the value of their work. To give other criteria equal merit would be self-serving and ultimately self-defeating to the profession. To suggest that a profession is equally committed to the protection and promotion of its members' well-being would suggest a value structure that places the public interest in competition with the welfare of the individual practitioner.

This is an intellectual and philosophic imperative. It has little to do with public relations and marketing. It does, however, have a great deal to do with research and the creation of expert knowledge. The public cannot be "sold" professional need in the same way it buys soap or vacations. In final review, professional action is driven by the social requirement of altruism.

The Nature of the Challenge

What would *you* do if you learned that

- music played at high decibel levels over sustained time periods was shown to be responsible for irreparable hearing loss?

- high-calorie diets contributed to obesity, diabetes, heart disease, and premature death?

- dental disease and tooth loss were linked to diets high in refined sugars?

- AIDS was transmitted only through the direct exchange of bodily fluids?

- physical inactivity was linked to psychological depression, loss of muscle tone, and numerous chronic illnesses?

- tobacco was linked to cancer of the mouth and lungs and contributed to respiratory diseases?

- Stereotypic grouping of people according to disability categories (e.g., mentally retarded, blind, mobility impaired) undermined individual freedom, stifled human growth and development, and served as a basis for discrimination?

If recreation experience ought to promote health and well-being, and I firmly believe that such a quality can be useful in distinguishing good from bad, how can one support programs that take place in environments contaminated by agents harmful to health? How can a responsible and reflective practitioner ignore the research in related disciplines? Because expert knowledge is based upon research, the moral imperative is undeniable.

For example, I have observed programs that stress dessert and junk foods as primary motivators for participation and programs where music is played so loud that meters would report levels shown to create hearing loss. The implication is direct and unavoidable. If health is important, the experiences ought to promote it. Professionals would not ignore the participants who are destroying their hearing by listening to excessively loud music. Those who say listening to loud music is normal and people with disabilities should have normal experiences, may be guilty of placing immediate personal happiness over the best interests of the participants. It does not take courage to turn down the volume; it takes professional knowledge and a degree of moral responsibility.

There are countless issues to be debated in the field. Some touch more lives than others, and some are of greater consequence to the people served by therapeutic recreators. On what should the field focus?

- Rooting out the incompetent practitioner?
- Creating healthier environments for clients?
- Advocating the rights of others?
- Creating casebooks and codes of ethics?
- Establishing ethical practices review boards?
- Raising the entry-level criteria for certification?

Whatever the field decides to do, the story will be written. There is no way to avoid the inevitability of creating history. Each day at work defines the moral meaning of the field. There is no agenda in place today that will secure the moral foundation of therapeutic recreation. Those interested in learning more about the moral meaning of their work need look first at what they did yesterday.

A Closing Thought

I want to share with you a story about Peg. She is 65 years old and lives in a state school with several hundred other people. Peg has lived in the institution for 62 years. I met her during a client review. Peg was nicely dressed and sitting alone at a table in a large, open room. She was drawing pictures with broken crayons taken from a big box. Behind her was a tiled wall where dozens of her drawings were taped. I sat next to her and we began to talk. Since the pictures she had drawn were clear, with easily identifiable images of houses and other things, I asked why she did not sign her name to any of them. She told me "Peg can't write her name; she is mentally retarded." I asked whether she could write a *P* for Peg, and again she responded that she was mentally retarded. I then wrote a *P* on the paper, gave her my pen, and asked whether she could copy what I had written. She cautiously took my pen and easily copied the letter *P*. I then turned to the group of staff who had brought me to met Peg. I didn't need to say the obvious,;their faces told me they knew the story of Peg--what had happened to her, what had *not* happened to her, and what *could be*!.

Later, at the staff meeting, I told them that Peg's future was up to them. It was their vision of what she could become that would determine the rest of her life. If they saw her as learning to write and read and eventually leave the institution, she would. But that would necessitate that the programs of the past be abandoned, that recreators would, out of a sense of moral responsibility, teach Peg to write her name! And then to read, and then . . ., and so on.

The field of therapeutic recreation will undoubtedly continue. The need for recreation services to individuals with special needs is unrelenting. Regardless of setting or population, recreation in its varied forms is part of human experience. Recreation as a form of health as well as a curative agent is accepted as part of enlightened, humane treatment. The kind of practitioner recruited and retained in the field will be a direct measure of the field's moral soundness. Should therapeutic recreators spend more of their days teaching people like Peg to write their names, the questions of "ought" will become less abstract while the moral basis for professional practice becomes more clear.

Study Questions

1. What should you read? Create an annotated bibliography for your class using the following categories:
   moral philosophy
   professional ethics
   therapeutic recreation ethics

2. Construct three case studies illustrating ethical dilemmas in therapeutic recreation practice. Develop one case for each of the following: clinical setting, community setting, outdoor setting.

3. Who should you study with? How will you know whether you are learning to be a reflective practitioner? What are the moral standards you expect of yourself, your teachers, and your colleagues?

4. What should professional societies do to ensure the highest ethical conduct of their members? Construct a plan of action for the ethics committee of either the National Therapeutic Recreation Society, American Therapeutic Recreation Association, National Council on Therapeutic Certification, or the American Association for Leisure and Recreation.

5. Critique the NTRS code of ethics. How does it compare to the codes of related fields of practice? What specific revisions do you recommend?

References

Dewey, J. (1944) . *Democracy and Education* . New York: Free Press.

Fain, G.S.(1984). Toward a Philosophy of Moral Judgment and Etical Practices in Leisure Counseling. In E.T. Dowd (Ed.) *Leisure Counseling: Concepts and Applications* (pp. 277-300). Springfield, Illinois: Charles C. Thomas.

Frankena, W. (1973). *Ethics.* Englewood Cliffs, NJ: Prentice-Hall.

Frye, V., & Peters, M. (1972). *Therapeutic Recreation: its Theory, Philosophy, and Practice.* Harrisburg, PA: Stackpole.

Haun, P. (1971). *Recreation: A Medical Viewpoint.* New York: Teachers College Press.

Heermance, E. L. (1924). *Codes of Ethics: A Handbook.* Vermont: Free Press Printing.

Hunnicutt, B.J. (1978) . A Rejoinder to the Twelve-year History of the National Therapeutic Recreation Society. *Therapeutic Recreation Journal , 3 ,* 15-19.

Hutchison, I.J., Jr. (1973) . Recreation and Racial Minorities. In T.A. Stein & H.D. Sessoms (Eds.), *Recreation and Special Populations* (pp. 323-352). Boston: Holbrook.

Kestenbaum, V., (1985). Professions, Ethics and Unity. *Therapeutic Recreation Journal,* 4,41-50.

MacIntyre, A. (1966). *A Short History of Ethics .* New York: Macmillan.

MacIntyre, A. (1981). *After Virtue: A Study in Moral Theory.* South Bend, IN: Notre Dame.

Nash, J.B. (1965). *Recreation: Pertinent Readings.* Dubuque, IA: William C. Brown.

Nesbitt, J.A., Brown, P.D., & Murphy, J.F.,(1970). *Recreation and Leisure Services for the Disadvantaged.* Philadelphia: Lea and Febiger.

Shapiro, I.G.,(1970). *A History of the Professionalization of Recreation Administration from 1930 to 1970.* Unpublished doctoral dissertation, University of North Carolina, Chapel Hill.

Sloan, D. (1980). The Teaching of Ethics in the American Undergraduate Curriculum, 1896-1976. In D. Callahan & S. Bok (Eds.), *Ethics Teaching in Higher Education* (pp. 1-57). New York: Plenum Press.

Assessment Issues

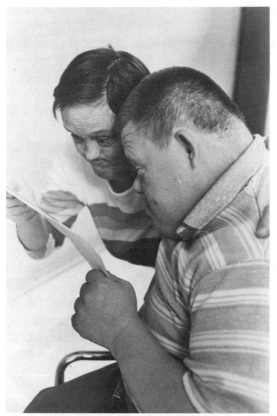

Does the leisure behavior of individuals with disabilities and special populations differ from the leisure behavior of the non-disabled?

—Janiece J. Sneegas

ASSESSMENT INSTRUMENTS IN THERAPEUTIC RECREATION:
To What Extent Do They Work?

Christine Z. Howe

Introduction

Assessment is one of the many professional responsibilities of the therapeutic recreation specialist (TRS) whether he or she is employed in a clinical, community, or transitional setting. Assessment is the first step in coming to know one's clients. Informally, personnel all "assess" each other, formulating impressions through conversation or other social intercourse. Formally, TRSs assess their clients in order to facilitate the clients' independent leisure functioning.

For the purpose of this chapter, leisure is considered to be the state of mind that clients achieve through engaging in recreational activities. As such, leisure is a complex, individualistic, and dynamic phenomenon. Leisure is characterized by feelings of freedom; novelty; enjoyment, pleasure, or fun; renewal; competence or mastery; and the reward of greater knowledge of oneself. Achieving leisure may involve the cognitive, affective, psychomotor, or social domains. Formal assessment is one means of systematically helping clients to achieve leisure, providing opportunities for growth and development through recreational activities that involve each of these domains. This means that the TRS must be prepared to expand beyond traditional professional roles into new, more scientifically based ones done within the context of leisure literacy. Thus, the assessment instrument or process is only as effective as the TRS using it.

The New Roles of the Therapeutic Recreation Specialist

There are a variety of roles for the contemporary TRS to undertake in order to stimulate the recreational engagement of clients and to facilitate their move toward informed, independent leisure functioning. These roles range from the traditional, historic role of a direct service provider to today's roles of broker and enabler and to the probable future roles of consultant and independent contractor. Although one may describe each of these roles as being relatively distinct, because of their multifaceted nature as practiced in reality, the roles are not truly discrete. TRSs seldom function in only a single role at a time. The most successful professionals draw on different dimensions of their roles depending upon their own skills and abilities, the needs and interests of their clients, and the given realities of their work settings (Howe & Carpenter, 1985, pp. 174-176).

However, when the TRS is specifically interested in developing the leisure literacy of the clients, then it is likely that he or she will find the leisure educator role to be most appropriate and will predominantly rely on it. Clients come to institutions, communities, and half-way houses with differing levels of leisure awareness, skill, and functioning. The therapeutic recreation profession has matured enough to offer a range of recreational services and programs along a continuum that matches needs, interests, and abilities with appropriate leadership, groups, and settings. An underlying dimension of this matching process is independence. Thus, at one end of the therapeutic recreation service delivery continuum, there may be a highly structured program (or agency) that provides for those who need a great deal of assistance with their pursuit of leisure. At the other end of the continuum are those programs (or agencies) in which a minimum of actual direction or supervision is needed. The clients' leisure pursuits are essentially self-managed, with some professional support or advisement (Teaff, 1985).

Leisure Literacy

Peterson and Gunn (1984, pp. 11-21) have proposed a Therapeutic Recreation Service Model which conceptualizes and defines therapeutic recreation services ranging from treatment to independent leisure functioning. Their model includes the roles of the TRS as they relate to the functional level of the client. Similar to Teaff's (1985) idea, independence is an underlying dimension of leisure service provision along a continuum of service categories (treatment, leisure education, and recreation participation).

How can this model be useful to the TRS concerned with assessment? The model provides a context in which the TRS who operates as a leisure educator promotes the independent leisure functioning of their clients and enhance their leisure literacy. Most communities have public park and recreation departments and other human service agencies that provide recreational activity programs for their "normal" and challenged participants. True treatment programs generally are limited to clinical or transitional settings. Leisure education programs may occur in all three environments. As a leisure educator, the contemporary TRS becomes a scientist or investigator who uses formal assessment to systematically collect information about the clients to determine their needs, interests, preferences, abilities, and problem areas in order to prepare and/or connect them with the appropriate program, leader, or group. The intent for the TRS as a leisure educator is to facilitate the ability of the clients to leisure, that is, to establish self-directed, freely chosen, healthy, intrinsically motivated, and pleasurable leisure lifestyles. Formal assessment is a means to this end.

As adapted for the purposes of this chapter, Peterson and Gunn's model is shown in Figure 1. The parts of the model of greatest relevance are the "Leisure education" and "Recreational activity participation" segments of the "Leisure lifestyle" line. According to Mundy and Odum (1979, pp. 2-3), leisure education is a developmental process through which individuals gain an understanding of themselves, leisure, their leisure choices, and the role of leisure in their own lives as well as in the fabric of society. The ultimate outcome of the process is to enable people to enhance the quality of leisure in their own lives. Thus, leisure education is a process through which people go in order to become self-determining or independent in their leisure. Recreational activity participation is that outcome--the free engagement in meaningful leisure experiences alone and with others.

Formal Assessment for Leisure Well-Being

The TRS performing as a leisure educator to advise or instruct helps in skill development, in awareness of leisure options, and in making leisure choices based upon knowledge of self and knowledge of leisure. As stated previously, the first step to uncovering this knowledge is through formal assessment. Stumbo and Thompson (1986) use a problem-solving approach to defining assessment as follows:

> Assessment is the process of gathering information about an individual in order that the most appropriate services may be provided to diminish or eliminate the individual's problems with their [sic] leisure. These problems may include certain barriers that the individual finds in the pursuit of meaningful and enjoyable leisure involvement. (p. 28)

Figure 1
Recreational Activity Participation Model

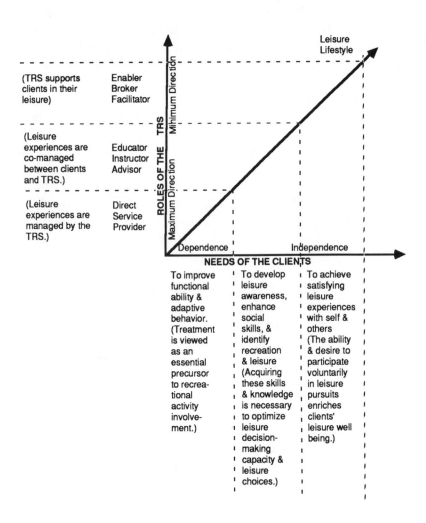

Source: C.A. Peterson & S. L. Gunn, *Therapeutic Recreation Program Design: Principles & Procedures,* 2nd. Ed.© 1984, p.12. Adapted by persmission of Prentice-Hall, Inc., Englewood Cliffs, New Jersey.

Stumbo and Thompson (1986) enumerate examples of leisure-related problems that reflect the four behavioral domains mentioned earlier. They continue by suggesting that in order to systematically identify these problems, the TRS should complete an assessment. They suggest a multiple-method approach, combining several instruments or procedures. They contend that when more than one instrument is used to gather information on a single or on several traits, a fuller, more accurate picture of the client is created. Further, a variety of procedures, such as questionnaires, interviews, and observations, may be used together to elicit a better understanding of the individual.

Others describe leisure assessment as a process of systematic inquiry about client attitudes, needs, interests, values, behaviors, and patterns where some type or degree of intervention is desired. The information derived from such an inquiry serves as one of the "guiding lights" the TRS may use to provide, develop, or facilitate the client's pursuit of leisure based on any changes, clarification, instruction, improvement, or reinforcement needed (Howe, 1984; Loesch & Wheeler, 1982; Witt, Connolly, & Compton, 1980).

Riddick (1986) reports that evidence suggests that the mental health of adults is influenced by the amount of satisfaction that they receive through their leisure pursuits. She also cites studies that suggest that satisfaction with leisure rather than satisfaction gleaned from a job, a family, health, or income is the primary determinant of mental well-being. In her own study, Riddick examined precursors to leisure satisfaction or predisposing factors such as age, sex, knowledge of leisure opportunities, and leisure values as motivators of an individual's actions. Her findings are important to leisure assessment. Riddick reports that the first and second most influential determinants of leisure satisfaction for her subjects were knowledge of leisure resources and leisure values. These determinants are illustrative of the many pieces of important information that can be discovered through a formal assessment process. However, as it currently exists in the field of therapeutic recreation, assessment is in the developmental stages, especially in terms of reliability , validity, and practical utility.

Reliability, Validity, and Practical Utility in Assessment

The traditional view of reliability and validity is that they are essential aspects of measurement. Measurement is the process of describing or representing properties of individuals, groups, or phenomena that under the positivist philosophy of science is usually quantified but has varying conventions. Tests are shorthand devices that elicit such information. These terms are sometimes confusing as they are used with the separate but highly interrelated activities of assessment, evaluation, and research.

The quality of the information that is collected and the confidence that the TRS can have in the results obtained from the information collection techniques (assessment devices) used depends on the degree of reliability and validity present in the process (Dunn, 1988; Weissinger & Caldwell, 1987). Dunn and Weissinger and Caldwell further state that these concepts are so fundamental to inquiry that their importance cannot be overstated. In terms of assessment, it is absolutely necessary for the TRS to consider reliability and validity (as well as practical utility) when developing or selecting information collection instruments or techniques. The aforementioned researchers provide extensive discussions of reliability and validity specifically within the contexts of leisure program evaluation and leisure research; for a detailed explanation and examination of the concepts, the reader is referred to them. This chapter is limited to a brief consideration of the issues surrounding reliability and validity as they apply to formal assessment.

Reliability in assessment

Reliability is the stability and consistency of observations or measurements over given periods of time and variable conditions such as different settings or instruments. The term *stability* suggests a relationship between reliability and external validity (Weissinger & Caldwell, 1987), whereas the term *consistency* suggests an emphasis on the inter-observer or within-the-instrument/internal-consistency form of reliability(Dunn, 1988). Dunn purports by writing that especially in the assessment of human behavior, various forms of error will erode the accuracy of one's observations or measurements. Thus, reliability in relation to error is the degree to which the obtained results are free from random or chance error and/or "reliability errors" of time sampling, content sampling, score differences, and content heterogeneity (Weissinger & Caldwell, p. 4).

Stability across settings or instruments

Weissinger and Caldwell (1987, p. 4) feel that the aspect of reliability that reflects stability of measurement across settings is the form "integrally related to external validity." This means that a reliable observation or measurement must possess stability across settings in order to be generalizable (to demonstrate external validity). Dunn (1988) states that the stability of an instrument rests on its ability to achieve similar results in repeated uses over time. Through the test-retest method, temporal reliability may be determined for an assessment.

Consistency between observers or internal to instruments

Weissinger and Caldwell (1987) find inter-observer reliability to be important because it implies a lack of investigator bias in a systematic inquiry. Whenever more than one investigator or observer is used to collect information, Weissinger and Caldwell recommend calculating the reliability of the information across observers. They believe that a lack of inter-observer reliability tends to negate the internal validity of the findings of an assessment. Not only are appropriate statistical analyses (correlations) recommended, but so are specialized training for observers, a careful and precise categorization system for observed behaviors, and the use of preestablished recording and coding schemes.

Internal consistency (or within-the-instrument reliability) is determined by comparing the results from items or elements of an assessment instrument with each other (Dunn, 1988). This is accomplished by subjecting the instrument to statistical analyses. The resultant internal consistency coefficients provide estimates of how the items in the instrument are related. The analysis selected depends on the validity of the content-sampling procedures, the homogeneity of the assessment instrument's content (the construct being measured), and the length of the scale. When a single scale has numerous items (or several subscales), both total scale and subscale coefficients should be considered by the TRS to gauge the reliability of the assessment instrument (Weissinger, & Caldwell, 1987).

Validity in assessment

Simply stated, internal validity describes how well the results obtained through using an assessment instrument match the intended purpose of the instrument. But to stop at such a simple statement would be misleading, for determining internal validity involves one's perceptions of the nature of reality or truth. What is real or true is a subjective question that is as yet unresolved by theologians, politicians, philosophers, scientists, and laypersons alike. In essence, internal validity becomes the value judgment of the user of an instrument that the instrument is a true reflection of reality or at least is measuring what it is supposed to measure to some extent. Dunn (1988, p. 64) suggests the following:

> Validity is indicated by degree; it is not an automatic property of a particular instrument. The degree of validity of any measurement strategy is established through the relationship of the instrument to the content, criterion, or construct which it purports to measure.

Dunn (1988) collapses the forms of internal validity into three major types: content, criterion-related, and construct validity. The extent to which one's measurements and operations (instruments, tests, or procedures) are valid can be judged by the TRS in terms of content, criterion-related, and construct validity. Before turning to those three major types of internal validity, though, external validity must be mentioned. External validity refers to the degree to which it is possible to generalize the results of an assessment process across alternate measures or instruments and across different types of persons, settings, and times (Weissinger & Caldwell, 1987). In essence, external validity considers the representativeness of the findings of an assessment or its replicability. Weissinger and Caldwell state the following:

> Neither internal nor external validity is typically assessed directly in leisure research studies. Rather, they are indirectly determined via the measurement of reliability and other forms of validity. That is, internal and external validity are primarily a matter of designing reliable and valid measurements and operations. (p. 5)

Content validity
Content validity is the professional's degree of confidence that an instrument or procedure exhaustively represents some specific content. It is the extent to which the instrument fully measures the subject at hand by sampling responses or behaviors. To paraphrase Dunn (1988), an assessment instrument is content valid if it yields an accurate description of the individual (in a specific domain) and his or her behaviors under varying situations. Thus, the better the content validity of an instrument, the more complete and representative the assessment of the client's affect and behaviors is.

Once the area of content has been specified and its relevance to the inquiry established, then the TRS focuses on the instrument's representativeness and completeness. Dunn (1988) suggests a blueprint method to be used in the developmental phase of instrument validation in which numerous questions are composed for all of the major content areas to be assessed. Once the question pool is narrowed and ready for use (or used), outside experts may confirm content validity through professional review.

Criterion-related validity

Criterion-related validity is derived by comparing the results of an assessment instrument to some external criterion or standard that is thought to measure essentially the the same phenomenon or characteristic. Criterion-related validity is determined by the capacity of an instrument or procedure to correlate with or predict an established or accepted criterion. Thus, criterion-related validity has two subtypes: concurrent and predictive, the difference being whether the instrument and criterion are being administered at about the same time or after some intervening period. In essence, criterion-related validity indicates how well an assessment instrument estimates current performance or future performance on some valued measure (criterion) or standard other than the instrument itself.

According to Dunn (1988), one of the greatest difficulties in establishing criterion-related validity is the paucity of relevant, unbiased, stable, and available criterion measures or variables. Weissinger and Caldwell (1987) consider predictive validity to be the "most important assessment of the relevance of measurements to the 'real world.'" However, in order to determine criterion-related validity, the TRS needs to possess some knowledge of correlational and predictive statistics in order to interpret the meaning of the validity coefficient that is derived from comparing the assessment instrument's score with the criterion.

Construct validity

Weissinger and Caldwell (1987) view construct validity as the degree to which an assessment instrument can be said to accurately measure a psychological trait or quality. A construct is an abstraction, or a postulated attribute or characteristic that summarizes, explains, or accounts for some phenomenon. In order to determine construct validity, the professional must first operationally define the target construct (and related constructs) as it is thought to exist in the body of knowledge.

Dunn (1988) suggests some constructs that would be of interest to a TRS when conducting an assessment: leisure satisfaction, leisure needs, leisure functioning, perceived freedom, and leisure behavior, all of which stem from theories of human behavior and leisure. The interrelationship between the development of construct validity and theory cannot be overstated. It is further essential to understand the conditions which may threaten validity (both in the design of the entire assessment and in its instrumentation) and to try to minimize them. Some of the strategies for reducing the influence of such threats are presented in the next section.

Practical utility in assessment

The third major characteristic of an assessment instrument or procedure is its practical utility. Inherent in the previous discussion is the exhortation to use the most reliable and valid assessment devices available. But the TRS must also have a sense of the appropriateness, usefulness, and context of the instruments or procedures employed. There are several criteria that can be used to aid the TRS in judging the practical utility of a reliable and valid assessment instrument.

However, some general comments are in order first. It must be recognized that the TRS's philosophy of professional practice, education, and past experience are explicit and implicit influences on his or her selection criteria. So, once again, there is a value judgment aspect to the TRS's decision making (Howe, 1984), which is the way it should be! The TRS should be the ultimate judge of the probable usefulness of a particular instrument or procedure for a particular client or situation, based on his or her professional knowledge, experience, and current context.

Specific criteria may include whether the instrument is norm- or criterion-referenced; readily available; easy to administer, score, and interpret; time efficient; cost effective; consistent with the purpose of the assessment; intended for the client population with whom it is being used; inclusive of a training manual; and sensitive to the rights, welfare, and dignity of the persons with whom it is being used (Howe, 1984; Stumbo & Rickards, 1986).

Stumbo and Rickards (1986) have developed a checklist which the TRS can use to determine the utility of an assessment instrument. Their checklist is organized under four areas of concern: program concerns, population/client concerns, staff concerns, and administrative/proce-dural concerns. An abbreviation of their checklist is presented for illustrative purposes as follows:

Abbreviated Checklist for Determining Utility of Assessments

PROGRAM CONCERNS
Does the assessment instrument/procedure
1. match the intent/goals/philosophy of the overall program?
2. align with the program documentation?
3. yield the right kinds of information to appropriately place clients into programs?
4. allow for information for both assessment and evaluation of the clients at a later date?
5. match the resources available within the therapeutic recreation department (including costs, staff expertise, time for administration and scoring)?
6. meet professional standards?
7. allow for collaboration with other disciplines?

POPULATION/CLIENT CONCERNS
Does the assessment instrument/procedure
1. match client abilities (if self-administered)?
   a. Can the client read the instrument?
   b. Can the client understand the questions on the instrument?
   c. Can the client tabulate the results (if required)?
2. match the client's
   a. performance abilities?
   b. needs?
   c. characteristics?

STAFF CONCERNS
Does the assessment instrument/procedure:
1. match the staff's abilities?
   a. Does the staff have the expertise to administer and interpret the data collected?
   b. Will they have the time to administer the assessment?
   c. Will they have time to score and analyze the results?
   d. Can they interpret the results in order to place clients into appropriate activities?
   e. Will they have the time to document the results?
2. provide similar results or interpretations for different staff members?

ADMINISTRATIVE/PROCEDURAL CONCERNS

Does the assessment instrument/procedure:

1. have sufficient accompanying material on administration and interpretation methods?
2. have sufficient accompanying material on validity and reliability for similar populations and programs?
3. fit within the budget allowed for assessment?
4. allow for public use (as opposed to restricted use by only select licensed professionals or under approval by author)?
5. allow for computer use in administration and scoring?
6. combine with or complement other assessments? have a history of use by similar agencies?

(From Selection of Assessment Instruments in Therapeutic Recreation Services by N.J. Stumbo and W.H. Rickards, 1986, paper presented at the Annual Congress of the National Recreation and Park Association. Copyright 1986 by N.J. Stumbo. Adapted by permission.)

Several of the items listed in the checklist represent the contextual factors that the TRS has to consider when selecting and using assessment instrumentation. These contextual factors are generic to all formal assessments whether the assessments are problem-solving oriented as in Stumbo and Thompson (1986) or systematic inquiry oriented as in Howe (1984) and Loesch and Wheeler (1982). These generic contextual factors may be grouped into three major areas: the purpose of the assessment; levels of skill, ability, and/or functioning; and resources.

It is the responsibility of the TRS to determine whether the purpose of the assessment is diagnostic, educational, or evaluative and then to select and use instruments or procedures accordingly. It is also incumbent on the TRS to objectively self-evaluate his or her own level of assessment-related skills, abilities, and/or functioning and choose assessments that he or she comprehends and can use within the boundaries of acceptable professional practice. The TRS must also judge the level of skill, ability, or functioning of the clients as a further consideration of what assessments to use. The instruments or procedures must also be comprehensible to the clients in order to elicit meaningful responses.

The resources that are realistically necessary and available for the assessment must be sought and committed. These include personnel time for the process; a budgetary allotment for materials; aids to information collection, analysis, and interpretation as needed; and opportunities and support for training and continuing education for using new or more sophisticated assessment instruments and procedures. This type of commitment is essential in order for assessment to be a part of the ongoing mission and process (programs and services) of the organization or agency in which the TRS is located.

Categories of assessment instrumentation

All of these criteria compose the basis on which the TRS makes the assessment instrument selection. Most recently, Stumbo and Thompson (1986) have presented seven categories of instruments and described their salient features. The reader is referred to their work and the others listed in the references at the end of the chapter for more detailed information. Briefly, the categories, which were originated with Loesch and Wheeler (1982) and were elaborated on by Howe (1984) and Howe and Carpenter (1985), include instruments that assess (1) leisure attitudes, (2) leisure values, (3) leisure states, (4) leisure behavior, (5) leisure satisfaction, (6) leisure interests, and (7) perceived freedom. These labels highlight the primary focus of the instruments.

The aforementioned authors and Wehman and Schleien (1980) have all discussed selected instruments that fall under each category, so such details are not duplicated here. However, the stature of the entire assessment process as it reflects the merits of the existing instruments and procedures deserves mention.

Status of Assessment

In 1989, as in 1984, it remains that assessment instruments and procedures should never be used alone and should be used with care and caution. In particular, to rely solely on a "paper and pencil test" would miss the richness and complexity of the individual client. Multiple forms of information collection must be used in order for an assessment to be truly meaningful. Undoubtedly, it is as true now as it was five years ago (cf Howe, 1984) that little new information has entered the literature regarding the reliability, validity, and practical utility of the instruments that are relatively easy to obtain. The available assessment instruments that are nonagency-specific are still sketchy, still evolutionary, and still conceptually cloudy. The tension between the applied and theoretical dimensions of the assessment process continues, especially with the continual proliferation of agency-specific assessment devices that are little more than interest inventories but are incorrectly used and touted for purposes way beyond those of such inventories. What remains needed is a coordinated, scientific approach to further testing, developing, implementing, evaluating, and revising assessment instruments and procedures.

This doesn't mean that the state of the art is so bad that formal assessment shouldn't be done at all. On the contrary, this means that there are still many things left to do! This languishing can serve as the call to action to review the tools of the trade, monitor and improve professional practice and the bases for decision-making, demonstrate and reinforce the scientific knowledge that underlies therapeutic recreation as a human services field for both accountability and efficacy, educate the public as to the real value of what a professional therapeutic recreation specialist does, and mandate the use of assessment instruments with wisdom and compassion. The intelligent application of the results of reliable and valid assessment instruments or procedures remains the best way to serve one's clientele. At this point in time, the whole, therefore, is greater than the sum of its parts.

It would be a misstatement to say that nothing has been accomplished in the past 5 years. The danger in making generalizations is the exception to the rule. One notable exception is the Leisure Diagnostic Battery (LDB). It is a superb model for the development, implementation, evaluation, and revision of assessment instrumentation. The original work on the LDB commenced in 1979, based on a grant obtained by David M. Compton at North Texas State University. By 1982 the project team directed by Peter A. Witt and Gary D. Ellis had developed adolescent and adult versions of the LDB plus an accompanying instruction manual, a remediation guide, and conceptual materials. Since then the material has been revised and updated. *The Leisure Diagnostic Battery User's Manual and Forms* (Witt & Ellis, 1987) is offered as a replacement for the original materials and is cited in the references listed at the end of this chapter. In addition, many reports of research using the LDB have appeared in print (cf Ellis & Niles, 1985; Ellis & Witt 1984; Ellis, Witt & Niles, 1982; Witt, & Ellis, 1985). The rigor with which the LDB was developed and tested is an exemplary and well-documented effort worthy of detailed review by the reader.

Assessment: The Professional and Professional Practice

The determination of the extent to which existing assessment instruments and procedures work ultimately rests with the TRS. These pages give the TRS some things to think about when making decisions about assessment. But, what these pages cannot give is the thorough and complete education needed to use assessment instruments or procedures well, mindful of both their strengths and their weaknesses. That training requires either formal degree work or continuing professional education. It takes time and study to gain the insight and skills to validate instruments, let alone to practice one's skills at assessment design, quantitative and qualitative data collection and analysis, and the interpretation and application of results. So, in that sense, any assessment is only as good as the TRS conducting it.

At least the reader may be alerted to the ties that exist between assessment, treatment, and placement and how assessment can be used to improve professional practice. Accountability is crucial to the proper practice of a profession. Using assessments is one means of ethically and judiciously doing this (Howe, 1984).

Further, to better understand and aid the human condition, to improve the quality of life, has always been a primary goal of the entire park, recreation, and leisure service profession as well as the allied health fields. One of the ways in which this goal may be achieved is through appropriately conducted assessments. Is not the human experience composed of cognitive, affective, and motor behaviors within some social context? Is it not through the pursuit of leisure that persons express themselves and, ideally, fulfill themselves? If so, then is it not the responsibility of today's TRS to ensure that the assessment process is fully integrated into his or her professional practice?

Assessments are tools that guide inquiry. Multiple inquiry demands the fusion of the scientific (rational) and artistic (intuitive) dimensions of the process and of the professional. Multiple inquiry sets the stage for the fullest enrichment of the clients' leisure repertoires and lives. The final measure of the TRS's success may be when the clients go out to play on their own as they are best able to do. The qualities of the instruments and the qualities of the TRS determine the extent to which assessment procedures work.

Study Questions

1. What is assessment? How does assessment differ from evaluation and research? How is assessment related to evaluation and research?

2. How is assessment related to the model presented in Figure 1? How can the therapeutic recreation specialist use assessment as a means of promoting and enhancing the leisure literacy and independent leisure functioning of clients?

3. What are reliability, validity, and practical utility as they are related to assessment instrumentation and the assessment process? How are these concepts related to each other? Why are they important to the therapeutic recreation specialist?

4. What contextual factors should the therapeutic recreation specialist consider when using assessment devices? Why?

5. To what extent do current assessment instruments work? To what extent should future assessment instruments work? What is the value of assessment?

6. What are the strengths and weaknesses of assessment? How can the weaknesses be remedied and the strengths reinforced?

7. What should the therapeutic recreation specialist know prior to conducting an assessment? What competencies should the professional possess? Where should these competencies be gained?

References

Dunn, J.K. (1988). Establishing Reliability and Validity in Evaluation Instruments. *Journal of Park and Recreation Administration,* *5*(4), pp.61-70.

Ellis, G.D., & Niles, S. (1985). Development, Reliability, and Preliminary Validation of a Brief Leisure Rating Scale. *Therapeutic Recreation Journal,19*(1), 50-61.

Ellis, G.D., & Witt, P.A. (1984). The Measurement of Perceived Freedom in Leisure. *Journal of Leisure Research, 16* (2), 110-123.

Ellis, G.D., Witt, P.A., & Niles, S. (1982). *Leisure Diagnostic Battery Remediation Guide.* Denton, TX: North Texas State University.

Howe, C.Z. (1984). Leisure Assessment and Counseling. In E.T. Dowd (Ed.), *Leisure Counseling: Concepts and Applications* (pp.234-253). Springfield, IL: Thomas.

Howe, C.Z., & Carpenter, G.M. (1985). *Programming Leisure Experiences: A Cyclical Approach.* Englewood Cliffs, NJ: Prentice-Hall.

Loesch, L.C., & Wheeler, P.T. (1982). *Principles of Leisure Counseling.* Minneapolis, MN: Educational Media.

Mundy, J., & Odum, L. (1979). *Leisure Education: Theory and Practice.* New York: Wiley.

Peterson, C.A., & Gunn, S.L. (1984). *Therapeutic Recreation Program Design: Principles and Procedures* (2nd ed.). Englewood Cliffs, NJ: Prentice-Hall.

Riddick, C.C. (1986). Leisure Satisfaction Precursors. *Journal of Leisure Research, 18*(4), 259-265.

Stumbo, N.J., & Rickards, W.H. (1986, October). *Selection of Assessment Instruments in Therapeutic Recreation Services.* Paper presented at the Annual Congress of the National Recreation and Park Association, Anaheim, CA.

Stumbo, N.J., & Thompson, S.R. (1986). *Leisure Education: A Manual of Activities and Resources.* State College, PA: Venture.

Teaff, J.D. (1985). *Leisure Services with the Elderly.* St. Louis, MO: Times Mirror/Mosby.

Wehman, P., & Schleien, S.J. (1980). Relevant Assessment in Leisure Skill Training Programs. *Therapeutic Recreation Journal, 14*(4), 9-20.

Weissinger, E., & Caldwell, L. (1987, May). *Validity and Reliability Concepts in Leisure Research..* Paper presented at the 5th Canadian Congress on Leisure Research, Dalhousie University, Halifax, Nova Scotia.

Witt, P.A., Connolly, P., & Compton, D.M. (1980). Assessment: A Plea for Sophistication. *Therapeutic Recreation Journal, 14*(4),- 5-8.

Witt, P.A., & Ellis, G.D. (1985). Development of a Short Form to Assess Perceived Freedom in Leisure. *Journal of Leisure Research, 17*(3), 225-233.

Witt, P.A., & Ellis, G.D. (1987). *Leisure Diagnostic Battery User's Manual and Forms.* State College, PA: Venture.

CAN WE REALLY MEASURE LEISURE BEHAVIOR OF SPECIAL POPULATIONS AND INDIVIDUALS WITH DISABILITIES?

Janiece J. Sneegas

Introduction

Measurement is accepted as an important concept with diverse applications across the scope of therapeutic recreation practice. Measurement, as cited by Dunn (1987), has been defined as "the assigning of numbers to individuals [or phenomenon] in a systematic way as a means of representing properties of the individual [or phenomenon]. Numbers are assigned . . . . according to a carefully prescribed, repeatable procedure" (Allen & Yen as cited in Dunn, 1987).

"The two essential qualities desired in measurement are reliability and validity" (Dunn, 1987). Reliability refers to consistency in measurement, whereas validity is the extent to which one measures what one purports to measure. (The reader is referred to Howe's chapter in this volume for a detailed discussion of these concepts.) Essentially, these two criteria serve to reflect the credibility of measurement efforts (Dunn, 1987).

Through measurement efforts in assessment and research, therapeutic recreation specialists attempt to gather a variety of information related to leisure behavior. This information serves to guide the provision of quality therapeutic recreation services to clients in order to facilitate the development, maintenance, and expression of an appropriate leisure lifestyle (Peterson & Gunn, 1984). Measurement through formal assessment procedures determines the placement of clients into appropriate therapeutic recreation programs. Measuring leisure behavior for research purposes is also critical. Through research, further knowledge and understanding may be gained and more effective interventions developed for improving the leisure lifestyle of clients.

The current, future, and oftentimes past leisure behavior of the client are important areas of focus for the therapeutic recreation specialist. Relevant information to be gathered may include leisure interests, use of leisure time, ability to participate in individual or group activities, ability to experience fun and enjoyment, leisure skills, leisure attitudes and awareness, and knowledge of leisure resources as well as any physical, cognitive, or social limitations affecting leisure lifestyle.

Yet the measurement of leisure behavior in individuals with disabilities and in special populations is not as simple as it might appear on the surface. The current state of the art for assessing leisure behavior is relatively undeveloped because obtaining valid and reliable measures of the leisure behavior of anyone (not even considering any additional problems presented by disability) is a complex process. Indeed, the question may be posed, "Can we really measure leisure behavior in special populations and individuals with disabilities?" This chapter will discuss the problems inherent in this process by focusing on the following questions:

1. What are the problems associated with measuring the leisure behavior of any population, including nondisabled persons?

2. What are the unique considerations in measuring the leisure behavior of disabled persons and special populations?

3. Can the assumption be made that the leisure behavior of individuals with disabilities and of special populations is the same as that of nondisabled persons? Or is it necessary to investigate the leisure behavior of individuals with disabilities and special populations in spite of the inherent difficulties?

Problems Associated with Measuring
Leisure Behavior of Any Population

The problems associated with measuring leisure behavior are the same for assessment purposes as for research purposes. These problems include difficulties in defining variables, lack of available instrumentation, and lack of methodological sophistication.

One of the most salient difficulties in measuring leisure behavior exists with the definition of variables. Defining leisure, and thus what constitutes leisure activities and leisure behavior, continues to be problematic. Leisure has been defined as free time and as activity. Leisure has also been defined experientially. "The notion that leisure is an experience or state of mind, that it is uniquely individual, and that the quality rather than quantity of leisure in our lives deserves attention has

. . . become a theme among leisure professionals and researchers" (Mannell, 1983, p. 10). This conceptualization of leisure is obviously more difficult to measure than is free time or activity. As stated by Howe (1985),

> because of the subjective nature of leisure and the contention that leisure behavior is best explained in terms of the interplay between internal (subjective or psychological) feelings and external/situational events (social group influences, etc.), difficulties exist. (p. 221)

Thus, identifying and measuring participation in various activities is alone not a valid and sufficient measure of the full spectrum of leisure behavior. In order to obtain more meaningful information, the antecedents and consequences of activity involvement—that is, the preexisting needs and subsequent effects of leisure involvement (Crandall & Lewko, 1976), as well as the subjective experiences of the individual—need to be examined.

However, the very nature of the leisure experience presents a problem in measurement. The "fragile nature of leisure," as phrased by Reynolds and O'Morrow (1985, p. 188), presents a challenge. Is it possible to measure this subjective component or to create a leisure experience to facilitate measurement? Or will the introduction of external observers or measurement instruments detract from the experience, removing it from the realm of leisure?

Even if the notion of leisure behavior as a subjective, complex, and multidimensional phenomenon is accepted and care is taken not to disturb the "leisure experience," the path to measurement is still strewn with methodological difficulties. There is currently a lack of appropriate measurement tools, or instrumentation, which reflect the complexity of leisure behavior. Whereas time diaries and activity checklists provide a measure of time use and activity involvement, they do not generally provide any information detailing the whys and wherefores of the behavior, information on the subjective experience of the individual's involvement.

A discussion of the existing instrumentation available for assessment purposes in therapeutic recreation is provided by Dunn (1984), Howe (1984), and Stumbo and Thompson (1986). Readers are referred to these sources for in-depth analyses of the current state of the art in therapeutic recreation assessment. Reliability, validity, and usability information for specific instruments is included. In sum, these researchers found that there are few instruments designed to obtain assessment information related to leisure behavior which demonstrate adequate reliability, validity, and practical utility.

Another problem in measuring leisure behavior, which becomes apparent when examining the published research, is the adherence to univariate studies (Tinsley, 1984).

> Investigators frequently look at single constructs in attempting to predict or explain important aspects of leisure behavior. Unfortunately, the important causes, attributes, and effects of all behavior, including leisure behavior, are almost always multivariate. This means that the explanatory power of univariate research is seriously limited. (p. 93).

Greater attention has been focused on qualitative methods of data collection in research, in order to capture the complexity of leisure behavior. Qualitative methods provide detailed descriptive and contextual information (Bullock, 1983).

> Qualitative data consist of *detailed descriptions* of situations, events, people, interactions, and observed behaviors; *direct quotations* from people about their experiences, attitudes, beliefs, and thoughts; and excerpts or entire passages from documents, correspondence, records and case histories . . . . The data are collected as open-ended narrative *without* attempting to fit program activities or peoples' experiences into predetermined standardized categories such as the response choices that comprise typical questionnaires or tests. (Patton, 1980, p. 22)

The focus of qualitative methods is on understanding the area of study from the subject's point of view. Examples of frequently used qualitative methods include participant observation, in-depth, unstructured interviews, and open-ended questionnaires.

Common concerns related to qualitative methods, including generalizability, reliability, and observer effect, have been discussed by Bullock (1983), Patton (1980), and Stake (1978). Generalizability, a key concern of the scientific method, generally refers to the degree to which the findings of a study can be applied to settings and subjects outside of the study limits (Bullock). Qualitative methods, however, stress the examination of phenomenon within a specific context; that is, the unique characteristics of a given context are a primary component of investigation. Therefore, as stated by Bullock, many qualitative researchers are not concerned with generalizability in the traditional sense. Stake notes that "naturalistic generalization [is] arrived at by recognizing the similarities of objects and issues in and out of context and by sensing the natural covariations of happenings" (p. 6).

Reliability is another common concern associated with qualitative methods. Reliability within the more traditional research paradigms refers to consistency in measurement, either over time or across researchers (Bullock, 1983). Reliability within the qualitative paradigm is more "concerned with accuracy and comprehensiveness of data. Qualitative researchers see reliability as a fit between what they record as data and what actually occurs" (Bullock, p. 42). Is the data recorded an accurate reflection of what happened?

As the qualitative researcher collects data in naturalistic settings, concerns are often voiced as to the effects of the researcher's presence on the phenomenon or behavior under examination. This is a concern within other research paradigms as well. Qualitative methodologists respond to this concern by stating that because the researcher is so ongoingly present, he or she "becomes a part of the worlds of those under investigation" (Bullock, 1983, p. 42). The argument is thus presented that there is less of a threat of observer effects in qualitative methods than in other approaches.

Despite these and other concerns, qualitative methods represent not necessarily an alternative approach but rather an additional approach, which can contribute to a more complete understanding of leisure behavior. Through qualitative approaches, quantification of leisure activities can be supplemented with more experiential, psychosociological measures. Experience-sampling studies providing both quantitative and qualitative data (Larson & Csikszentmihalyi, 1983; Samdahl, 1986) have contributed much in this direction, yet to date, few if any such studies have focused on the leisure behavior of disabled and special populations.

The preceding discussion has presented an overview of some of the difficulties involved in measuring the leisure behavior of anyone, without consideration given to disability. The next section identifies some additional problems involved in measuring the leisure behavior of special populations and individuals with disabilities.

What are the Unique Considerations for Measuring the Leisure Behavior of Special Populations?

There are a number of considerations that further complicate the measurement of leisure behavior of individuals with disabilities. These include disability-specific considerations, small numbers of available subjects, setting characteristics, and ethical concerns.

The inherent characteristics of some disabilities present difficulties in measuring leisure behavior. Physical impairments with associated communication deficits present challenges to obtaining valid and reliable information with some individuals. Examples might include some persons with cerebral palsy or traumatic brain injury. With hearing-impaired individuals, not only the difficulties in verbal communication but also the subtle variations in vocabulary and syntax in manual communication (e.g., American Sign Language) present obstacles to obtaining valid and reliable information (Wachter, 1987).

Cognitive impairments present yet other difficulties. Individuals with mental retardation who are unable to process information cognitively, as well as psychiatric clients who are not reality-based, pose significant challenges to measurement. Individuals with severe or profound mental retardation who have both cognitive and communication difficulties present even greater challenges.

Another problem in measuring the leisure behavior of individuals with disabilities is "the lack of adequate numbers of subjects for between-groups comparisons" (Reynolds & O'Morrow, 1985, p. 188). The number of subjects available is often inadequate to allow for more than descriptive statistics. Some disabilities are low-prevalence disabilities (e.g., visual impairments, spinal cord injury), and difficulties often exist in trying to locate individuals with disabilities within community settings. (Confidentiality concerns limiting access to individuals is discussed in more detail below.) Although institutional settings may offer a convenient sample, another set of problems comes with the territory (Reynolds & O'Morrow; Witt, 1986).

Within many institutional settings, staff are neither provided the time nor the financial resources to collect valid and reliable information on the leisure behavior of their clients. External researchers must work within "existing agency routines. This often requires large amounts of agency support and cooperation and removes the ultimate control . . . from the researcher" (Reynolds & O'Morrow, 1985, p. 188). Ensuring adequate experimental control is difficult in both clinical and community settings. Control refers to the ability to clearly separate out external influences and potential bias from the variables under investigation. That is, are the results obtained a true reflection of only the variables examined? "Problems of maintaining intact groups, controlling for unforeseen events, and controlling other potential explanations for dependent variable change may cause significant... problems" (Witt, p. 30). Qualitative methods, as discussed earlier, may serve to offset these particular difficulties associated with more structured experimental designs.

Ethical concerns also have an impact on the measurement of leisure behavior in some special populations. The clearest example, perhaps, is that related to substance abusers, including alcoholics. Although assessment of the leisure behavior of these clients while they are in a treatment facility is not particularly more difficult than with other clients, follow-up of their leisure behavior once they leave the facility and return to the community is extremely difficult due to confidentiality issues. Likewise, it is very difficult to locate individuals in the community to participate in research studies examining the leisure behavior of chemically dependent persons. While Alcoholics Anonymous would provide an interesting and convenient subject population, the organization is by its very nature anonymous, precluding most research attempts (Ward, 1983).

Another ethical concern which affects the measurement of leisure behavior in therapeutic recreation research is the right to treatment. "This concept... has as a corollary the principle that it is unethical to deny or withhold beneficial treatment" (Reynolds & O'Morrow, 1985, p. 188). Thus, it becomes difficult to attempt to manipulate variables or interventions which may restrict or affect the leisure behavior of a segment of the client population. As a significant amount of the research in therapeutic recreation focuses (or should!) on the efficacy of therapeutic recreation services in improving the leisure lifestyle of clients, this is a genuine concern.

It has been argued that measuring the leisure behavior of anyone is difficult. It has further been argued that measuring leisure behavior in special populations and individuals with disabilities may be subject to additional problems. If it can be assumed that there are no significant differences between the leisure behavior of such individuals and populations and that of nondisabled individuals, then it would not be necessary to specifically examine the leisure behavior of individuals with disabilities, fraught as the process is with problems. If this assumption cannot be made, however, then further investigation is warranted despite the difficulties.

Does Leisure Behavior of Individuals with Disabilities Differ from that of the Nondisabled?

The leisure behavior of individuals with disabilities and special populations has been shown to be affected by real and/or perceived barriers. McGuire (1984) states, "Any force which limits choice also limits leisure. By constricting the range of choice, constraints are placed on leisure behavior" (p. 323).

Special populations—including individuals with physical, mental, or emotional disabilities; the aging; and individuals who are economically disadvantaged—are limited by barriers imposed by their impairments and/or by the societal response to them. Unfortunately, the limitations associated with an illness or disability, as well as the attitudinal and architectural barriers imposed by our society, often inhibit or prohibit the leisure expression and involvement of these individuals (Peterson and Gunn, 1984).

Architectural barriers may include physically inaccessible buildings, facilities with inappropriate lighting for individuals with poor vision, or areas where background noise creates difficulties for individuals with hearing impairments. Architectural barriers, while not always precluding involvement, make it more difficult for individuals with disabilities to dine out, attend sporting events, travel, visit in the homes of nondisabled friends, or participate in a number of other leisure opportunities in which their nondisabled counterparts are not affected.

Attitudinal barriers, while not as visible as architectural barriers, may also serve to limit the leisure behavior of individuals with disabilities. These barriers may exist on the part of the disabled individual or on the part of society. Examples of attitudinal barriers may include fear, pity, admiration, or any other response which focuses on the disability rather than on the person as an individual with unique strengths and limitations.

The constraints presented by attitudinal barriers become apparent in discussions of risk-recreation for individuals with disabilities. Robb and Ewart (1987) include the following factors in an explanation of why few risk recreation activities are traditionally provided for special populations: (a) attitudes of overprotectiveness, (b) segregated services which are many times no longer acceptable to individuals with disabilities and/or their advocates, (c) discrimination by insurance company rulings and service-provider policies and (d) misunderstanding of risk recreation as dangerous rather than as "controlled, planned or perceived risk that is manipulated to achieve a desired outcome or experience. This perception is compounded for persons with disabilities by virtue of their ascribed societal status" (p. 61).

In addition to architectural and attitudinal barriers, a number of other barriers exist for individuals with disabilities that may significantly constrict their leisure involvement. These barriers include a lack of leisure-related knowledge, lack of activity skills, lack of awareness of the value of leisure, lack of available resources adapted to their needs, lack of social skills, lack of decision-making or planning skills, as well as a lack of an acceptance of personal responsibility for their own leisure. In addition, the physical, social, emotional, or cognitive impairments of some individuals may also restrict the number of opportunities available for experiencing leisure.

The above discussion of the existence of barriers affecting the leisure lifestyles of special populations is not mere conjecture and speculation. Although the documentation of the leisure behavior of special populations is by no means voluminous, research has been completed that indicates that the leisure involvement of special populations is limited by barriers. Investigations of the leisure behavior of individuals with mental retardation, the elderly, and individuals who are economically deprived will be briefly mentioned as examples.

Dattilo (1987)—citing Katz and Yekutiel (1974), Luckey and Shapiro (1974), and Owen (1977)—states, "Persons with mental retardation do not participate in recreation as often as individuals without mental retardation.... More of their free time is spent around the home than appears to be true with the general population" (p. 10). Dattilo, in a comprehensive review of the literature, identifies a number of reasons for the lack of recreation participation of individuals with mental retardation. These reasons include (a) an overall lack of recreation opportunities for this population, (b) a lack of awareness of those recreation opportunities which are available, (c) a lack of social networks outside of school, and (d) a lack of age-appropriate leisure skills.

A number of studies have been conducted that specifically examine constraints on the leisure behavior of the elderly (Buchanan & Allen, 1985; Goodrow,1975; McGuire, 1979, 1984; Trela & Simmons, 1971). McGuire conducted telephone interviews with 125 people aged 45 and older. Results of this study indicated such individuals were constrained from participating in leisure activities. Clusters of constraints which were derived from a list of 30 constraints included lack of external resources, lack of time, need for approval, lack of leisure experiences, concern about physical well-being, lack of mobility, and poor self-image. Identified constraints from other studies include poor vision (Goodrow, 1975), lack of facilities (in this case, senior citizen centers), and lack of knowledge of available facilities (Harris & Associates, 1976).

Kaufman, Hultsman, and Hultsman (1987) conducted a review of the literature on recreation and the poor. This review revealed that reduced income (Hendon, 1981), inadequate mass transportation (Department of the Interior, 1974), a lack of education (Chubb & Chubb, 1981), a lack of adequate public funding, and a lack of recreation opportunities were tangible factors contributing to "the problem of recreation participation by the economically disadvantaged [which] is substantial in scope. [However,] . . . the primary barrier to participation appears to be related to *perceptions* of constraint" (Kaufman et al., p. 52). These perceptions included fear of hostility and discrimination.

In summary, there is no doubt that the opportunities for leisure involvement are limited for special populations when compared to the opportunities which exist for the nondisabled. Also, the literature supports the conclusion that the leisure behavior of individuals with disabilities differs quantitatively from the nondisabled. Although little work has been done to determine whether leisure behavior differs qualitatively between these groups, the fact that quantitative differences exist warrants further exploration despite the inherent difficulties.

Can We Really Measure the Leisure Behavior of Special Populations and Individuals with Disabilities?

The previously cited literature indicates that the leisure behavior of special populations and some individuals with disabilities can be measured with acceptable levels of reliability and validity insofar as leisure behavior is operationalized as time and activity. Work done in investigating the more qualitative, experiential aspects of leisure behavior with nondisabled persons could also be applied to those disabled individuals whose impairment does not affect cognition or communication. Clearly, ongoing efforts should be made to creatively measure the leisure behavior of such people who are not accessible through existing methods used with nondisabled individuals.

In order to increase the quality and quantity of efforts to measure the leisure behavior of special populations and individuals with disabilities, a number of areas need to be addressed, including the following:

1. There is a need to increase the measurement and research skills of individuals with an interest in, knowledge of, and access to special populations and individuals with disabilities. There are related curricular implications for both undergraduate and graduate programs in therapeutic recreation. There are also implications for continuing education opportunities for therapeutic recreation professionals.

2. There is a need for theoretical and empirical work to more clearly define what constitutes leisure behavior and the leisure experience for some individuals with disabilities, such as individuals with severe or profound mental retardation. Equal weight must be given to the investigation of the qualitative experience of leisure.

3. Ongoing efforts are necessary to develop and improve instrumentation providing reliable and valid information about the leisure behavior of individuals with disabilities. Creative approaches to data collection need to be developed for those persons with cognitive and communication difficulties.

4. There is a need to employ a greater variety of methods, including more qualitative approaches, to examine the full spectrum of leisure behavior.

5. Efforts should also be undertaken to increase cooperation between external investigators and practitioners in clinical and community settings.

Study Questions

1. How does measurement of leisure behavior for assessment purposes differ from the measurement of leisure behavior for research purposes?

2. What are the advantages and disadvantages of qualitative and quantitative approaches to the measurement of leisure behavior?

3. What skills and knowledge are required to measure leisure behavior? What additional skills are necessary to measure the leisure behavior of individuals with disabilities?

4. Why is measuring the leisure behavior of special populations and individuals with disabilities important?

5. Speculate on how leisure experiences of some individuals with disabilities may be qualitatively different from those of other groups.

    * In spite of awkwardness, both of the terms *individuals with disabilities* and *special populations* are used. Although the term *special populations* is generally considered to include individuals with disabilities, the writer prefers *individuals with disabilities* as the least offensive terminology. *Individuals with disabilities* does not include some client groups, however, such as aging individuals or persons who are chemically dependent or economically disadvantaged.

References

Allen, M.J., & Yen, W.M. (1979). *Introduction to Measurement Theory.* Monterey, CA: Brooks/Cole.

Buchanan, T., & Allen, L.R. (1985). Barriers to Recreation Participation in Later Life Cycle Stages. *Therapeutic Recreation Journal, 19*(3), 39-50.

Bullock, C.C. (1983). Qualitative Research in Therapeutic Recreation. *Therapeutic Recreation Journal, 17*(4), 36-43.

Chubb, M., & Chubb, H.R. (1981). *One Third of Our Time.* New York, NY: John Wiley & Sons.

Crandall, R., & Lewko, J. (1976). Leisure Research, Present and Future; Who What, Where. *Journal of Leisure Research, 8*(3), 150-159.

Dattilo, J.D. (1987). Recreation and Leisure Literature for Individuals with Mental Retardation: Implications for Outdoor Recreation. *Therapeutic Recreation Journal, 21*(1), 9-17.

Department of the Interior, Committee on Interior and Insular Affairs. (1974). *The Recreation Imperative: A Draft of the Nationwide Outdoor Recreation Plan.* Washington, DC: U.S. Government Printing Office.

Dunn, J.K. (1984). Assessment. In C.A. Peterson & S.L. Gunn (Eds.) *Therapeutic Recreation Program Design: Principles and Procedures* (2nd ed.), 267-320. Englewood Cliffs, N.J.: Prentice-Hall.

Dunn, J.K. (1987). Establishing Reliability and Validity in Evaluation Instruments. *Journal of Park and Recreation Administration 5*(4), 61-70.

Goodrow, B.A. (1975). Limiting Factors in Reducing Participation in Older Adult Learning Opportunities. *The Gerontologist, 15,* 418-422.

Harris, L., & Associates. (1976). *The Myth and Reality of Aging in America.* Washington, D.C.: National Council on Aging.

Hendon, W.S. (1981). *Evaluating urban parks and recreation.* New York, NY: Praeger.

Howe, C.Z. (1984). Leisure Assessment Instrumentation in Therapeutic Recreation. *Therapeutic Recreation Journal, 18* (2), 14-24.

Howe, C.Z. (1985). Possibilities For Using a Qualitative Research Approach in the Sociological Study of Leisure. *Journal of Leisure Research, 17*(3), 212-224.

Katz, S., & Yekutiel, E. (1974). Leisure Time Problems of Mentally Retarded Graduates of Training Programs. *Mental Retardation, 12,* 54-57.

Kaufman, J.E., Hultsman, J.T., & Hultsman, W.Z. (1987). Recreation and the Poor. *Therapeutic Recreation Journal, 21*(1), 51-57.

Larson, R., & Csikszentmihalyi, M. (1983). The Experience Sampling Method. In H.T. Reis (Ed.), *New Directions for Naturalistic Methods in the Behavioral Sciences.*, 41-56. San Francisco: Jossey Bass.

Luckey, R., & Shapiro, I.G. (1974). Recreation: An Essential Aspect of Habilitative Programming. *Mental Retardation, 12,* 33-36.

Mannell, R.C. (1983). Research Methodology in Therapeutic Recreation. *Therapeutic Recreation Journal, 17*(4), 9-16.

McGuire, F.C. (1979). *An exploratory study of leisure constraints in advanced adulthood.* Unpublished doctoral dissertation, University of Illinois, Urbana-Champaign.

McGuire, F.C. (1984). A Factor Analytic Study of Leisure Constraints in Advanced Adulthood. *Leisure Sciences, 6*(3), 313-326.

Owen, J.P.W. (1977). An Investigation of the Quality of Life of Ex-patients in the Community in Terms of Interests and Leisure Activities. *Research Exchange and Practice in Mental Retardation, 3,* 147-152.

Patton, M.Q. (1980). *Qualitative Evaluation Methods.* Beverly Hills, CA: Sage.

Peterson, C. A., & Gunn, S.L. (1984). *Therapeutic Recreation Program Design: Principles and Procedures* (2nd ed.). Englewood Cliffs, NJ: Prentice-Hall.

Reynolds, R.P., & O'Morrow, G.S. (1985). *Problems, Issues and Concepts in Therapeutic Recreation.* Englewood Cliffs, NJ: Prentice-Hall.

Robb, G.M., & Ewert, A. (1987). Risk Recreation and Persons with Disabilities. *Therapeutic Recreation Journal, 21*(1), 58-69.

Samdahl, D.M. (1986). *The Self and Social Freedom: A Paradigm of Leisure.* Unpublished doctoral dissertation, University of Illinois; Urbana-Champaign.

Stake, R.E. (1978). The Case Study Method in a Social Inquiry. *Educational Researcher, 7,* 5-8.

Stumbo, N.J., & Thompson, S.R. (1986). *Leisure Education: A Manual of Activities and Resources.* Peoria, IL: Central Illinois Center for Independent Living and Easter Seal Center.

Tinsley, H. (1984). Limitations, Explorations, Aspirations: A Confession of Fallibility and a Promise to Strive for Perfection. *Journal of Leisure Research, 16*(2), 93-98.

Trela, J.E., & Simmons, R.W. (1971). Health and Other Factors Affecting Membership and Attrition in a Senior Citizen Center. *Journal of Gerontology, 26,* 46-51.

Wachter, C.H. (1987). *The Relationship Between Mode of Communication, Leisure Participation, and Leisure Satisfaction in Hearing Impaired Adults.* Unpublished master's thesis, University of Illinois, Urbana-Champaign.

Ward, D. (1983). *Alcoholism: Introduction to Theory and Treatment* (2nd ed). Dubuque, IA: Kendall/Hunt.

Witt, P.A. (1986). Problems and Solutions in Undertaking Efficacy Research in Therapeutic Recreation Settings. *Abstracts from the 1986 Symposium on Leisure Research.,* 30-31 Alexandria, VA: National Recreation and Parks Association.

Reimbursement Issues

photo courtesy of Bradford Woods

What is the ultimate survival skill that many therapeutic recreation professionals feel is needed? It is the ability to better understand how to collect for therapeutic recreation services from insurance companies (third-party payers).
—Joseph L. Wilson

THIRD-PARTY PAYERS: ARE WE GETTING OUR SHARE?

Mary S. Reitter

The current economic climate in the United States clearly does not lend itself to growth or expansion of human services. Health care services in particular bear the scars of recent extensive cost-containment efforts. Undoubtedly, each therapeutic recreation practitioner will feel the impact of the limitations and constraints imposed on service provision by changes in health care financing. Therapeutic recreation managers will be faced with ensuring that services are cost-effective and of high quality.

Understanding the means by which therapeutic recreation services in clinical settings are financed is of paramount importance. It is no longer enough to respond to changes in health care financing after they are implemented. Those disciplines that are adequately prepared, anticipate changes, and take action in advance to minimize the impact of revisions in financing policy will have the best opportunity to survive in today's highly competitive health care environment.

This chapter contains an overview of health care financing and examines the efforts and status of therapeutic recreation relative to third-party payment for services. It is not intended to answer the question posed by its title; rather, that challenge has been reserved for the reader.

Health Care Financing : An Introduction

"Despite its great size, the health insurance industry is about as functional as a dinosaur." (Ehrenreich & Ehrenreich, 1970, p.111)

In the early 1900s, financing health care services was relatively simple. People went to their physicians, were treated, and paid out of their own pockets for the services they received.

The evolution of Blue Cross and the enactment of the Social Security Act of 1935 fostered the involvement of both the private sector and the federal government in health care financing. The advent of Medicare in 1965 and the expansion of commercial insurance carriers in the health insurance industry irrevocably changed health care financing. Retrospective cost-based reimbursement by third parties became the usual mode of financing health care services. This was usually referred to as "third-party reimbursement" or simply "reimbursement."

Medicare permitted hospitals to be reimbursed for the "reasonable costs" of providing services to patients. Hospitals used two primary methods to independently determine their reasonable costs under Medicare regulations. The per diem rate (also known as the "routine service charge" or "room rate") was established as a fixed rate by the hospital. The costs of many services routinely provided by the hospital, such as meals, nursing, and housekeeping, were included in this charge. Services for which separate charges were billed were known as "ancillary services." Diagnostic and therapeutic services provided at the discretion of the physician were generally considered to be ancillary. These services could generate revenue for the hospital by increasing the quantity of services provided. Retrospective cost-based reimbursement thus offered hospitals financial incentives for providing more services to patients.

Each third-party payer had its own methods of determining which services would be covered. However, commercial carriers tended to adopt the policies and methods utilized by Medicare, as did many Medicaid programs, for two main reasons. First, in some states, legislation mandated that particular health care services be covered under certain health insurance policies. Second, Medicare and Medicaid used the commercial insurance carriers as fiscal intermediaries. Intermediaries were responsible for determining the medical necessity of a hospital admission and the services received (Jonas 1981). Each intermediary was allowed to develop its own methods of review, which led to wide variation in review policies. Only infrequently, however, would an intermediary deny payment for services because it had determined the services were not medically necessary.

Between 1960 and 1973, national expenditures for health care tripled. Medicare and Medicaid became the largest single purchasers of health care services (Franklin & Rodgers 1983). The cost of health care was astronomical and continued to rise unchecked. This rise in costs was accompanied by increased hospital revenues. The virtually limitless financial resources permitted by retrospective reimbursement stimulated the growth of the health care industry. Myriad new services became routinely provided to patients. Innovative and often expensive medical technology and specialization by service providers flourished.

It soon became widely recognized that modifications in the methods of health care financing were necessary in order to control and reduce health care costs. Among early attempts were the Social Security Amendments of 1972 (PL 92-603). Section 249 F(b) established the Peer Standards Review Organization (PSRO) to "promote the effective, efficient, and economical delivery of health care services of proper quality" (SEC. 1151:1429). Section 223 established limits on the amount a hospital could be reimbursed for routine services.

In an effort to maintain their previous levels of income, hospitals began to encourage services previously considered routine to pursue reimbursement as an ancillary service. Resource allocations within clinical settings became related to the amount of revenue provided by a service. Competition for health care dollars ensued.

Despite these efforts, health care costs continued to escalate. A second major revision in health care financing was introduced in 1982: The Tax Equity and Fiscal Responsibility Act (TEFRA) (PL 97-248) changed reimbursement methods three ways. First, a per case system of reimbursement replaced the per diem system. Second, case-mix was incorporated into the payment system. Finally, the rate of increase in reimbursable Medicare costs per case was limited. In addition, peer review organizations (PROs) replaced PSROs. This change reinforced the intentions of TEFRA, for "unlike their predecessors, PROs will focus on containing costs and working with the insurance industry rather than monitoring cost and quality and working with providers and practitioners" (Mattson, 1984, p. 607). TEFRA also expanded Section 223 limits to ancillary services.

The Social Security Amendments of 1983 (PL 98-21) further elaborated on these changes. In an initiation of perhaps the most significant change in health care financing since the establishment of Medicare, retrospective cost-based reimbursement was replaced by the Medicare prospective payment system (PPS) (Reitter, 1986). Under the PPS, hospitals were paid rates which had been fixed in advance according to diagnosis-related groups (DRGs). DRGs were assigned to patients upon discharge from the hospital according to diagnosis, age, sex, necessary medical procedures, and length of stay.

This system fundamentally altered financial incentives for hospitals. Rather than encouraging increased quantity of services as the previous system had, the PPS rewarded hospitals for operating efficiently. If the actual cost of treating a patient were less than the DRG payment, a hospital would make money. If, however, treatment costs exceeded the DRG payment, the hospital absorbed the loss. Hospitals began to focus on decreasing length of stay and on cost containment.

In keeping with earlier trends, some private insurance carriers adopted the PPS. Others instituted different measures aimed at cost containment. Among these were preadmission certification programs, mandatory second opinions, and higher deductibles and co-payments. Private review of the medical necessity of hospital admissions and services (modeled after PROs) began to be used extensively. Managed care systems were developed. Under such systems, case managers for insurance carriers predetermine the appropriate level of treatment and where the treatment should be provided prior to a patient's admission, and monitor the patient's status during the admission.

Health care financing in the late 1980s is a complex entity, undergoing constant metamorphosis. The Medicare PPS continues to be developed, regardless of the fact that hospitals actually profited by as much as 15 percent during the first 2 years of its implementation. Alcohol and drug DRGs were instituted in 1987. Research on methods of developing a PPS for nursing homes is in progress. Conversion of physician payments, from the present system based on usual and customary charges to a relative value scale which establishes a physician fee schedule, is being pursued. Capitation plans are being investigated for children's, rehabilitation, psychiatric, and long-term hospitals, since extensive attempts to develop DRG-based payment systems in these settings have largely been unsuccessful.

Alternative health care delivery settings have grown dramatically. Among those experiencing the greatest expansion are home health care; outpatient services, including ambulatory surgery, day hospital programs, and free-standing emergency services; and long-term care facilities. Health maintenance organizations (HMOs) and preferred provider organizations (PPOs) have been further developed as alternatives to traditional commercial insurance.

HMOs provide comprehensive health care services for a prepaid fee regardless of the number of services utilized. In theory, HMOs provide unlimited health care services. In reality, they employ many mechanisms designed to ration treatment services, because they lose money if patient services are overused. In order to survive, they must operate efficiently.

In a PPO, physicians, hospitals, pharmacies, nursing homes, home health agencies, and other providers contract to provide discounted health care services to beneficiaries. Most PPOs are based on the fee-for-service model, although some use capitation payment plans. Basically, patients opting to receive treatment from the "preferred provider" are reimbursed at a higher rate than those electing to seek treatment from other providers. Extensive utilization review programs assist in the control of expenditures.

It is anticipated that both the health care industry and methods of financing health care services will continue to change. Investigation of relatively minor modifications to existing methods of financing, such as a voucher system, continues. Major changes, including national health insurance, are under discussion as well. Truly, "what will emerge in the 1990s will bear little resemblance to what we know today" (Porter, 1987, p. 6).

> "If a therapeutic recreation service is to be broad and effective, it does require well-based financial support." —Charles Brightbill (Frye & Peters, 1972, p. 175).

In the early days of the field of therapeutic recreation, financial matters were not a primary concern. Organizational, educational, and philosophical issues dominated the attention of the National Therapeutic Recreation Society (NTRS), which emerged as the field's professional organization in 1966 (Frye & Peters, 1972). Therapeutic recreation services in clinical settings were financed primarily through the per diem rate charged by hospitals.

Resources granted by hospitals for therapeutic recreation services (where such services existed) were limited. Fundraising efforts were frequently used to supplement budget allocations. The role and purpose of therapeutic recreation services within clinical settings was not clear. "Too frequently, recreation was associated with diversionary activities." (Briggs & Shafter 1971, p. 41).

In the early 1970s, NTRS initiated discussions with the Health Care Finance Administration's (HCFA) Office of Coverage Policy. HCFA administers the Medicare program; the Office of Coverage Policy aids in determining which services will be covered by Medicare, as well as the extent of coverage. These discussions were of short duration, and their intent and outcome are unclear.

Section 223 limits on routine service reimbursement in 1972 threatened to jeopardize the financial foundations of therapeutic recreation services in hospitals. Following the lead of other health care disciplines, the field desired to increase financial support through reimbursement as an ancillary service. In order to do so, "therapeutic recreation specialists, like those representing other fields, must be able to justify allocations and expenditures of funds for programs and services in their field" (Frye & Peters 1972, p. 193). Hospital administrators receiving requests for additional staff and supply resources for therapeutic recreation services advised the service to seek methods of generating revenue. Increased competition and the youth of therapeutic recreation at the time made this a difficult undertaking.

"Development of a Self-Sufficient Therapeutic Recreation Service" (Patterson, 1976) was the landmark publication that described the status of therapeutic recreation with respect to third-party reimbursement. In most instances, therapeutic recreation services were considered to be routine. However, services provided in psychiatric settings that met the criteria for active treatment could be reimbursed on an ancillary basis. In order to constitute active treatment, services had to be provided under an individualized treatment plan, be supervised or evaluated by a physician, and be reasonably expected to improve the patient's condition or be given for the purpose of diagnosis. Patterson recommended that discussions with state and area Medicare, Medicaid, and private insurance carriers be pursued in order to gather additional information about reimbursement policies and mechanisms prior to seeking reimbursement on a ancillary basis.

Efforts made by occupational therapy to secure third-party reimbursement provided the foundation for information contained in "Issues and Guidelines for Establishing Third-Party Reimbursement for Therapeutic Recreation," which was intended to provide practitioners a handbook describing methods of increasing reimbursement (Ingber, 1978). Absence of a definition of therapeutic recreation was seen as a significant barrier to pursuing reimbursement. "If we as practitioners cannot agree on a definition of our special expertise relative to health care, how can we expect to be accepted by third-party payers, physicians, and hospital administrators?" (Ingber, p. 5).

Lack of curriculum standards resulted in substantial differences in the basic educational preparation of therapeutic recreation students at colleges and universities. This exacerbated the difficulty of establishing practice standards and of developing and implementing requirements and procedures for credentialing within the field, which were necessary in order to pursue reimbursement.

Differences in the methods of pursuing reimbursement through government and private insurers complicated matters more. Determining the cost of providing therapeutic recreation services, identifying existing problems in receiving reimbursement (such as denial of claims), and contacting insurance representatives were suggested in order to pursue reimbursement from commercial carriers (Ingber, 1978).

Overall, the piecemeal efforts made by a few therapeutic recreation practitioners to pursue reimbursement had encouraging results. Third parties were found to be interested in learning more about the field and, in some cases, approved reimbursement for therapeutic recreation services. NTRS sponsored a miniforum on third-party reimbursement in 1979 and responded to escalating interest in the topic among practitioners with the establishment of the NTRS Third-Party Reimbursement Committee in 1980.

One of the first actions of this committee was to conduct a survey intended to identify the means by which therapeutic recreation services were financed. The survey considered services that were paid for either as an ancillary charge or through the per diem rate to constitute receipt of third-party payments. The majority of respondents (158) stated they did not receive third-party reimbursement. Only 44 (22 percent) stated they did receive third-party reimbursement. This is an interesting response since the vast majority of health care services were being financed by third parties at the time (Fein 1986). Of the 44, 15 received payment as an ancillary charge, while the remaining 29 were funded as a routine service.

Billing for therapeutic recreation services on an ancillary basis was reported under a variety of names, including "recreation therapy," "occupational therapy," "activity therapy," and "therapeutic recreation." Blue Cross, Prudential, Equitable, Travelers, and Aetna were among the third parties reported to have paid claims. Payments were most often made for services provided in rehabilitation or psychiatry. Almost 40 percent (17) of those paid on an ancillary basis reported having had claims denied at some time. Usually, claims were denied because the third party felt the services provided did not constitute active treatment but were instead of a diversionary nature.

Benefits of receiving third-party reimbursement were identified by respondents as placing the therapeutic recreation service in a better bargaining position, improving the administrator's attitude toward the service, and allowing expansion into other areas. Recommendations made to the NTRS by the committee, based on the results of the survey, included these:

1. Develop a strategy to initiate contact with Medicare to clarify who we are and what services we provide.
2. Develop a brochure to educate insurance carriers about therapeutic recreation's role in active treatment.
3. Publish selected research literature documenting the therapeutic value of services specific to service settings and disability groups.
4. Devote a special issue of *Therapeutic Recreation Journal* to fiscal matters.
5. Define the NTRS philosophical position statement operationally.
6. Further define the standards of practice (West, 1983).

These recommendations came at a time when NTRS was in the process of attempting to redefine itself (Meyer, 1985). When originally formed, NTRS was intended to be the national organization for all those providing any type of therapeutic recreation service in any setting to any disabled population. The NTRS philosophical position statement adopted in 1982 reflected this: "The purpose of therapeutic recreation is to facilitate the development, maintenance, and expression of an appropriate leisure lifestyle for individuals with physical, mental, emotional, or social limitations" (NRPA, p. 1). It had become apparent, however, that the professional issues and needs of those delivering therapeutic recreation services in clinical settings were different from those providing services in community settings.

In February 1983 the NTRS Third-Party Reimbursement Committee reinitiated discussions with the HCFA Office of Policy Coverage in an attempt to clarify the policy of Medicare with respect to reimbursement of therapeutic recreation services. In particular, the disparity in coverage of services between psychiatric patients and others was discussed. It was found that Medicare legislation was actually broad enough for therapeutic recreation services provided to any patient to be considered active treatment (providing such services met active treatment criteria). Historically, however, Medicare generally considered therapeutic recreation services as diversional, except services provided to psychiatric patients. A request for review of Medicare coverage policy by NTRS in order to obtain broader coverage of therapeutic recreation services in both inpatient and outpatient settings could have been made. In order to pursue this, the field would need

1. a definition describing therapeutic recreation as active treatment;
2. research demonstrating the therapeutic value of services for various conditions;

3. information about services customarily provided by therapeutic recreation practitioners in a variety of settings; and
4. standards of practice and materials describing methods of monitoring and quality control of services (West, 1983, p. 1—2).

It was recommended that NTRS employ an attorney experienced in health legislation, as other disciplines had, to assist in this endeavor.

TEFRA and the Medicare prospective payment system (PPS) had dramatic impact on the pursuit of reimbursement by the field. While attempts were being made to coordinate national and state efforts to pursue reimbursement, the sudden changes in financing made the strategies customarily used in such efforts obsolete.

During further discussions with the HCFA Office of Policy Coverage in 1984, the Medicare policy on coverage of therapeutic recreation services described above was reiterated. In addition, the importance of the fiscal intermediary in making decisions about whether therapeutic recreation services would be covered as a routine or ancillary service in psychiatry was illustrated. "The intermediaries would base such determinations on local practice and the advice of their medical consultants" (Streimer, 1984, p. 1). With regard to services provided to other inpatient populations, outpatients, in clinics, and in the patient's home, Medicare had not yet established a basis for covering therapeutic recreation services on an ancillary basis. Information about the efficacy of therapeutic recreation services in these settings was needed for Medicare to make coverage decisions (Streimer, 1984).

Recognizing the change from the "more is better" philosophy of providing health care to the "cost containment" philosophy instituted through the PPS, the need to "define how therapeutic recreation service can be expected to improve the patient's condition with limited cost to insurers" (Brady, 1983, p. 3) became the two-pronged challenge facing therapeutic recreation.

The *Therapeutic Recreation Journal (TRJ)* issue devoted to fiscal accountability recommended by the Third-Party Reimbursement Committee became a reality in 1984 and could not have been more timely. The editors reminded practitioners "therapeutic recreation is not a free service" (West & Thorn, 1984, p. 10). and delineated the fiscal realities which were affecting health care and, concomitantly, therapeutic recreation. Noting that the field could no longer "be all things to all people," the editor suggested relevant issues which needed to be addressed if the field were to respond to the demands for fiscal accountability advanced by the changes in health care financing.

In *TRJ*, the status of therapeutic recreation with respect to reimbursement was reviewed, and strategies that practitioners could undertake in responding to the PPS were recommended. These strategies included conducting both cost-based and clinical research, development of effective quality assurance programs, and expanding therapeutic recreation services to alternative health care settings. Monitoring of the developments and results of the PPS in order to continue efforts to obtain third-party payment for therapeutic recreation services was advised (Reitter, 1984).

West (1984) presented productivity measurement as a necessary precursor to investigation of the efficiency and effectiveness of therapeutic recreation services. The process of development of a productivity management system as a tool to demonstrate fiscal accountability was detailed. It was observed that concepts and techniques formerly used exclusively by the business industry were being adopted by the health care industry (Thom, 1984). Improving service quality, expansion, and demonstrating the treatment value of therapeutic recreation services to third-party payers through development of an integrated marketing plan were encouraged.

Other issues discussed were risk management, educational preparation for fiscal management, and exploration of private foundations as alternative funding resources. This issue of the *TRJ* quickly became recognized as the most comprehensive resource concerning fiscal issues relevant to therapeutic recreation available at the time.

During 1984 Mary Peters, legislative representative of the National Association of Private Psychiatric Hospitals, compiled the following suggestions to assist the field in securing third-party payments:

1. Determine the costs of the departments on a cost per case or per DRG (diagnosis-related group) basis.
2. Train therapeutic recreation staff in techniques to reduce length of stay, including getting referrals earlier.
3. Gear patient evaluations to those areas causing the patient to stay in the hospital and focus treatment on those areas.
4. Be involved with effective treatment team and discharge planning.
5. Identify DRGs or diagnoses that therapeutic recreation has had a measurable impact with and concentrate on those patients.
6. Increase the management skills of therapeutic recreation directors to better prepare them to address the new demands for increased productivity.
7. Decrease paperwork and increase patient contact time.

8. Communicate the efforts to increase the department's reimbursement status with the hospital administration.
9. Research and demonstrate the influence of therapeutic recreation services on patient care. Outcome and cost-effectiveness studies that are tied to decreased length of stay, need for nursing home, need for home health care, and outpatient costs would be particularly helpful.

In the future, Peters anticipated, "there will be a need to substantiate treatment and show that whatever is being provided to the patient works and has a measurable outcome" (1984, p. 7).

A new national organization for therapeutic recreation professionals, the American Therapeutic Recreation Association (ATRA), was established in late 1984. The focus of professional activities again turned to philosophical and organizational concerns as practitioners debated which organization to join. This did not impede efforts to secure third-party payment, as one might expect. Rather, it provided a new impetus and energy to attempts to address this issue.

In 1985 NTRS and ATRA joined forces in a reimbursement coalition to request further clarification of Medicare coverage policies related to therapeutic recreation. The HCFA response noted there was a variation in coverage from state to state (in some states, services were deemed routine, in others ancillary) (Wren, 1985). Differences in the common or established practice of therapeutic recreation providers between and within states and the differences in the ability of intermediaries to make independent coverage determinations were recognized as primary factors causing these variations. The ATRA Roundtable on Health Care Delivery, Financing, and Standards in 1986 identified several areas the field needed to address relative to financing. Among those highlighted were the need to identify the established therapeutic recreation practice for patients with similar diagnoses, and the ability of the field to demonstrate that certain therapeutic recreation treatment services could save money while maintaining economic competitiveness with other disciplines (*ATRA Newsletter* , July 1986).

Areas the field could emphasize (or readily implement where not usually practiced) to portray therapeutic recreation services as a tool for cost containment included offering services 7 days per week, during the evening in addition to daytime hours, and in group situations wherever clinically appropriate. In addition, the relatively low cost of therapeutic recreation services compared to other allied health disciplines such as occupational therapy was considered advantageous (Ollson, 1986).

Smith (1986) found five components necessary in order for therapeutic recreation services to become reimbursable: administrative support, accurate documentation, physician's orders, fee schedules and codes, and itemized bills. Documentation of the outcomes of service provision was seen as critical in pursuing and justifying third-party payments for therapeutic recreation services. Using terminology accepted by third-party payers instead of that used within therapeutic recreation was noted to be important.

Two studies conducted in 1987 added to available information about the status of reimbursement within the field. The first explored the status of therapeutic recreation financing in hospitals in the United States (Van Hyning & Teaff). Of the 320 hospitals which responded to this survey, 86 were found to offer therapeutic recreation services. These were primarily specialty (such as rehabilitation) or general medical facilities. Hospitals which did not have therapeutic recreation cited budget constraints, the type of hospital, and absence of need or demand for therapeutic recreation services as significant reasons such services were not offered.

Financing of therapeutic recreation services was found to be through diverse sources, including direct third-party payments, per diem rate allocations, public allocations, private support, and the facility overhead, as well as indirectly, through other hospital departments such as physical therapy. Thirty-three hospitals with therapeutic recreation services received third-party payments, primarily from commercial carriers. Many of these hospitals reported that payment of claims had been denied at some time. Undeterred by this, those hospitals which persevered in their efforts to receive third-party payments were often later approved for payment. Billing was done under a variety of names, including "recreation therapy," "occupational therapy," "activity therapy" and "ancillary services." Investor-owned facilities were found to be aggressive in their pursuit of third-party payments for therapeutic recreation services.

The second study consisted of a sample survey of therapeutic recreation professionals involved with the reimbursement issue. Conducted by the ATRA Third-Party Reimbursement Committee, the study found that 41 percent of the 50 respondents received third-party payments for the services they provided. Of these, the majority (52 percent) billed insurance companies for "therapeutic recreation" services, while 31 percent billed for "occupational therapy" or other names. Almost all respondents reported requiring a physician's order before services would be provided (Hutchinson-Troyer, 1987).

In 1987 the status of reimbursement for therapeutic recreation services by Blue Cross was found to mimic coverage by Medicare. "Some Blue Cross and Blue Shield Plans provide coverage for these services under psychiatric and substance abuse benefits, but there is, however, no standard definition of therapeutic recreation used by all the Plans. Each Plan responds to local practices and state law(s)"(Rial, p. 1).

A definition of therapeutic recreation was adopted by ATRA in November 1987:

> Therapeutic recreation is the provision of Treatment Services and the provision of Recreation Services to persons with illness or disabling conditions. The primary purpose of Treatment Services, which is often referred to as Recreation Therapy, is to restore, remediate or rehabilitate in order to improve functioning and independence as well as reduce or eliminate the effects of illness or disability. The primary purpose of Recreation Services is to provide recreation resources and opportunities in order to improve health and well-being. Therapeutic Recreation is provided by professionals who are trained and certified, registered, or licensed to provide Therapeutic Recreation. (*ATRA Newsletter*, May, 1987)

Therapeutic recreation literature has tended to minimize the importance of financial concerns, including third-party payments. For example, one textbook included the topic in a chapter entitled "Epilogue" and devoted little more than two pages to it. A later textbook covered the topic in less than one page, although the authors did advise, "Professionals in the field can expect this to remain a critical issue through the 1980s and 1990s" (Howe-Murphy & Charboneau 1987, p. 238). Practitioners interested in obtaining third-party payment find gathering information about health care financing and methods of pursuing payment a time-consuming venture. Contacting other practitioners, attending conferences, investigating the efforts of other disciplines, and utilizing often outdated publications are the primary means of developing a base of knowledge from which to begin. Perhaps it was the lack of readily available, accurate information in the field which prompted one practitioner to inquire in 1987, "Is there anyone currently receiving third-party reimbursement for therapeutic recreation services?" (*SRAC Newsletter*, p. 5).

It is important to note that therapeutic recreation is not the only discipline to face the issues which are intertwined with financial concerns. Educational preparation, credentialing, research, establishing standards of practice, defining the scope of services, and communication with funding sources have been concerns of all allied health disciplines at some time. Each has addressed these in different yet similar ways. Some have progressed more than others; however, none has been entirely successful. This is ensured by the fact that health care financing is not static. All, however, relentlessly continue their attempts to maintain and increase their share of the health care dollar.

Summary

"It can also be stated with some degree of certainty, that unless therapeutic recreation professionals make their presence known, there is very little that will be accomplished in providing this service in the distant future." — James J. Ticehurst (Riley, 1987, p. 41).

Interest in pursuing direct third-party payment for therapeutic recreation services has steadily grown. Initial interest was generated as therapeutic recreation managers sought to increase staffing and supply resources in order to provide more (and higher quality) services to patients. The retrospective cost-based reimbursement system used at the time fostered a "more is better" philosophy, leading to the growth and development of the health care industry. Hospital administrators responded to early modifications made in this system by advising therapeutic recreation professionals that the additional resources requested could be obtained—if the department generated revenue. Therapeutic recreation departments observed that health care disciplines already receiving third-party reimbursement as an ancillary service were becoming larger and better equipped as they increased revenue production.

Recent changes in health care financing resulting from the implementation of the Medicare prospective payment system have led to a focus on cost containment which pervades health care. Interest in third-party payment within therapeutic recreation has been renewed. Payment for services on a pre-established basis dependent upon patient diagnosis offers hospitals incentives to offer only those services which are deemed "reasonable and necessary" for the treatment of the patient. Alternative health care delivery systems and settings have resulted, and the growth of the for-profit health care industry has been stimulated. Competition for shrinking health care dollars has intensified as acupuncturists, hypnotists, and nutritionists rival "traditional" allied health disciplines for financial resources.

For therapeutic recreation to survive in today's health care economy requires that each practitioner take an active role in addressing critical issues. All must continue efforts to address the needs for research; standardized curricula and credentialing systems; as well as universal acceptance of a definition of, and further development of standards of practice for, therapeutic recreation services. Future communications with funding sources must be well prepared and coordinated. Careful monitoring of the continually changing health care environment and timely dissemination of updated information within the field is needed. National and state therapeutic recreation organizations must take the lead in these efforts if the field is to have the very best opportunities to determine its own destiny.

Study Questions

1. Describe the changes in health care financing since 1975. How have these impacted therapeutic recreation? What is the impact of the 1983 amendments to the Social Security Act?

2. The emergence of HMOs and PPOs has altered health care delivery significantly. Discuss the role of therapeutic recreation in these organizations.

3. Discuss the difficulties in billing for therapeutic recreation services on an ancillary basis through occupational therapy.

4. Does current Medicare legislation support therapeutic recreation as a direct reimbursable service? What needs to be done to change the law? Where does HCFA stand in all of this? How can they be influenced to change current practices?

5. Why is it essential to "define our practice"? How can we be more definitive in identifying the outcomes of our clinical intervention? What role does research assume in the definition of practice?

References

American Therapeutic Recreation Association. (May, 1981). *Newsletter,4*(3), p.1.

Briggs, J.F. & Shafter, A.J. (1971). Two Administrators Look at Mental Health, Professionalism, and Activity Therapy. *Expanding Horizons in Therapeutic Recreation , 1*, 33-42.

Carter, M.J., VanAndel, G.E., & Robb, G.M. (1985). *Therapeutic Recreation: A Practical Approach.* St Louis, MO: Times Mirror/ Mosby.

Commerce Clearing House. (1965). *Medicare and Social Security Explained.* Chicago, IL.

Ehrenreich,B., & Ehrenreich, J. (1970). *The American Health Empire: Power, Profits, and Politics.* New York: Vintage Books.

Fein, R. (1986). *Medical Care, Medical Costs.* Cambridge, MA: Harvard University Press.

Franklin, D.A., & Rodgers, M.J. (1983). Legislative Control of Federal Health Care Costs. *The Urban Lawyer, U15* , 947—971.

Frye, V., & Peters, M. (1972). *Therapeutic Recreation: Its Theory, Philosophy, and Practice.* Harrisburg, PA: Stackpole Books.

Health Care Finance Administration, HSQB. (1977). *Legislative History of PSRO: Provisions of the Social Security Act Amendment.* (USDHEW Publication No. NRP-0025-916). Springfield, VA.

Health Care Finance Administration. (1985). Medicare and Medicaid Programs; Utilization and Quality Control Peer Review Organization (PRO): Assumption of Medicare Review Functions and Coordination with Medicaid. *Federal Register, 50,* 15312-15374.

Howe-Murphy, R., & Charboneau, B.G. (1987). *Therapeutic Recreation Intervention — An Ecological Perspective.* Englewood Cliffs, NJ: Prentice-Hall.

Hutchinson-Troyer, L. (1987). Third Party Reimbursement Update. *ATRA Newsletter, 3*(6).

Ingber, F.K. (1978). In R. West (Ed.), *Issues and Guidelines for Establishing Third-Party Reimbursement for Therapeutic Recreation.* Alexandria, VA: National Recreation and Park Association.

Jonas, S. (1981). *Health Care Delivery in the United States.* New York: Springer Publishing Company.

Kraus, R. (1978). *Therapeutic Recreation Service: Principles and Practices* (2nd Ed.). Philadelphia: W.B. Saunders.

Mattson, M.R. (1984). Quality Assurance: A Literature Review of a Changing Field. *Hospital and Community Psychiatry ,35* , 605-616.

Meyer, L. (1985). *Specialization Among Park and Recreation Professionals: The Need for Clarification and Differentiation.* Paper presented at the meeting of the Maryland Recreation and Park Society, Ocean City, MD.

National Recreation and Park Association. (1982). *National Therapeutic Recreation Society Philosophical Position Statement.*

National Therapeutic Recreation Society. (1987). *SRAC Report.* Alexandria, VA: National Recreation and Park Association.

Ollson, R. (1986). The Prospective Payment System: Implications for Therapeutic Recreation. *Therapeutic Recreation Journal*, *20*(1),7—17.

Patterson, R. (1976). The Development of a Self-Sufficient Therapeutic Recreation Service. *Expanding Horizons in Therapeutic Recreation,* 3,:49—52.

Patterson, R., Brady, C., & Erlandson, M.E. (1983). *Techniques for Pursuing Third-Party Reimbursement for Therapeutic Recreation Services.* Paper presented at the Congress of the National Recreation and Park Association, Kansas City, MO.

Peters, M. (1984). *Reimbursement Issues Affecting Therapeutic Recreation.* Paper presented at the Congress of the National Recreation and Park Association, Orlando, FL.

Porter, S. (1987, August 16). New Forms of Health Care Emerging. *Raleigh News and Observer,* pp.6-1.

Reitter, M.S. (1984). Third-Party Reimbursement: Is TR Too Late? *Therapeutic Recreation Journal* ,*18*(4)13—19.

———. (1986a). *PROs and Private Review: New Challenges for Therapeutic Recreation.* Unpublished manuscript, University of North Carolina, Chapel Hill.

———. (1986b). *The History of Current Attempts to Reduce Health Care Costs.* Unpublished manuscript, University of North Carolina, Chapel Hill.

Reynolds, R.P., & O'Morrow, G.S. (1985). *Problems, Issues and Concepts in Therapeutic Recreation.* Englewood Cliffs, NJ: Prentice-Hall.

Rial, W.Y. (1987). Letter to Ray West, director of recreation therapy, North Carolina Memorial Hospital.

Smith, L. (1986). *Speaking the Language of Reimbursement.* Paper presented at the Congress of the National Recreation and Park Association, Anaheim, CA.

Staff. (1986). Mid-Year Roundtables. *ATRA Newsletter* , *2*(4).

Streimer, R.A. (1984). Letter to Randall Rutta, policy associate, National Easter Seal Society.

Thom, B. (1984). Marketing Therapeutic Recreation Service. *Therapeutic Recreation Journal* , *18*(4),42—47.

Ticehurst, J.J. (1987). Medical Peer Review, the Government, and the Practitioner: Partners in Quality of Care. In B. Riley (Ed). *Evaluation of Therapeutic Recreation Through Quality Assurance.* (pp.37—42). State College, PA: Venture Publishing.

Van Hyning, T.E., & Teaff, J. (1987). *Financing of Therapeutic Recreation Services in the United States.* Unpublished master's thesis, Southern Illinois University, Carbondale, IL.

West, R.E. (1982). [Third-Party Reimbursement Survey: Responses]. Unpublished raw data.

West, R.E. (1983). Memorandum to Third-Party Reimbursement Committee, National Recreation and Park Association, Alexandria, VA.

West, R.E. (1984). Productivity Analysis as a Method of Fiscal Accountability for Therapeutic Recreation. *Therapeutic Recreation Journal, 18*(4), 27—36.

West, R.E. (1985). Letter to Barry Tindall, Division of Public Affairs, National Recreation and Park Association.

West, R.E., and Thorn, B. (Eds.). (1984). Special Issue on Fiscal Accountability *Therapeutic Recreation Journal,18*(4).

Wren, R.E. (October, 1985). Personal Correspondence to Barry Tindall, Director, Division of Public Affairs, National Recreation & Park Association.

ALTERNATE SOURCES OF FUNDING:
Potentials and Pitfalls

Joseph L. Wilson

Introduction

Although some therapeutic recreation professionals feel their time is not well-spent in having to deal with obtaining cost reimbursement, today's health care market is making it more and more necessary for therapeutic recreation programs to recoup some if not all of their costs by obtaining outside funding. With the beginning of Medicare's prospective payment system using DRGs (diagnostic-related groups) in 1983, and with the shift away from a cost-based reimbursement system, the entire health care system has had to make major adjustments. Because there is a need to make hospital care more cost-effective, many hospitals have begun to eliminate or reduce services that are ancillary or infrequently used and that are not revenue producing, such as therapeutic recreation services.

In a recent article, Ray E. West (1984) makes the following observation: "Hospitals are forced to be more businesslike in terms of management practices (cost accounting, marketing, etc.), planning (long term, short term, and strategic), and labor productivity analysis." A related article in *Business Week* ("Upheaval," 1983) states, "Hospitals are diversifying and developing alternative delivery systems for outpatient and clinical services, home health, and long term care, and are also merging into corporate chains or regional and national affiliations in order to spread the cost to a larger financial base or benefit from cooperative ventures (i.e., purchasing, marketing, etc.)."

How will the therapeutic recreation profession respond to this challenge? What will happen to our profession if we do nothing to obtain reimbursement? Will our profession's growth be stunted? Will therapeutic recreation die? Do we have the people with the competencies and skills to work toward the development of necessary information to help recoup our costs for service? Is it time to open our minds to new ideas and the sharing of information?

Some therapeutic recreation departments are currently receiving third-party insurance payments. Those that are not may not be doing enough to prove to their insurance carriers that they have viable programs. We all need to work together and share what we are learning through our individual efforts. Successful formats should be shared with others.

It is imperative to gather information from professionals in the field. One hundred therapeutic recreation professionals were contacted and asked to share their concerns and suggestions for solving the funding problems facing therapeutic recreation. A strong effort was made to contact people from all types of facilities who are professional members of the National Therapeutic Recreation Society. Fifty percent of the people contacted responded.

Nearly half of those responding to the inquiry indicated that their therapeutic recreation programs are funded from the daily room or bed rate for their facility. Many of these professionals felt very uneasy and concerned about relying on this funding source. Are they uneasy because of the recent changes in health care payments? Are they concerned because they have no proven way to help contribute financially to the overall budget of their facilities?

Alternate Sources of Funding

Can your department be fiscally accountable? Can your department currently justify its worth, value, and therapeutic effect to your clients? As your health care agency becomes more cost conscious, will you be able to expand to new activities and staff without increasing your funding base? If your needs are growing, how are you expanding your budget? Or is the opposite happening—are you actually losing programs, staff, supplies, and support because of your limited funds? Can you continue to do more with less?

Because the trend is toward more money, it would seem to be highly prudent for recreation therapists to learn how to diversify their funding base. But if we branch out and take on this responsibility, what will we be giving up in patient contact and care? What trade-offs are we willing to make?

Diversification means to be supported by funds from many different sources rather than from just one source. Diversification has some general assets (advantages) and liabilities (disadvantages). According to Compton (1987), the assets are these:

- Expanded funding base and possibly discretionary funds are available.
- New ventures and programs are now feasible.
- Extended services are possible.
- Additional personnel can be hired.
- New or used equipment, areas, and buildings may be acquired.
- Stipends, traineeships, camperships, and so on are available.
- New operating capital is available.

The liabilities are these:

- Funds may be earmarked for certain things only.
- Funds may be short-lived, temporary, one-time.
- Strings may be attached, due to political realities.
- Donors may require matching funds.
- Nothing is ever free!
- Quality personnel are difficult to hire and retain.
- A funded program may need support later or die; there are trade-offs in many cases.
- Additional and oftentimes unforeseen operating costs may come with your "gift."
- Gifts or funds may not be realized for a long time, as in the case of a will, insurance premiums, and so on.

In order for a therapeutic recreation department to effectively pursue generating additional resources, it is important for the department to first evaluate itself and to look at the relevant aspects of its program. Some questions to ask yourself:

1. What is the major concern or philosophy of your organization?
2. What is the focus of your department?
3. What program areas are you now offering?
4. What population is being served?
5. What benefits does your program offer to the people being served?
6. What are the carry over benefits your program provides to your clients?
7. How many staff members are needed to carry out your program?
8. From where are you generating funds to provide the program?
9. What type of financial support do you need for a successful program?
10. What resources are available?

Funds can be generated in many ways, some of which are very elementary but time consuming. Most recreation therapists feel that there is a big advantage to be gained by exploring funding ideas with other professionals. In many communities, therapeutic recreation professionals meet on a quarterly basis to share ideas, ask questions, and provide input to each other on many aspects of the field, including the development of materials to generate outside funding. Such meetings act as support networks and important educational sources for many therapeutic recreation professionals.

Short-term fund raisers

Funding sources may range from short-term events to long-term commitments. Short-term, possibly one-time, events can include such things as selling a product (candy, greeting cards, light bulbs, posters, T-shirts, etc.), garage sales, arts and crafts sales, special suppers, car washes, or sponsoring special workshops. These events generally take some time to organize and need to be publicized to be successful. Selling a product can provide a good income if the product is popular with the community. However, selling a product can require a lot of record keeping, makes it necessary for people to push a product, and may sometimes require a large time investment. Other special sales may be beneficial if not conducted too frequently. Workshops and special seminars are good fund-raisers, provide the service of educating those attending, and can be set up to award CEUs (continuing education units) to those desiring them.

If you choose to try some of these suggestions for raising funds, you will have to consider the pros and cons: Is this a prudent use of your time? Do you have the time and talent to be a salesperson? Is marketing the product or service going to interfere with your client contact time? Will others (staff, volunteers, administration) support the plan?

Special event fund-raisers

A fund-raiser that focuses on a special time of the year, event or person can be a popular and successful, continuing source of funds. Ice cream socials, walk-a-thons, holiday dances or suppers, bingo, tele-thons, and special sporting events are examples of special events. These events can be given catchy titles and are generally held at the same time every year. A fee is charged to participants in all but the telethon. The intended outcome is to make a reasonable profit after expenses are taken out. By getting services or products donated or discounted, the cost of sponsoring these events can be kept to a minimum. Annual sporting events identified with your organization can become very popular and at the same time provide a good service to the public.

The event can also be humorous. Easter Seals Society of Iowa, Inc., has a "Goat Day" once a year. Live goats are donated for the day. People call in the name of a person whom they want to be the "goat for the day" and pay a fee to have a goat delivered to that person. Volunteers deliver the goat, and if the person receiving the goat does not match the fee paid by the first person, the goat stays with him or her all day. Hundreds of dollars are raised this way in different sections of the state each year.

The drawback to special events is that they take a long time to plan and need excellent organization and generally lots of volunteers to be successful. As with any type of fund-raiser, good publicity is vital.

Sponsorships

Generally, service clubs, civic clubs, business associations, and unions have special funds earmarked to support specific purposes or recipients, such as programs or events for disabled or disadvantaged persons or for equipment purchases. A specific request from a therapeutic recreation program to these groups could result in cash or equipment donations. Many of these organizations look for specific causes they can support each year. In some cases, funds from these organizations will provide funds year after year, but other times their donations are one-time support. They also expect the recipient to pay the costs of using the equipment and maintaining it.

Ongoing ventures

In some hospitals, special institutions, or community recreation programs that have therapeutic recreation programs, it is possible to have a profit-making area that contributes its earnings to the therapeutic recreation budget. Examples of these ventures are gift shops, snack shops, game machines, and vending machines. These ventures need physical space in a facility and need a good group of volunteers or paid employees to operate them. Such a venture may be a good training experience for a disabled person who is being placed back into the community or a good way to teach a disabled person valuable job skills.

Other Funding Sources

Although all of the preceding ideas can be used to raise funds, these are not the methods we would want to use on a daily basis, nor would we want to rely on them for a significant portion of a budget.

Overuse of these ideas would seem to do little to further the esteem our profession is held in . How many other therapeutic entities do you know that spend their time funding their programs this way? We need to turn our attention to improving our profession and demonstrating its worth. And we need to develop more highly productive means of financial support.

Grant writing

Two sources of funding that generally require the writing of grant proposals are governmental entities and foundations. There are no special characteristics needed by a grant writer other than the ability to follow the printed guidelines and good English composition and spelling skills. In general, the answers to the following three questions (Hall, 1977) need to be understood by the grant writer before attempting to write a grant proposal: (a) What are the goals and needs of your organization? (b) How would you assess the competence of your organization? (c) Does your organization have the essential support systems? If there is a solid understanding of these three areas, it is much easier to pursue any type of external funding.

Grants are usually specific in scope and may provide funds for a limited number of years. Financial assistance through grants is initiated in one of two ways: solicited or unsolicited (Hall, 1977). A solicited grant comes from a funding source that announces its desire to grant monies for a specific type of program and may give very specific guidelines and criteria. Usually this announcement comes in the form of a request for proposals (RFP), a combination program announcement and application form. An unsolicited grant comes when a needy individual or organization makes the initial contact to a possible funding source.

The major components of a typical proposal are the title page, abstract, problem statement, objectives, procedures, evaluation, dissemination, and discussion of facilities and equipment, personnel, and budget (Hall, 1977). A new grant writer may well feel discouraged at first when assessing the amount of work and time required in the development of a good grant proposal. But even if the first attempts at receiving external funds fail, the writer should not give up. There are billions of dollars available each year through many sources. Experience comes only through writing and submitting proposals. The time and effort invested in preparing a proposal in which one is interested is really never lost.

Also, for a new writer, improvement can come more quickly by asking a more experienced person to serve as the project director. It might also be helpful to collaborate with another group. As one gains experience, one becomes more realistic in choosing likely sources of support. All of this can lead to a greater likelihood that your proposals will be funded (Hall, 1977). Although grant proposals generally require a lot of time and work to put together, if they are funded they can be highly beneficial to any program.

Foundations

Private foundations should be considered as potential sources for funding projects initiated by recreation therapists. Foundations are governed by boards of trustees and generally have their own particular interests, populations, geographical areas, and projects that they will fund. Foundations are required by law to distribute at least 5 percent of their total assets each year. This amounts to billions of dollars (Fine, 1984).

There are basically three types of foundations: independently endowed foundations, community foundations, and corporate foundations (White, 1979). The name of an independently endowed foundation usually contains the name of the person giving the money. Approximately 70 percent of these foundations hire paid staff. Many of the major independently endowed foundations prefer funding large projects with national exposure, while smaller foundations generally donate at the local level (Fine, 1984).

Community foundations can be excellent sources of funds. These foundations receive their monies from private individuals who benefit by receiving tax breaks. The more than 250 community foundations in the United States generally give out monies only in their own geographic locations (Fine, 1984).

Corporate foundations receive funds directly from their parent corporations, which may give away up to 10 percent of their gross assets before taxes. These foundations generally set a certain percentage to give to each type of cause (Fine, 1984).

Foundations will expect to receive a lot of information about who you are and how you plan on spending their funds if you receive them. Almost all foundations will require this information to be presented in the form of a grant proposal. Most libraries have information about foundations and their addresses.

Governmental agencies

According to Hall (1977), state agencies are good sources of grant money because (a) they serve as channels for federal monies to be given locally; (b) when they are awarded grants, they look for agencies or organizations to help them fulfill requirements of the grants, (c) they serve as the administrators of state grant-in-aid programs and look for local programs to fund; and (d) they often purchase services or products to help them carry out their responsibilities.

The competition for these state dollars is less than that for national money, making it advantageous to consider state agencies, especially for the inexperienced grant writer. Hall (1977) observes that states often do not go out of their way to let potential applicants know of upcoming grant opportunities, so it is up to the grant writer to become acquainted with key people within the state agencies. Also, contact them frequently because being put on one mailing list may not automatically put you on the list for subsequent mailings.

There are also hundreds of federal agencies and offices offering grant and contract money (Hall, 1977). It is important to identify the agencies and key personnel and to communicate with them concerning your interests and abilities. You can find these agencies by checking federal directories and newsletters which relate federal information, by contacting your state's United States senators or representatives, and by contacting the Federal Assistance Programs Retrieval System (FAPRS), which disseminates information listed in the *Catalog of Federal Domestic Assistance*. When you make contact with federal agencies, ask to be put on their future mailing lists for grant- and contract-related mailings.

Although there seems to be millions of dollars available from federal agencies, there is sometimes a lack of reliability in the actual disbursement of the promised funds. With budget changes occurring each year, these funds could disappear overnight. States are becoming more reluctant to raise their tax bases and thus have less federal revenue sharing dollars to channel. A recipient should be cautious about relying too heavily on these "soft money" sources for a significant percentage of the budget.

Fees and charges

For many therapeutic recreation programs, especially those offered through community park and recreation departments, it is now a reality to charge a fee for the services provided. With a public service entity, the public is willing to pay for services if (a) the service is desired by the public; (b) the service is of high quality; (c) there is good management; and (d) the service is one which the public feels is worth the money being charged (Sharkey, 1987). For many programs, user fees are a main source of funding. Charging for services encourages the department to provide activities really wanted by the community and leads to a higher level of normalization for disabled persons. Also, in several hospital and community programs, the people being served are being charged the cost of the supplies used in the activities rather than actually paying the cost of staff salaries.

Several hospital-based programs report that they are receiving income by offering special services and programs. Therapeutic recreation staff who have training in such areas as stress management, relaxation techniques, and biofeedback techniques, are potential providers of special programs that bring in income.

Outpatient programs from some hospitals charge patients directly for therapeutic recreation services. In most cases, people are willing to pay for programs that lead to their functional improvement. In fact, some insurance companies are also willing to pay for functional improvement, especially if it is accomplished through range-of-motion activities.

Charging fees for therapeutic recreation services is still not readily accepted, and for some professionals is controversial at best. Some legitimate concerns include the effect on services for lower income people; if they cannot pay, will they be denied services? Yet it would seem that more disabled people would be willing to pay for a service that has a high restorative value to them and that is provided by qualified individuals through well-designed programs with good resources.

Third-party payments

What is the ultimate survival skill that many therapeutic recreation professionals feel is needed? It is the ability to better understand how to collect for therapeutic recreation services from insurance companies (third-party payers). Olsson (1985) states:

> The first step in obtaining third-party reimbursements is gaining some insight as to what a third-party reimbursement is. Basically there are three parties other than accreditation bodies concerned with the stay of a client at a hospital: a) the hospital (provider), b) the client (consumer), and c) the insurance company ... The hospital (party 1) has a direct reciprocal relationship (contract) with the client (party 2). The hospital agrees to provide treatment and services to the client; in return, the client agrees to pay for these treatments and services. Prior to this agreement the client, by paying an insurance premium (or meeting governmental requirements) contracted with an insurance company to pay all or part of hospital treatments and services if the

consumer (client) ever needs hospitalization or treatments. Now the insurance company becomes the third party and, although it has no direct contract with the hospital, it does make the hospital accountable for providing *needed* and *quality* treatment before it will pay the claims (bills) sent by the hospital. (p. 29)

Recreational therapists who are currently receiving third-party payments feel that it is important for those hoping to receive these payments to begin by studying the historical patterns of insurance companies and by observing how they pay for services rendered. The therapeutic recreation profession lacks a consensus on what is the best fee for services and how to code these for proper payment. A proper set of fees and codes needs to be established. That this is important is emphasized by burlingame (1987):

Our lack of knowledge about CPTs (*Physicians' Current Procedural Terminology*, Fourth Edition) could mean ill health to our profession. In 1966 the American Medical Association printed the first edition of the CPT manual. It listed the assessments, treatment procedures, and services that the AMA felt to be medically indicated. Each listing was given a five-digit code and categorized first by medical speciality (e.g., surgery), then by body part (e.g., integumentary system), then by diagnosis (e.g., pressure ulcers), and then by specific service rendered (e.g., #15936 = excision, sacral pressure ulcer, with over flap closure).

This coding made it easier for the medical profession to standardize treatment modalities and greatly simplified data as a means to streamline their bookkeeping. Within a short period of time their computer programs would not process a bill UNLESS it was written in CPT codes. And therein lies our problem. In a time that more and more of us are switching to third-party reimbursement, we as a profession have never submitted any of our treatment modalities to the AMA for review and inclusion in the CPT manual. Many insurance companies are rightfully leery about paying for services that are not publicly recognized by the AMA.

Because billings are usually processed by the finance office of our institutions, CTRSs receiving third-party reimbursement have been isolated from the need to have CPT codes specifically developed for therapeutic recreation. The billing departments usually translate our services to either P.T. or O.T. codes. (The ethical and legal implications of this gives me great discomfort!) Typically, therapeutic recreation services are coded under Physical Medicine #97139 (physical medicine treatment to one procedure), #97240 (pool therapy or Hubbard tank with therapeutic exercises; initial 30 minutes, each visit), and #97540 (activities of daily living [ADL] and diversional activities; initial 30 minutes, each visit). The last one makes me uncomfortable. By law (in states where O.T.s are licensed) any CTRS who uses that code can ONLY be billed for diversional activities because CTRSs are not licensed to provide ADL treatments. (p. 5)

There are some basic guidelines to follow which enhance the likelihood of receiving third-party reimbursement:

1. There must be overall administrative support for submitting requests for payments to third-party payees (Smith, 1986).
2. There must be a physician order for recreation therapy, and it should be written before there has been any contact between the patient and the recreational therapist. It is important to show that the physician order was written within 24 to 48 hours after admission.
3. A written, comprehensive leisure assessment must be done on the patient, usually within 48 hours, and must include goals and objectives.
4. Daily and/or weekly notes must be kept on the patient and recorded on the charts. These must show that an active treatment plan is being followed.
5. A recreation therapist must have input into the development of the master plan of each patient; updates are added to this plan when needed.
6. A complete and thorough discharge summary must be submitted.

It is the opinion of many therapeutic recreation specialists that if the above steps were followed, insurance companies would be more likely to consider accepting therapeutic recreation as a reasonable and necessary service. Some professionals also think that it makes a big difference if the services provided are called "recreation therapy" rather than "therapeutic recreation" to more strongly emphasize the therapy aspect of the services.

Summary

So, where does this discussion on the issue of cost reimbursement bring us? Is it all that undesirable to be receiving payment for our services from the standard room rate? After all, isn't that what the standard room rate should cover? As long as we develop proper guidelines for providing therapeutic recreation services, does it really matter from where the fees are collected as long as they are proper, ethical, and, above all, supportive to the profession? Or should we make the effort to have therapeutic recreation services recognized as a legitimate treatment modality in its own right?

The suggestions presented throughout this chapter attempt to give the reader some insight into the possibilities for action. The suggestions are intended as starting places; adjustments will need to be made to fit the many different types of therapeutic recreation settings. All of the suggestions will require paperwork and time commitments, all have advantages and disadvantages, and each requires a measure of support and skills on the part of staff members. Some are more basic than others yet could possibly provide the same level of financial support. Each therapeutic recreation program will have to determine, by study and possibly even trial and error, which works best for it.

Like it or not, we need to be aware that we are caught up in the "medical arms race" ("Study," 1988). Competition in the medical field has driven costs up over the past few years, despite DRGs. If we are not astute in seeing into and planning for the future, therapeutic recreation could be one of the casualties of this arms race, and one of the most beneficial treatments to disabled people will be lost.

Study Questions

1. In an era of burgeoning health care costs, is it likely that therapeutic recreation will become a fully reimbursed service? What factors will work against this action? Is it desirable?

2. Discuss the rationale for diversifying the funding base of a therapeutic recreation service. List five principal sources of income beyond a basic budget allocation from the agency.

3. What state and federal funds are available to augment therapeutic recreation services? Visit a local city, county, or special district where therapeutic recreation services are offered and inquire as to their sources of funding. Prepare a brief report delineating the sources of funding. Contrast this agency with others from the area.

4. Recently there has been an increase in the use of "fees and charges" as a mechanism to raise operating capital. Discuss the pros and cons of such a move.

References

burlingame, j. (1987). CPT's Impact on Therapeutic Recreation. *ATRA Newsletter*, 111(2), 5.

Compton, David. (1987). *Alternate Sources of Funding: Assets and Liabilities.* Unpublished manuscript.

Fine, Aubrey H. (1984). Private Foundations: A Need for Further Explorations. *Therapeutic Recreation Journal 18*(4), 48-55.

Hall, Mary. (1977). *Developing Skills in Proposal Writing* (2nd ed.). Portland, OR: Continuing Education Publications.

Olsson, R. (1985). Third-Party Reimbursement: A Practical Application For Therapeutic Recreation. *California Parks and Recreation, 41*(4), 29-30, 41.

Sharkey, Linda. (1985, March). *Creative Funding Strategies for Community Therapeutic Recreation.* Paper presented at Annual Conference of the New Jersey Recreation and Park Association, Atlantic City, New Jersey.

Smith, L. (1986, October). *Speaking the Language of Reimbursement.* Paper presented at the Annual Conference of the National Recreation and Park Association, Anaheim, CA.

Study: "Medical Arms Race" Driving Up Hospital Costs. (1988, February 5). *Waterloo-Cedar Falls* (Iowa) *Courier,* p. 1

The Upheaval in Health Care. (1983, June 25). *Business Week,* pp.44-56

West, Ray E. (1984). Productivity Analysis as a Method of Fiscal Accountability for Therapeutic Recreation. *Therapeutic Recreation Journal, 18*(4), 29.

White, V. (1979). *Grants.* New York: Plenum Press.

Issues Related to Standards of Practice

photo courtesy of City of Las Vegas

The lack of practice standards is scary and frustrating. There appears to be an absence of a standard set of clinical procedures and valid or reliable instruments available for use in therapeutic recreation.

—Terrance P. Robertson

PLAYING THE STANDARDS GAME: CONSIDERATIONS FOR THE 1990s

S. Harold Smith
Chester Land

Introduction

The term standard(s) has many possible definitions. For the purpose of this discussion, we simply state that standards are rules, principles, or procedures for conduct (Websters, 1986). Standards are developed for at least two major reasons: first, to guarantee a minimum level of service provision; and second, to assure the safety of the consumer. In general, there are two types or levels of standards. The first are termed external standards because they are set by agencies/institutions outside of the direct service industry. The second are called internal standards because they are set by and within the direct service industry at its various levels of service provision. Relating this to therapeutic recreation, it should then be understood that the therapeutic recreation industry must address external standards that are set by agencies/institutions outside of therapeutic recreation and internal standards that are set by the recreation/therapeutic recreation service industry itself.

External standards that are most frequently addressed in therapeutic recreation are those set by such groups as: the Joint Commission on the Accreditation of Healthcare Organizations (JCAHO) (1988) , formerly the Joint Commission on the Accreditation of Hospitals (JCAH) (1985); the Commission on the Accreditation of Rehabilitation Facilities (CARF) (1986); the Health Care Finance Administration (HCFA) (1976); and to some degree "Third-Party" type providers (Donovan, 1987, pp. 26-31). Internal standards in therapeutic recreation come from a variety of levels within the recreation/therapeutic recreation service industry and include standards set by such groups as: the National Therapeutic Recreation Society (NTRS) (1979, 1980, 1982, 1984); the American Therapeutic Recreation Association (ATRA) (1987); the National Council for Therapeutic Recreation Certification

(NCTRC) (1987); and, the National Recreation and Park Association/ American Association for Leisure and Recreation Sponsored Council on Accreditation (COA) (1986). To better understand the potential influence of these and similar standards in the next decade, we must examine each of the types/levels of standards individually and then in relation to one another. A discussion of each of these areas follows.

External Standards

Standards set by outside, overseer type, agencies/institutions usually provide one of two major challenges to a specific service industry like therapeutic recreation. The first challenge is that the standards may be so stringent or out of line with current practice that they stand in the way of successful service provision. The second challenge is that, for whatever reason, no standards are set, thereby allowing no guarantee of service provision in that particular area. The major issue faced by therapeutic recreation related to external standards falls within the second area of concern, lack of adequate service standards. The issue being, if therapeutic recreation is not mentioned in the standards of groups like JCAHO, CARF, and HCFA then there is no philosophical, administrative or programmatic justification for having therapeutic recreation in the facilities/programs that rely on these groups to accredit, and in the case of HCFA, fund their operations. A second, but directly related, issue is that third-party providers do not and will not provide funding for services not approved and governed by these major health care accrediting agencies. In fact, it is often the case that HCFA will not provide funding for services in certain facilities without that facility first having CARF accreditation.

Today some JCAHO standards do address areas related to recreation and therapeutic recreation and CARF and HCFA have proposals under study (Donovan, 1987). A specific example in point are the current CARF standards where therapeutic recreation (recreation therapy) is not listed as a required program/service in the Standards for Individual Programs or Services as indicated by Figure 1.

Figure 1

III.A. Comprehensive Inpatient Rehabilitation
Admission criteria for program
Affiliation and consultation

Evidence of personnel credentials (degrees, licenses, etc.)
Case Records
Evidence of education activities with patients, staff, and
   community
Written plan for quality of care and utilization reviews
Written policy and program for prevention and control of
   infection
Roster of staff assigned to the rehabilitation program
Evidence of physiaian and staff contacts with patients

III.B. Spinal Cord Injury Programs

Formal agreements for acute hospital services. If the
   program is not part of an acute hospital
Individual case records
Policies and procedures for admission
Affiliation or consultation agreements

III.C. Chronic Pain Management Programs

Individual case records
Affiliation and consultation agreements
Written educational program for patients, families, staff,
   professionals and lay community
Evidence of personnel credentials (degrees, licenses)

III.D. Brain Injury Programs

Formal program for education, support and advocacy for
   patients and families
Acute Programs
   Affiliation or consultation agreements
   Evidence of personnel credentials (degrees, licenses,
      etc.)
   Formal agreement with an acute hospital. If the pro-
      gram is not part of an acute hospital
   Individual case records
Post Acute Programs
   Statement of expected functional outcomes for the
      program(s)
   Evidence of personnel credentials (degrees, licenses,
      etc.) listing professional staff
   Affiliation or consultation agreements

III.E. Outpatient Medical Rehabilitation

Policies and procedures for referring and prescribing physicians

Individual case records

Affiliation or consultation agreements

Patient care policies

Written utilization review plan

Minutes of utilization review committee meetings

Written infection control policy and program

III.F. Infant and Early Childhood Developmental Programs

Written description of program's design, structure and content

Individual case records

Affiliation or consultation agreements

Evidence of prevention and conservation activities

Evidence of case finding, screening, and verification program

III.G. Vocational Evaluation

List of assessment capabilities and resources

Evidence of qualifications of person(s) administering tests in the vocational area

Examiner's manuals

Individual case records

Unit worksheets

III.H. Work Adjustment

List of adjustment capabilities and resources

Individual case records

Descriptions of specialized adjustment programs or classes

III.I. Occupational Skill Training

Individual case records

Course descriptions

Course outlines and/or curricula

Minutes of meetings to review curriculum content

Written policies covering work done for others

III.J. Job Placement

Individual case records

Records of involvement with community employers
Placement records
Records of job openings
(CARF, 1986, pp. 143-144)

On the other hand, however, if therapeutic recreation is a part of the total program or any one of the listed services provided by the agency being reviewed, the therapeutic recreation program/service must meet each of the requirements for the specific program/service as listed in Figure 1. In addition therapeutic recreation must also conform to each of the standards listed in *Section II Standards For All Programs* as listed in Figure 2.

Figure 2   T.R. must conform

II. Standards for all Programs

II.A. Intake and Orientation
Written admission criteria for each program
Individual case records
Intake policies and procedures
Records of those declared ineligible for services
Orientation procedures

II.B. Assessment and Individual Program Planning
Evaluation procedures
Individual case records

II.C. Individual Program Management, Treatment, and Training
Policies and procedures for case coordination or case management
Individual case records
Human rights policies
Policies governing the use of restrictive procedures
Policies governing medications
Affiliation and consultation agreements

II.D. Referral, Discharge, and Follow up

Individual case records
Exit criteria for each program
Discharge procedures
Follow up procedures

II.E. Case Records
Individual case records
Case Record Review Committee minutes
Case record policies

II.F. Assessment of Program Quality for Individuals Served
Written system for review of individual's programs
Minutes or reports of review findings
Individual case records
(CARF, 1986, pp. 142-143)

The implications of these two major issues are quite obvious. Administratively it is difficult to justify a service that is not "recognized" and that adds additional costs to an already overburdened health care system. This places a great burden on many therapeutic recreation programs in JCAHO, CARF, and HCFA related facilities because of their continual need to justify their services both financially and philosophically. It is, therefore, quite understandable why therapeutic recreation specialists who work in these programs are extremely concerned about impacting standards in these areas.

Fifteen years ago there were virtually no standards related to the provision of therapeutic recreation service provided by JCAHO, CARF, and HCFA (Van Andel, 1981). Today, JCAHO has published five sets of standards: the *Accreditation Manual for Hospitals* (1988); the *Consolidated Standards Manual for Child, Adolescent and Adult Psychology, Alcoholism and Drug Abuse Facilities and Facilities Serving the Mentally Retarded/Developmentally Disabled* (1985); the *Long Term Care Standards Manual* (1986); the *Hospice Standards Manual* (19883); and the *Ambulatory Health Care Standards Manual* (1986). Three of these standards manuals address therapeutic recreation standards: the *Long Term Care Standards;* the *Consolidated Standards Manual;* and the *Accreditation Manual for Hospitals* (Donovan, 1987). An example of the JCAHO standards for therapeutic recreation are found in Figure 3.

Figure 3
RH 2.5 Recreation Therapy

RH.2.5.1 In the physical rehabilitation setting, recreational and other leisure-time activity services provide for the development, maintenance, and expression of an appropriate leisure/social life-style for individuals with physical, mental, emotional, or social limitations.

RH.2.5.1.1 Recreational therapy services provide, but need not be limited to the following:
RH.2.5.1.1.1 An assessment of the patient's leisure, social, and recreational abilities, deficiencies, interests, barriers, life experiences, needs, and potential;
RH.2.5.1.1.2 Treatment services designed to improve social, emotional, cognitive, and physical functional behaviors as necessary prerequisites to future leisure/social involvement; and
RH.2.5.1.1.3 Leisure Education designed to help the patient acquire the knowledge, skills, and attitudes needed for independent leisure/ social involvement, adjustment in the community, decision-making ability, and appropriate use of free time.
RH.2.5.1.2 Recreational therapy services staff monitor the extent to which goals are achieved relative to the use of leisure time and the acquisition of socialization skills.
(*Accreditation Manual for Hospitals*, 1988, pp. 199-200)

These 1988 standards reflect a change from the 1985 *Consolidated Standards,* Chapter Thirty, "Rehabilitation Services" (see Figure 4) in that they conform directly to the Philosophical Position Statement on Therapeutic Recreation Service espoused by the National Therapeutic Recreation Society (NTRS 1982). This in itself could be an "issue" in that not all therapeutic recreation practitioners agree with or accept the NTRS philosophical position statement. On the other hand it could be veiwed as a giant step forward because it is a specific example of an external standard conforming directly to an internal standard.

Figure 4
Rehabilitation Services Guidelines

1. Provide activity services
2. Have a written plan for organization
3. Plan on using community resources
4. Write down goals and objectives
5. Write down policies and procedures
6. Plan activities throughout the week
7. Document medical records
8. Give patients leisure time
9. Do not label vehicles
10. Hire qualified supervisor
11. Hire sufficient staff
12. Review goals, objectives, and roles
13. Keep statistical records
14. Plan a staff development program
15. Be active in committees and conferences
16. Be trained for emergencies
17. Encourage studies, evaluation, and research
18. Have sufficient space, equipment, and facilities
19. Ensure quality and appropriateness of patient care
20. Continuously monitor important aspects of care
21. Give a periodic assessment of monitors
22. Document findings
23. Make sure your activities QA program is part of a facility QA program   (Donovan in Riley, 1987, pp. 27-28)

Much of the credit for the current positive relationship with JCAHO must be given to Dr. Nancy Navar who over the past ten years has almost single-handedly shouldered the responsiblity of working with JCAHO in the development of standards related to therapeutic recreation service provision (Riley, 1987).

As important as her work in standards development has been, perhaps the most important thing that Dr. Navar has done is give us a model of how to address these issues in the future. Her model is not new or unfamiliar. It is, however, one with which we in therapeutic recreation are not overly comfortable.   Her model: *Informed, Assertive Lobbying!*

Although it may seem overly simplified, Dr. Navar's work has indicated that to have an influence on any group, governmental or private, that does not understand the mission and role of therapeutic recreation in the Health Care Industry, therapeutic recreation, as an industry, must spend a great amount of time and effort in working directly with those groups on a one-to-one basis. For therapeutic recreation to be successful in this endeavor, it must, *unitedly* identify a plan of action that addresses directly each of the issues that are of concern in each of these areas. It is of great importance for this to be a united effort from within the profession for at least two reasons. First, it is not going to be an easy job to impact on these governing bodies. Much time, effort, and resources are going to have to be spent to successfully accomplish the task. If therapeutic recreation is not united in the effort, it is doubtful that enough resources can be generated to be successful. Second, therapeutic recreation must put its "best foot forward" in this effort. If the industry is not united in its approach to these groups they, (JCAHO, CARF, etc.) are going to question the validity of the industrys' existence. If not careful, therapeutic recreation could become its own worst enemy.

Perhaps the greatest issue or question that must then be asked is: " has therapeutic recreation matured enough as a profession/service industry to come together to develop a single, focused legislative agenda / action plan that actively addresses each of the issues that relate to external standards?"   If it has, then surely a mechanism that will include involvement of all impacted parties can be developed that will allow successful development of this agenda /action plan.   If not, therapeutic recreation must then seriously ask itself what must be done to reach that level of maturity.

The temptation is to challenge either NTRS or ATRA to take the lead in the development of this needed work. They, however, may not be the best forum for this type of action. Perhaps those practitioners and facilities that are most directly impacted by these standards should lead the way, using the related professional societies as support and back-up.

Or maybe a national forum on the development of standards in therapeutic recreation needs to be called and presented by one of the many great university programs in the country. The "how" of this action could be accomplished in a variety of ways. The "why" is evident. The "who" is the big question. Yes, who will take the lead?

Internal Standards

As previously discussed, internal standards are those standards that the recreation/therapeutic recreation industry has established, at its various levels, to govern its professional actions and service provision. A review of literature indicates that internal standards are addressed at a variety of interesting levels (NCTRC, 1987; NTRS, 1982; Peterson, 1984; Riley, 1987; Reynolds, 1985). First, there are standards that govern professional preparation, and hopefully professional competence, e.g., COA, (1986),NCTRC (1987), and state licensure (Utah, 1984). The NCTRC certification paths are presented in Figure 5 as an example of this area.

Figure 5
NCTRC Certification Paths

Professional Level Certification Paths
Academic Path - Baccalaureate degree or higher in therapeutic recreation or in recreation with an option in therapeutic recreation which meets all criteria established for a major in therapeutic recreation.
Equivalency Path - Baccalaureate degree or higher in one of the specified related degree areas with five years or more work experience in therapeutic recreation and with completed academic coursework in therapeutic recreation/recreation.

Provisional-Professional Certification Path (this standard will be eliminated after the April, 1991 Review)
Provisional Path - Baccalaureate degree or higher in therapeutic recreation or in recreation with an option or degree in therapeutic recreation but completed academic work does not meet the criteria for a major in therapeutic recreation.

Paraprofessional Level Certification Paths
Academic Paths - Associate degree in therapeutic recreation or in recreation with an option in therapeutic recreation meeting all criteria for an associate degree-major in therapeutic recreation, or associate degree in recreation with work experience.

Equivalency Paths - Associate degree or higher in one of the specified related degree areas with work experience, or   Completion of the NTRS 750-Hour Training Program, or Completion of four years full-time work experience in therapeutic recreation

(NCTRC Standards, 1988, p. 2)

Second, there are standards of practice and/or service provision, e.g., Standards of Practice for Therapeutic Recreation Service (NTRS, 1980). (Figure 6)

Figure 6
Standards of Practice for Therapeutic Recreation Service
(Standards and Criteria only)

Standard I. Scope of Service
Comprehensive therapeutic recreation program services area available to all clients in the agency/facility.
   Criteria
   A. Treatment services are available that are goal oriented and directed toward (re)habilitation, amelioration, and/or modification of specific physical, emotional, mental, and/or social behaviors.
   B. Leisure Education services are available.
   C. There are general recreation services that provide a wide range of activities designed to meet the needs, competencies, capabilities, and interests of clients during leisure time.

Standard II. Objectives
Specific objectives are stated for each type of therapeutic recreation service based on the philosophy and goals of the therapeutic   recreation unit/agency/department and translated into operational terms.
   Criteria
   A. The statement of objectives is in writing.
   B. The statement is prepared by the therapeutic recreation staff in consultation with appropriate professional staff of the agency/facility (for example, medical, educational, recrational, and/or designated representatives of the administration).

C. The statement is used as a program planning and evaluation tool.

Standard III. Individual Treatment/Program Plan

The therapeutic recreation staff develop an individual treatment/program plan for each client referred to the unit/agency/department.

Criteria
A. The plan is based on complete and relevant diagnostic/assessment data.
B. The plan is stated in behavioral terms that permit the progress of the individual to be assessed.
C. The plan is periodically reviewed, evaluated and modified as necessary to meet the changing needs of the client.
D. The plan differentiates among short-term, long-term, and discharge/transition goals.
E. The plan is documented in the personal record of the client.
F. The plan reflects an integrated approach.

Standard IV. Documentation

Therapeutic recreation personnel record specific information on assigned clients for the client/participants's record on a regular basis in accordance with the policies and procedures of the agency.

Criteria
A. The individualized therapeutic recreation treatment/program plan is recorded in the client/participant's record.
B. Progress of the individual and his or her reactions to the therapeutic recreation program are systematically recorded in the client/patient's record and reported to all appropriate parties (for example, interdisciplinary team, parents).
C. A discharge/transition plan is included in their personal record.
D. Client records are reviewed regularly by therapeutic recreation staff in accordance with standards of regulatory agencies, and documentation of such review is entered in the personal record.

Standard V. Scheduling of Services

Specific times are allocated for therapeutic recreation program.
Criteria
A. The master schedule is established in cooperation with other programs and services provided for the client.
B. Each client receives a schedule of the comprehensive therapeutic recreation program or has easy access to posted schedules and scheduled changes.

Standard VI. Ethical Practices
Therapeutic recreation service delivery is designated to respect the personal rights of the individual clients and their families.
Criteria
A. It conforms with the local, state, and federal guidelines such as the "Patients' Bill of Rights" and Mental Health/Mental Retardation Act.
B. It conforms with the National Recreation and Park Association/National Therapeutic Recreation Society Code of Ethics.

Guidelines for Administration of Therapeutic Recreation Service in Clinical and Residential Facilities (NTRS, 1982), and Guidelines for Community-Based Recreation Programs for Special Populations (NTRS, 1979). Finally, there are standards related to professional behavior and conduct, e.g., NTRS Code of Ethics (NTRS, 1984).

National Therapeutic Recreation Society Statement of Professional Ethics

Introduction
The National Therapeutic Recreation Society (NTRS), a branch of the National Recreation and Park Association (NRPA), is a professional organization committed to the provision of recreation services for all persons regardless of age, race, sex, national origins, religious beliefs, or physical, social or mental abilities. NTRS maintains open membership to all persons employed in an occupation that provides recreation services for special populations (e..g. mentally ill, retarded, physically handicapped, aged, correctionally incarcerated, socially disadvantaged, etc.) and who subscribe to the professional standards and ethical practices endorsed by the governing board of the society.

NTRS affirms its commitment to the goals ofd the park and recreation movement as represented by the Constitution of NRPA and acknowledges its a priori adherence to standards and principles embodied in the related health disciplines from which it draws much of its heritage of concern and standards of practice.

In this spirit, the theraputic recreation professional subscribes not only to the ethical code adopted by NRPA, but equally subscribes to those general principles of ethical conduct endorsed by all health related disciplines.

The statement

I. The therapeutic recreation professional believes in the value and importance of special recreation services for persons who are limited in their opportunities because of physical, social or mental disabilities. He/she is committed to the continuous task of learning and self-improvement to increase his/her competency and effectiveness as a professional.

II. Above all else, the therapeutic recreation professional is guided by the accepted responsibility of encouraging and providing quality service to the client/consumer. He/she demonstrates respect for the dignity of the client/consumer as an individual human being. He/she makes an honest effort to meet the habilitative, rehabilitative and leisure needs of the client/consumer and takes care that the client/consumer is not exploited or otherwise abused. This includes but is not limited to the guarantee of basic human rights under law.

III. The therapeutic recreation professional engages only in those activities that bring credit to himself/herself and to the professsion. He/she shows respect for fellow colleagues in word and deed. When he/she becomes aware of unethical conduct by a colleague or fellow professional, appropriate and prescribed professional channels will be followed in reporting said conduct.

IV. The therapeutic recreation professional observes the principle of confidentiality in all written and verbal communications concerning clients/consumers, fellow colleagues and/or matters of professional privilege.

V. The therapeutic recreation professional serves as an advocate for therapeutic recreation by interpreting the purposes and values of the profession to clients/consumers, other professionals, and the community at large. He/she accepts responsibility for improving communications and cooperative effort among the many professional fields serving special populations. He/she encourages and participates in demonstration and investigative projects aimed at upgrading professional services and communicates the results of his/her efforts.

VI. The therapeutic recreation professional obligates himself/herself to providing consultation service to consumers, other professionals, community agencies and institutions. Fees for services, where appropriate, are made known to clients/consumers prior to entering into any contractual relationships.

Historically these standards represent critical steps in the maturation of the industry into a profession and provide an indication of the insight and interest needed to guarantee basic levels of service provision and professional conduct.

The primary issue that must be addressed in the future related to internal standards is that, with the exception of a few state licensure laws, all are voluntary in nature. A second issue is that most, if not all, current internal standards in therapeutic recreation have been proposed by bodies that do not represent the industry as a whole. These two issues place therapeutic recreation in a difficult position, because even though there are standards developed, there is no guarantee that the standards will be followed either at the individual or programmatic level. A third issue that also impacts on current internal standards is that as yet there, is no research verification that compliance to the stated standards guarantees either superior service provision or facilitates client safety/care.

These issues are not new, they have been discussed many times at several different levels (Reynolds, 1985; Riley, 1987). The question then continues, "Who/what will govern the maturation and development of the industry/profession through the next decade? Again, it must be stated, "therapeutic recreation, your destiny is in your own hands. To successfully address this issue, therapeutic recreation practitioners must learn to separate involvement in a professional society from the development of the profession. It is true, philosophically, that one should foster and support the other. Pragmatically, however, the two seem to be antagonists. For the effort at this level to be successful there must again be a unity of definition and mission. As was discussed with external standards, the question must be asked, "Has therapeutic recreation matured enough to accept the challenge of designing, implementing, and researching internal standards that have application and acceptance at all levels within the service system?" Therapeutic recreation practitioners espouse the professional ability to assess problems/needs, plan and implement programs, and evaluate success with their consumers. The time has now come for therapeutic recreation, as an industry, to take advantage of these same abilities in helping its own cause in the development of internal standards through the creation of a therapeutic recreation *master plan* for the 1900s. Who will take the lead?

Plan of Action

It is never an easy process to develop a plan of action that is acceptable to all parties involved. That, however, is exactly what needs to happen in therapeutic recreation if it is to be successful in the future development of both external and internal standards. Indeed, the model seems to be one of having acceptable internal standards before meaningful external standards can be developed. A good case in point is the work of the NRPA/AALR Council on Accreditations work with the Council on Post Secondary Accreditation (COPA) (NRPA, 1986). COA, a representative body within the recreation profession, worked for many years and went through numerous exercises, visitations and revisions before it ever tried to approach COPA for its stamp of approval. If therapeutic recreation is to be successful in having any long term influence with the development of mandated external standards in the Health Care Service System, it must first be willing to do its homework by developing functionally applied and universally accepted internal standards that guarantee a minimum level of service provision, quality of care and safety for its consumers.

Study Questions

1. What is an external standard? Why are they important?

2. What is an internal standard? Why are they important?

3. Explain the relationship between internal and external standards.

4. Identify and discuss at least for groups that regulate external standards that have a direct impact on therapeutic recreation.

5. Identify and discuss three or four types of internal standards that have been established in therapeutic recreation. Explain their significance.

6. Identify and discuss three or four issues that relate to the development of both internal and external standards in therapeutic recreation in the next ten years.

7. Who do you feel should take the responsibility for the future development of both internal and external standards in therapeutic recreation?

References

American Therapeutic Recreation Association. *A Message From the President.* Sand Springs, Oklahoma.

Commission on Accreditation of Rehabilitation Facilities (1986). *Standards Manual for Organizations Serving People with Disabilities.* Tucson, AZ.

Donovan, G. (1987). You Want Me to do What? Regulatory Standards in Therapeutic Recreation. In Riley, B. (eds.) (1987). *Evaluation of Therapeutic Recreation Through Quality Assurance.* Venture Publishing, Inc. State College, PA 16803.

Federal Register, Subpart J, Forty-Second Code (1976). *Conditions of Participation: Hospitals.* Washington, D.C.: United States Government Printing Office.

Joint Commission on Accreditation of Hospitals (1988). *Accreditation Manual for Hospitals.* Chicago, IL.

_____ .(1986). *Ambulatory Health Care Standards Manual.* Chicago,IL.

_____ .(1986). *Long Term Care Manual.* Chicago, IL.

_____ .(1985). *Consolidated Standards Manual.* Chicago, IL.

_____ .(1985). Consolidated Standards Manual for Child, Adolescent, and Adult Psychiatry, Alcoholism and Drug Abuse Facilities; and Facilities Serving MR/DD. Chicago, IL. (1983). *Hospice Standards Manual.* Chicago, IL.

National Council for Therapeutic Recreation Certification (1987).*Certification Standards for Therapeutic Recreation Personnel.* Spring Valley, NY 10977.

National Recreation and Park Association (1986). *Standards and Evaluative Criteria for Recreation, Park Resources and Leisure Services Baccalaureate Program.* Alexandria , VA.

National Therapeutic Recreation Society (1979). *Guidelines for Community-Based Recreation Programs for Special Populations.* Alexandria, VA: National Recreation and Park Association.

_____. (1980). *Standards of Practice for Therapeutic Recreation.* Alexandria, VA: National Recreation and Park Association.

_____. (1982). *Guidelines for Administration of Therapeutic Recreation in Clinical and Residential Facilities.* Alexandria, VA: National Recreation and Park Association.

_____. (1982). *Philosophical Position Statement.* Alexandria, VA: National Recreation and Park Association.

_____. (1984) *Code of Ethics.* Alexandria, VA: National Recreation and Park Association.

Peterson, C.A. and Gunn, S.L. (1984). *Therapeutic Recreation Program Design: Principles and Procedures.* Prentice-Hall, Inc., Englewood Cliffs, NJ 07632.

Reynolds, R.P. and O'Morrow, G.S. (1985). *Problems, Issues and Concepts in Therapeutic Recreation.* Prentice-Hall, Inc., Englewood Cliffs, NJ 07632.

Riley, B. (1987). *Evaluation of Therapeutic Recreation Through Quality Assurance.* Venture Publishing, Inc., State College, PA 16803.

State of Utah (1984). Recreation Therapy Practice Act of 1975 as awarded by session hours 1985, Title 58, Chapter 40, with Recreational Therapy Rules of 1984.

Van Andel, G.E. (1981). Professional standards: Improving the quality of services. *Therapeutic Recreation Journal. 15*(2), p. 24.

Websters (1986). Ninth New Edition, Collegiate Dictionary.

STANDARD VERSUS PRACTICE: IS THERE A GAP?

Terrance P. Robertson

Introduction

In the past few years, the topic of standards has received considerable review, discussion, and debate by individuals in a variety of health care professions, including therapeutic recreation. The scope of these exchanges has been broad, with individual items including everything from the historical and philosophical elements of practice standards to the different settings, formats, and regulating bodies associated with standards. Issues related to the improvement or refinement of standards have also been of recent interest and discussion. Collectively, these efforts indicate only continued interest and an increased necessity for therapeutic recreators to become more informed and involved in the area of practice standards.

The purpose of this chapter is to pose one fundamental question: Is there a gap between practice and standards? Literature review reveals that the answer to this question often depends upon one's perspective on the meaning of the terms *standards* and *practice.*

Professionals in the therapeutic recreation field have also contributed to the confusion by making comments about the lack of practice standards and their frustration with this lack (Reynolds & O'Morrow, 1985; Riley, 1987). Practitioners, however, appear to be providing services throughout the country, meeting or exceeding a variety of standards, and functioning within the conceptual foundations of the profession. Thus, a direct answer to our question is not clearly available, so the purpose of this chapter becomes to generate thought and discussion about the extent to which a gap exists between standards and practice.

Coming to a Definition

Paraphrased definitions of the term *standard* range from rule, guideline, benchmark, criterion, average/mean, median, norm, par, flag, beam, or an upright support (Commission on Accreditation of Rehabilitation Facilities, 1986, p.3; Donabedian, 1982; Donovan, 1987, pp. 26-27; Carf, 1986, p. 3; Reynolds & O'Morrow, 1985, pp. 104-105; *Webster's*, 1986, pp. 420, 526). While definitions of *practice*, on the other hand, were found to indicate repetition, habit, systematic exercise for proficiency, routine, or the exercise of a profession (Donabedian, 1982; Donovan, 1987, p. 26-27; Carf, 1986, p.3; Reynolds & O'Morrow, 1985, p.104-105; *Webster's*, 1986, p.420 & 526).

These various definitions are further clouded by consideration of the specific settings (e.g., school, clinical, community-based), the populations (e.g., DD/MR, geriatric, psychiatric), and the values (quality assurance, evaluation, utilization review) (Kennedy, Austin, & Smith, 1987; Riley, 1987; Steffen, 1988; Voelkl, 1988) to which they are applied.

The focus on practice standards can be traced back to Hippocrates. His Hippocratic Oath (addressing ethics and the scope of practice), his recording of successful treatment methods by symptoms (diagnostic-related groups or DRGs), and his case study method of care (individualized treatment) are the mainstays of modern medicine (Carter, Van Andel, & Robb, 1985). It should be noted that these original elements of care (established standards of practice) have maintained their place in modern medicine and, with the exception of ethics, have basically remained firm within the foundation of practice. In fact, the *Journal of the American Medical Association* (*JAMA*) has, as regular sections, a forum for sharing case histories, information on DRGs, and insight into professional development (e.g., "*JAMA*: A Hundred Years Ago").

Dr. Doris Berryman is credited with the initiation of the first significant effort to develop standards for therapeutic recreation (Van Andel, 1981). Dr. Berryman developed "Recommended Standards with Evaluative Criteria for Recreational Services in Residential Institutions" in 1971 as part of a grant funded by the Department of Health, Education, and Welfare. Berryman's work was the framework for the development of standards through the 1970s, serving as the basis for the National Therapeutic Recreation Society's (NTRS) "Standards of Practice" (1980) and their "Guidelines for Administration of Therapeutic Recreation Service in Clinical and Residential Facilities" (1980) (Donovan, 1987).

The focus of these "original" standards was to standardize service in such a way that a prescribed amount and type of care should be maintained. Further, these original standards implied that individuals receiving services could be assured of a satisfactory level of service.

However, circumstances have changed, and with these changes have come new perspectives on the use of the standards. Standards are no longer used simply as guidelines or support systems. There are now both internal standards (within peer or professional organizations) and external standards (as regulatory or credential-establishing criteria). External standards are being used to divide care and service into one of two categories—the haves and the have nots, or that which is in compliance and that which is out of compliance (Reynolds & O'Morrow, 1985). Along with services, the scope of practice has also changed to meet increasing and diversifying needs in a variety of different environments, but our standards of practice have not changed drastically since 1971. So, instead of guiding us in our practice, standards are now being used as measuring, evaluative criteria and even as criteria for punitive action (Bluestien, 1988a, 1988b; Couch, 1988a).

In a recent *ACURP* article, Rodriguez (1988) stated that "as 'cost restraints' and 'utilization review' emerged as the predominant signposts of U.S. health care from 1975-1985, so quality is emerging as the antecedent marker for the next years" (p. 61). This statement is supported not only by the volumes of potential standards we can become subject to (from such agencies as JCAHO, CARF, HCFA, NTRS, NCTRC, or one's own individual agency) but also from political and economic trends such as (a) resource allocation methodologies (by DRGs or resource utilization groups, or RUGs; (b) proposals for physician fellowships and resident practices in quality assurance and utilization review; (c) studies on the cost, legality, and ethical concerns regarding quality assurance, peer medical reviews, and PSROs/ SERP; and (d) the impact of all of this on morale (_____, 1988; Colvin, 1988; Couch, 1988; Linn & Robinson, 1988; Rodriguez, 1988; Ziegenfuss, 1988). To further this, the recent Presidential signing of the Health Care Quality Improvement Act of 1986 helps solidify the thought that practice standards of all types (e.g., QA/UR, credentiality, clinical privileges) are going to be continuously scrutinized through QA/UR and thus are of grave importance to the therapeutic recreation profession. So, to better facilitate our investigation, the term practice shall mean "the exercise of a profession" (*Webster's*, 1986, p. 923), and the term standard shall mean "criterion" (*Webster's*, p. 1148).

Examples and Samples of Present Standards

The following information is provided to give insight into some of the different standards a therapeutic recreator might encounter. Listed in Tables 1 and 2 are examples of specific established standards.

Table 3 and 4 indicate the content of some of these sets of standards. Examples have been divided into internal and external standards and also into personnel and professional standards. Specific information has been paraphrased here, but such guidelines should be reviewed in their entirety before use in building or evaluating services.

Table 1
Example Standards: Personnel

Personnel (Internal)

1) National Council for Therapeutic Recreation Certification (NCTRC)
2) National Therapeutic Recreation Society (NTRS) 750-hour training certification
3) Certified Leisure Professional (NRPA)

Personnel (External)

1) Marriage and Family Counselor/Therapist
2) Substance Abuse Counselor/Therapist
3) Utah State Law/ Utah Recreational Therapy Practice Act of 1975.

Table 2
Example Standards: Professional

Professional (Internal)

1) TR Education: Guidelines for a competency-based, entry level curriculum (NRPA/NTRS - 1977)
2) Guidelines for Community Based TR for Special Populations (NRPA/NTRS) - 1979)
3) Standards of Practice for TR Service (NRPA/NTRS - 1980)
4) Guidelines for Administration of TR in Clinical and Residential Facilities (NRPA/NTRS - 1984)
5) Standards for Field Placement inTR (NRPA/NTRS - 1986)

Professional (External)

1) Joint Commission on Accreditation of Hospitals (JCAHO)/ 5 different sets of standards [eg. for Hospitals Psychiatric and Substance Abuse (1980), MR/DD

(1985), Long Term Care (1986), Hospice (1983), and Ambulatory Health Care (1986)].
2) Commission on Accreditation of Rehabilitation Facilities (CARF) (1986).
3) Health Care Finance Admiistration (HCFA - Medicare & Medicaid guidelines) Draft, June (1988).
4) Insurance Providers (for reimbursements).
5) State Health Care Associations

Sample content from selected examples are provided below in Tables 3 and 4.

Table 3
Sample: Professional Service

A. The NTRS Standards of Practice (1980) provide for the following:
   1. Comprehensive Services Available:
      A. Clinical
      B. Leisure Education
      C. General Recreation
   2. Objectives Written
   3. Individual Treatment Plans
   4. Medical Record Documentation
   5. Specific Times Allotted for Therapeutic Recreation
   6. Ethical Practices
B. JCAHO Standards (1986) in Long-Term Care provide for the following:
   1. Organize and staff to actively meet needs of patients/residents.
   2. Make the staff responsible for developing, documenting, and maintaining activities.
   3. Hire a qualified patient-activities coordinator.
   4. Hire a sufficient staff.
   5. Acquire suitable activity space.
   6. Acquire suitable supplies and equipment.
   7. Organize activities suited to needs.
   8. Offer a variety of activities.
   9. Make an activities schedule available.
   10. Offer independent activities.
   11. Create assessment areas.
   12. Monitor quality and appropriateness of activities.
C. CARF (1986), Activity Service standards provide for the following:
   1. Lists of activity resources and capabilities.
   2. Curricula and course outlines for areas of instruction.
   3. Individual case records.
   4. Written grievance and appeal procedures.
   5. Minutes of meetings of those served and management.

6.   A daily activities schedule providing free-time (30 hours of activities outside the home integrated with the community and evidence (documentation) of client choice.*

*This applies to residential services only.

Table 4
Sample: Professional Standards

A.   State of Utah (1985) Recreational Therapy Practice Act (Title 58, Chapter 40) Licensing Requirements are as follows:

1.   Every applicant for licensure under this chapter shall make written application, pay the proper license fee, and give such information as the board may require including, but not limited to, satisfactory evidence that he:

a)   Is of good moral character as it relates of the functiions and responsibilities of the practice of therapeutic recreation; and

b)   Has satisfactorily completed an examination approved by the board for the license.

2.   The application for a therapeutic recreation technician license shall include, in addition to the requirements of subsection(1), satisfactory evidence that the applicant:

a)   Has completed an approved high school education, or the equivalent as determined by the board; and

b)   Has completed:

i)   two years of full-time paid experience in the therapeutic recreation field;

ii)   two hundred clock hours of in-service training in therapeutics; or

iii)   a combination of subsections (b) (i) and (ii) that the board determines to be adequate.

3.   The application for a therapeutic recreation specialist license shall include, in addition to those requirements of subsection (1), satisfactory evidence that the applicant:

a)   Has received a baccalaureate degree or its equivalent from an accredited college or university with:

i)   an emphasis in therapeutic recreation.

ii)   a major in recreation and one year of experience in the therapeutic recreation field; or

iii)   a degree in a field related to therapeutic recreation and two years of experience in the therapeutic recreation field; or

b)   Has received a master's degree from an accredited college or university with a major in recreation or other field related to therapeutic recreation.

Table 4 (cont.)

---

4. The application for a master therapeutic recreation specialist license shall include, in addition to those requirements of subsection (1), satisfactory evidence that the applicant:

    a) Has a master's degree or its equivalent from an accredited college or university with:
    - i) an emphasis in therapeutic recreation and has two years of experience in the therapeutic recreation field; or
    - ii) a major in recreation and three years of experience in the therapeutic recreation field; or
    - iii) a major in a field related to therapeutic recreation and four years of experience in the therapeutic recreation field.

    b) Has a baccalaureate degree from an accredited college or university with:
    - i) an emphasis in therapeutic recreation, five years of experience in the therapeutic recreation field and six credits of work at the graduate level;
    - ii) A major in recreation, six years of experience in the therapeutic recreation field and twelve credits of work at the graduate level; or
    - iii) a major in a field related to therapeutic recreation, seven years of experience in the therapeutic recreation field and eighteen credits of work at the graduate level.

Utilization and Application

With all of the changes within our profession and in the direction of health care provision, we must reexamine our use and application of practice standards. As mentioned previously, our original standards were developed in an attempt to standardize an element of service either the amount or the type of service. This concept is still consistent with other allied health professions, but an essential difference is in the type and scope of practice with which we are concerned (e.g., our practice may be viewed as questionable in terms of sophistication, specialization, and precision). Even so, therapeutic recreation is not the only profession having difficulty maintaining, developing, or regulating practice standards.

A quick examination of 1988's *JAMA* indicates that even the medical profession is having difficulty in developing and regulating practice standards (Linn & Robinson, 1988; Mulley & Eagle, 1988), as well as in defining what quality medical care is (Steffen, 1988, p. 56).

Some have tried to find out what quality care isn't; Mulley and Eagle (1988), for example, commented on practice standards in an attempt to refocus the reader to the trends of the marketplace and the responsibility of the medical profession:

"Though wide variations in the application of medical technologies have been recognized for decades, they have only recently become the object of intense scrutiny and debate" (p. 540).

They then cite a number of studies in which routine surgeries were judged for their appropriateness and/or relation to a practice standard. The results indicated that between 17% and 34% of rated surgeries were deemed inappropriate. The focus then turns to the consumer (e.g., client, insurance company, city) and the marketplace. The concluding thought is that eventually the consumer or the marketplace will determine what is appropriate (billable) and that informed consumers are as important as developing a need (real or perceived) within the marketplace.

So where does this leave therapeutic recreation? We do not have precise surgery, dentistry, diagnostic, or pharmacological actions or treatments to review from which to develop standards. We do not have volumes of case histories or proven and accepted symptom-relief formulas to utilize. So, for what purpose are we trying to develop standards. And why?

Leaders in our profession and other health professions seem to agree that there is a need for a reexamination of our standards, but for a variety of reasons. In a recent meeting for therapeutic recreators in Utah, John Chambers reported, "The apparent assumption of standards is that they will lend one credibility – and thus privileges (clinical). The bottom line is money and who can bill for it and who can't! It's not who can save it or even best utilize it" (Robertson, 1988). This statement, while pointed, is not too far off from more traditional comments about our needs for review of our standards:

Selected elements of service serve as the underpinnings of the standards of practice. Evaluation of such elements provides an empirical foundation for motivationally derived standards of practice, and in essence supports or refutes their validity. (Riley, 1987, p.20)

Therapeutic recreation has shown extraordinary adaptive capacities, but to continue to do so will require further research into standards of practice so as to ensure quality assurance. The practical task of establishing reliability and validity in our standards is formidable, but it must be done. (Reynolds & O'Morrow, 1985, p. 108)

Credibility, clinical privileges, money, validity, adaptability, quality assurance, reliability, standardization, advancement of our professional technology—whatever the reason, the reality is that a thorough review and analysis of our standards of practice must take place on a regular basis. This review and analysis should coincide with changes in service technology (e.g., prevention, diagnostic, or treatment), consumer or marketplace needs, and the improvement or enhancement of services (e.g., to represent levels of care, quality assurance, or DRGs).

Presently the bulk of our practice standards (internal professional) seem to center on elements relative to the unsubstantiated but widely accepted therapeutic recreation process model and not on specific preventive, diagnostic, or treatment technology. Thus, our present standards force a single perspective in the review of service (therapy, education, participation) relative to our standards. This perspective is usually dichotomous in nature (i.e., met or not met) and does not allow for qualitative judgments, much less intervals, ratios, or continuous gradations in service. So the utilization and application of our practice standards may be appropriate, but are our standards consistent with the state-of-the-art technologies being practiced?

Scenarios for Further Thought

For further examination of the relationship between standards and practice, the following four scenarios have been developed. Associated with each brief scenario is a specific but hypothetical view on the present relationship between standards and practice. The individual scenarios view the relationship between standards and practice as either overdone, satisfactory, underprepared, or nonapplicable.

Overdone

According to Howe-Murphy and Charboneau (1987), some futurists have indicated that the nature of our society and trends in other professions will force professions to develop more general standards rather than more specific ones. If the scope of our profession is expanding, we need generic, flexible standards to accommodate both a minimal service standard and yet allow for a creative, dynamic research or demonstration project, or even a new developing program. Further, our standards should not be goals toward which we should work, but minimal entrance-level criteria. Thus, the move to less prescriptive standards is encouraging. Standards should reflect gradations in the service process and be based on available resources and outcome, without a forced comparison to other, outside programs. Thus, a situation perspective is needed. At present, the volumes of standards we now are forced to follow are overdone!

Satisfactory

So far, so good! Our original concept of practice standards is right on track with what we and other health professions have desired for therapeutic recreation. They are also general enough to be flexible, yet specific enough to be measured.

The standards don't fence us in, but they provide good support or framework for services. Further, multiple service providers seem to consistently meet or exceed standards without having to artificially generate documentation or alter services. If it's not broken, don't fix it, and if we don't need it, don't get it. Be happy with where you are, know your limitations, and satisfaction guaranteed!

Underprepared

The startling lack of practice standards is scary and frustrating. There is neither a standard set of procedures nor enough valid or reliable instruments available for use in therapeutic recreation. We want all of the privileges but without any observable or measurable data to back up such a request. Presently, there is too much room for geographic and programmatic differences. The general lack of precision and specification in our standards does not allow for comparison. Thus, not only are we not able to be reviewed and given credit for what we do, but we also can't determine where we have problems and why. The only thing our standards do tell us is that we are under-prepared.

Not Applicable

There are at least two assumptions associated with practice standards, including, first, that there are elements of service that occur regularly enough and with enough consistency to establish a standard of practice. The second assumption is that there is a need for a standard to be set in our case, that we need either to protect the consumer from a wrongful or unlawful service or to legitimize our service.

But as you know, there is no documented proof that shows that our services help or hurt individuals. The medical profession can't agree on what should be routine or appropriate, so how can we ever hope to? Throughout the course of our history, volunteers have often been our direct care givers, so how could a voluntary experience (recreation) being provided by volunteers be considered unlawful or wrongful? Our standards of practice seem to be irrelevant and probably *not applicable.*

Concluding Perspective

Practice means the exercise of a profession, and a standard means a criterion. But where do we stand professionally in relation to our actual practice and our present standards? Can we show any treatment effects? What are the consequences of not meeting our present standards? Do we have punitive outcomes or responsibility? Do we make a difference? Many of us practice—is there a standard? Is there a gap? If yes, why, how, or so what? If no, should there be; why or why not? Should we even be concerned with them? What's the true focus of standards, and where do they fit in? How should they be established in terms of the scope of practice, as minimal, average, or superior performance? Who should determine this and how would it be determined? The concluding perspective is left to the reader.

Study Questions

1. Is there a gap between practice and standards? Where, how, why, in what way?
2. What are standards used for, and how are they used?
3. Could you write a behavioral description of a standard treatment in TR?
4. Which of the four hypothetical scenarios (overdone, satisfactory, underprepared, or not applicable) best represents your thoughts, and why?
5. Which of the four hypothetical scenarios least represents your thoughts, and why?
6. Could you develop a short list of standards for either credential-

ing, professional preparation, or practice? Try to put them in the context of a group to be served or in a setting employing therapeutic recreators.

7.   Examine the process and content of therapeutic recreation as you know it to be. Ask yourself how we could either standardize or generalize these.

Recommendations for Future Development of Practice Standards

1.   Develop, collect, share, and publish case histories (successes and failures), with focus on TR treatment.
2.   Develop, collect, share, and publish standardized treatment formats and procedures.
3.   Develop, collect, share, and publish on prevention, treatment, and diagnostic techniques.
4.   Develop, collect, share, and publish diagnosis and prognosis statements concerning leisure deficits.
5.   Develop, collect, share, and publish research on the efficacy of TR.
6.   Continue dialogue and interfacing with professional organizations/agencies developing and regulating external standards.
7.   Develop more specific internal standards with a peer review system to compensate for the less specific outcome-oriented external standards.

References

American Medical Association Council on Quality Assurance.(1988). Guidelines for Quality Assurance. Council Report, *Journal of the American Medical Association* , *259*, 2572-2573.

Bluestein, P.A. (1988). Commentary: The Price of Miracles. *Quality Assurance and Utilization Review,* American College of Utilization Review Physicians, *3*(1), 42-43.

Bluestein, P.A. (1988). The Nuts and Bolts of Utilization Review. *Quality Assurance and Utilization Review.* American College of Utilization Review Physicians, *3*(1), 11-13.

Carter, M.J., Van Andel, G. E., & Robb, G. M. (1985). *Therapeutic Recreation: A Practical Approach.* St. Louis, MO: Times Mirror/Mosby College.

Colvin, R.S. (1988). Quality Assurance/Utilization Review as a Practice Option: The Influence of a Residency Program. *Quality Assurance and Utilization Review*, American College of Utilization Review Physicians, *3*(2) 50-52.

Commission on Accreditation of Rehabilitation Facilities. (1986). *Standards Manual for Organizations Serving People with Disabilities* Tucson, AZ:Author.

Commission on Accreditation of Rehabilitation Facilities. (1986). *The CARF Story*. Tucson, AZ: Author.

Couch, J.B. (1988). Legal Aspects of the Medical Staff Peer Review Process. *Quality Assurance and Utilization Review*, American College of Utilization Review Physicians, *3*(1), 24-26.

Couch, J.B. (1988). Medical Care Value Purchasing: Medicolegal Promises, Pitfalls, and Progress. *Quality Assurance and Utilization Review*, American College of Utilization Review Physicians, *3*(1) 32-26.

Donabedian, A. (1982). *Explorations in Quality Assessment and Monitoring: Vol. 2.: The Criteria and Standards of Quality*. Ann Arbor, MI: Health Administration Press.

Donovan, G. (1987). You Want Me to Do What? Regulatory Standards in Therapeutic Recreation. In B.Riley, (ed.), *Evaluation of Therapeutic Recreation Through Quality Assurance*. State College, PA: Venture.

Federal Register, Subpart J., Forty-Second Code. (1976). *Conditions of Participation: Hospitals*. Washington, DC: United States Government Printing Office.

Howe-Murphy, R., & Charboneau, B.G. (1987). *Therapeutic Recreation Intervention: An Ecological Perspective*. Englewood Cliffs, NJ : Prentice-Hall.

Joint Commission on Accreditation of Hospitals. (1980). *Accreditation Manual for Hospitals*. Chicago, IL.

Joint Commission on Accreditation of Hospitals. (1983). *Hospice Standard Manual*. Chicago, IL.

Joint Commission on Accreditation of Hospitals. (1985). *Consolidated Standards Manual*. Chicago, IL.

Joint Commission on Accreditation of Hospitals. (1985). *Consolidated Standards Manual for Child, Adolescent, and Adult Psychiatry, Alcoholism and Drug Abuse Facilities; and Facilities Serving MR/DD*. Chicago, IL.

Joint Commission on Accreditation of Hospitals. (1986). *Ambulatory Health Care Standards Manual*. Chicago, IL.

Joint Commission on Accreditation of Hospitals. (1986). *Long -Term Care Manual.* Chicago, IL.

Jones, D.J. (1988). Editorial: Quality Assurance or Reassurance? *Quality Assurance and Utilization Review,* American College of Utilization Review Physicians, *3*(2), 31.

Kennedy, D.W., Austin, D.R., & Smith, R.W. (1987). *Special Recreation: Opportunities for Persons with Disabilities.* New York, NY: CBS College Publishing.

Linn, B.S., & Robinson, D.S. (1988). The Possible Impact of DRGs on Nutritional Status of Patients Having Surgery for Cancer of the Head and Neck. *Journal of the American Medical Association 260*(4), 514-518.

Mulley, A.G., & Eagle, K.A. (1988). What's Inappropriate Care? *Journal of the American Medical Association , 260*(4), 540-541.

National Therapeutic Recreation Society. (1980). *Guidelines for Administration of Therapeutic Recreation Service in Clinical and Residential Facilities.* Alexandria, VA: National Recreation and Park Association.

Peterson, C.A., & Gunn, S.L.1984. *Therapeutic Recreation Program Design: Principles and Procedures.* Englewood Cliffs, NJ: Prentice-Hall.

Reynolds, R.P. & O'Morrow, G.S. (1985). *Problems, Issues and Concepts in Therapeutic Recreation.* Englewood Cliffs, NJ : Prentice-Hall.

Riley, B. (Ed.). (1987) *Evaluation of Therapeutic Recreation Through Quality Assurance.* State College, PA: Venture Publishing.

Robertson, T.R. (1988). Personal communication, TEAM-TR correspondence at Utah Meeting of Therapeutic Recreation, Salt Lake City. July 1988.

Rodriguez, A.R. (1988). Literature Review: Focusing on Quality. *Quality Assurance and Utilization Review,* American College of Utilization Review Physicians. *3*(1), 61-63.

Rodriguez, A.R. (1988). Literature Review: On Risk Management and Mismanagement. *Quality Assurance and Utilization Review, 3*(2) 28-29.

Sabin, P., Meyer, T. C., & Von Ehren, M. (1988). The Cost of Quality Assurance: An Exploratory Study. *Quality Assurance and Utilization Review.* American College of Utilization Review Physicians, *3*(1) 14-20.

State of Utah. Recreation Therapy Practice Act of 1975, as awarded by session hours 1985, Title 58, Chapter 40, with Recreational Therapy Rules of 1984.

Steffen, G.E. (1988). Quality Medical Care: A Definition. *Journal of the American Medical Association*, 260(1) 56-61.

Van Andel, G.E. (1981). Professional Standards: Improving the Quality of Services. *Therapeutic Recreation Journal, 15*(2) 24.

Voelkl, J.E. (1988). *Risk Management in Therapeutic Recreation: A Component of Quality Assurance*. State College, PA: Venture Publishing.

Webster's, (1986). *Webster's Ninth New Collegiate Dictionary*. Merriam-Webster, Inc. Springfield: MA.

Ziegenfuss, J.T. (1988). Toward an Educational Model for Physician Fellowships and Residencies in Quality Assurance and Utilization Review. *Quality Assurance and Utilization Review, 3*(1) pp.2-9). American College of Utilization Review Physicians.

Clinical and Community Practice Issues

photo courtesy of Bradford Woods

The issues with which community-based therapeutic recreation programs must deal are not totally distinct and different from the issues faced by more clinically-oriented therapeutic recreation programs.

—Kathleen J. Halberg

ISSUES IN COMMUNITY-BASED THERAPEUTIC RECREATION SERVICES

Kathleen J. Halberg

Introduction

The purpose of this chapter is to identify and examine current issues in community-based therapeutic recreation services. As a basis for exploring current issues and their implications to the future of such services, the history and current status of these services will also be reviewed.

The issues with which community-based therapeutic recreation programs must deal are not totally distinct from the issues faced by more clinically oriented therapeutic recreation programs. Rather, differences are found in the specific impact of an issue in the two areas of practice. For example, while adequate dealing with the prospective payment system for reimbursement of health care services has more specific impact on clinically-oriented programs, it also is an issue, albeit less critical, for community-based programs; while community-based practice is more directly involved with integration and the rights of individuals to leisure services, they also are major issues for clinical practice. Although clinical and community practice in therapeutic recreation are at times addressed separately for educational and discussion purposes, it is important to recognize that the therapeutic recreation profession currently continues to be a single profession with one basic philosophy and pattern of professional preparation even though widely differing views do exist.

History of Community-Based Therapeutic Recreation Services

Early years

The roots of community-based therapeutic recreation services in the United States go back, in a sense, to the beginnings of the park and recreation movement. The park and recreation movement began in the early part of this century with the concern for the availability of human and leisure services to those outside the mainstream who had not yet gained true equality, primarily recent immigrants who worked and lived in unpleasant and unhealthy environments. However, such concerns were not applied to individuals with disabilities during this era because the limited services which did exist occurred primarily in institutional settings. "Few community-based programs were recorded in the first half of the twentieth century. The Easter Seal Society has provided day and residential camping since the 1930s, and a few public school systems offered after-school programs" (Howe-Murphy & Charboneau, 1987, p. 153).

During the 1950s and early 1960s, community-based recreation services to individuals with disabilities slowly developed. A few municipal park and recreation departments and other programs began to provide services to individuals with disabilities (Reynolds & O'Morrow, 1985).

Mid - to late 1960s

"Although there was a concern for the ill and disabled in the community, it was not until the mid-1960s that a definite trend toward the provision of such services was established" (Reynolds & O'Morrow, 1985, p.7). Studies in the mid- to late 1960s in the U.S., however, suggest that individuals with disabilities were not receiving community-based leisure services to a large extent (Andres, 1970 [1967 study]; Hayes, 1969; Marson, 1965 [cited in Thompson, 1969]; Mitchell & Hillman, 1969; Stracke, 1969). Although these studies varied as to geographical area and populations examined, Nesbitt (1970) concluded that approximately 35 percent of the nation's local park and recreation departments offered some type of recreation program to individuals with disabilities. He further concluded that the proportion of resources devoted to such services was small, only a small proportion of those needing services were receiving them, and the personnel directing these programs had limited professional preparation (p. 35).

The 1970s

As a part of the larger human rights movement in the U.S., which focused upon equal opportunity for various groups of devalued citizens (e.g., blacks and other ethnic minorities, women, older people) during the 1960s and 1970s, individuals with disabilities also began to advocate their right of equal opportunity. Significant legislation was enacted for people with disabilities, recognizing their right to equal access to all services, including leisure services. Among these laws are the Architectural and Transportation Barriers Act of 1968; the Rehabilitation Act of 1973, especially Section 504; the Education for All Handicapped Children Act in 1975; the Developmental Disabilities Act in 1975; and the Rehabilitation Act of 1978. Because of some of this and earlier legislation, a significant number of individuals with disabilities who had formerly resided in large state hospitals and schools, were now living in the community or at least in smaller residential settings located in the community . Therapeutic recreation specialists who practiced in community settings thus were faced with attempting to meet the leisure needs of a considerably larger number of less able participants (Brown, 1975; Pomeroy, 1974; Stevens, 1971).

During the 1970s, issues related to the rights of individuals with disabilities to receive leisure services were frequently discussed in the therapeutic recreation literature. In addition to the legislation which was enacted, the introduction of the principle of normalization (Wolfensburger, 1972) created further discussion and writings, both in the U.S. and Canada.   These writings addressed the relationship between therapeutic recreation and community recreation programs (Abrahams, 1971; Lindley, 1972); described and discussed clinical therapeutic recreation programs which were oriented toward community participation (Dunham, 1971; Hoffman & Ely, 1973); and discussed community recreation programs designed for individuals with disabilities (Bernheim, 1975; Cappel, 1974; Chapman, 1975; Mitchell, 1971; Pomeroy, 1974; Woods, 1971). Normalization was described and applied (Bullock, 1979; Dixon , 1978; Mathews, 1977; Pomeroy, 1974; Reynolds, 1979); moving beyond the medical model as a philosophy and definition of therapeutic recreation was suggested (Rowthorn, 1978; Rusalem, 1973; Witt, 1977); and the role of the therapeutic recreation specialist as an advocate was explored (Edginton & Compton, 1975; Kinney, Edginton, & Granek, 1977; Robb, 1975; Weiner, 1975). A special issue of the *Therapeutic Recreation Journal*, "Mainstreaming Handicapped Individuals in the Community," appeared late in 1979 (Hitzhusen).

Canadian recreators, who have typically expressed the advocacy-oriented philosophy that it is the responsibility of providers of typical leisure services to respond to the right that individuals with disabilities have to these services, produced many more writings in the area. These publications most often explored critical issues in greater depth, since the integration efforts appeared to be more focused and widespread. Notable among these are the *Journal of Leisurability* and Hutchinson and Lord's book, *Recreation Integration* (1979), which provided the first extensive theoretical examination, and also included practical applications, of normalization and integration in leisure services.

Studies conducted in Texas (Hayes & Smith, 1973) and Iowa (Edginton, Compton, Ritchie, & Vederman, 1975) around the time of the legislation, however, reflected only somewhat higher proportions of municipal park and recreation departments providing services to individuals with disabilities than had been reported in the earlier studies. Percentages of departments providing services, which were reported according to population served, ranged from 47 percent providing services to individuals with mental retardation to 6 percent providing services to individuals with emotional disturbances. In both states, department personnel directing the programs were few and had limited preparation. In Texas a little over half (52 percent) of the departments reported that they did feel a responsibility to provide services to special populations. In Iowa a larger proportion (76 percent) either strongly or moderately agreed that the department did have a responsibility to provide services to special populations, although agreement was strong for only 35 percent. Concerning the kind of information and/or assistance that departments in Texas believed would be of value in providing services to people with disabilities, additional staff was listed most frequently, followed by additional finances, special knowledge about handicaps, specially trained staff, and in-service training for staff. In Iowa, lack of funds was the most common reason for not providing services, with fewer respondents indicating lack of skills necessary to organize services and lack of awareness of the need for services.

Two state-level studies conducted later in the 1970s reflected little change, although departments were offering services to individuals with a wider range of disabilities. Percentages of departments in Indiana which provided services (Austin, Peterson, &z Peccarelli, 1978) ranged from 38 percent to individuals with physical disabilities or mental retardation to 6 percent to those who were chemical abusers. A higher share of departments were providing services to individuals with emotional disturbances than in previous studies. The majority of programs were conducted by the general staffs of departments. Eighty percent of departments either strongly or moderately agreed that they had a responsibility to provide services to special populations, with 44 percent strongly agreeing. Lack of funds and the services being provided by other agencies were the reasons that departments were not providing programs.

For Oregon, Williams (1979) reported that 47 percent of municipal park and recreation departments provided service to individuals with disabilities. Cited as reasons for not offering services were lack of funds, lack of interest, and inaccessible facilities.

Nolan (1978) conducted a national study to replicate Stracke's 1969 study of the attitudes of community recreators about therapeutic recreation. During the 9 years between the studies, there were significant increases in the number of community recreation directors and supervisors who had a therapeutic recreation staff member (although only 15 percent had such staff members) and in the number of persons with disabilities using community facilities in a group. Other positive changes included significant decreases in community recreators who felt that individuals with disabilities were difficult to program for in a community recreation setting, in those who felt that the recreation needs of people with disabilities were different from those of other people, and in the attitude that the field of therapeutic recreation is confined to medical settings. Less positive changes also occurred in two areas, with a significant decrease of community recreators who would encourage referrals from therapeutic recreation specialists and a significant increase of those who felt that programming for participants with disabilities is expensive.

Current Status of Community-Based Practice
in Therapeutic Recreation

The 1980s in the U.S. have represented a very different approach to assuring the rights of devalued populations to equal opportunity. While the concern continued to be apparent, the role of government and legal remedies to assure equal access was de-emphasized, and efforts were made to weaken, if not eliminate, the significant legislation which had been adopted in the 1960s and 1970s (DeJong & Lifchez, 1983; Goldman, 1984).

While the volume and depth of writing concerned with normalization and integration continued in Canada, publications and discussions of these issues declined in the U.S. during the 1980s. Most of the articles discussed mainstreaming in community and educational settings and focused on leisure education (Chinn & Joswiak, 1981; Collard, 1981; Dixon, 1980; Pollingue & Cobb, 1986; Voeltz &

Wuerch, 1981). Dunn (1981) and McDonald (1985) discussed main-streaming in transitional programs, while West (1982), Schleien, Olson, Rogers, and McLafferty (1985) and Richardson, Wilson, Wetherald, and Peters (1987) produced articles which addressed mainstreaming in community-based programs. Integration issues relative to more severely disabled individuals were addressed by Certo, Schleien, and Hunter (1983), Crawford (1986), and Schleien, Krotee, Mustonen, Kelterborn, and Schermer (1987); and the attitudes of able-bodied preschoolers were studied by Hoenk and Mobily (1987). The lack of articles in the area may be related to regulatory changes which provided severe challenges to therapeutic recreation programs in clinical settings and the resulting need to focus professional efforts in that area. However, as Hutchison (1983) suggests:

> Examples of sound integration effort are still few and far between; the reality is that many individuals who live with a handicap still have little opportunity to be full participants in their communities. It seems that there are still many questions which need to be answered about the integration process before we can hope to move significantly beyond the current level of integration activity. (p. 26)

A study that examined services in Minnesota (Schleien & Werder, 1985) indicated that larger proportions of departments were providing services to a wider range of individuals with disabilities, ranging from 57 percent providing services to people with mental retardation to 11 percent to adjudicated offenders. Fifteen percent of departments had full-time therapeutic recreation specialists responsible for services to special populations, while in 53 percent of departments, general recreation staff held this responsibility.

This study also examined community education agencies, as well as municipal park and recreation departments. Most of the respondents from both types of agencies felt that the responsibility for leisure services for people with disabilities should be shared among agencies. However, 78 percent of municipal park and recreation departments felt that community education programs should be primarily responsible, while 93 percent of community education programs felt that the municipal park and recreation department should have primary responsibility. Thirty-three percent of community agencies (municipal park and recreation and community education) indicated that the reason for not providing services was because they believed other agencies provided such services, while 43 percent indicated that lack of funds was the reason for not providing services.

The only recent national study found that 43 percent of municipal park and recreation departments provided services to individuals with disabilities (Halberg, Mitchell, Hendrick, Breshears, and Hillman 1986). The results of this study reflect some increase in the proportion of departments providing services, but that increase is small, considering the number of years which had passed in general and in relationship to the legislation which mandated equal opportunity for individuals with disabilities. Of those departments which did not provide such services, 47 percent felt that they had a responsibility to do so. Thus, over 30 percent of departments either did not provide services to people with disabilities or did not feel that they have the responsibility to provide these services. The largest reason that services were not offered was the perception that another agency provided the service, followed by insufficient funds, no demands for services, and lack of trained staff.

The main reasons for not providing community leisure services to individuals with disabilities have remained relatively constant over the years (i.e., lack of financial resources, lack of trained staff, and architectural barriers). However, Wilkinson (1983) has suggested that attitudes and philosophy are seen as the major barriers by those with experience in mainstreaming, while the more typical reasons are given by those without such experience. Kennedy, Austin, and Smith (1987) address this issue.

Although these problems are formidable, Vaughan and Winslow (1979) have presented a number of specific solutions for dealing with each of them. Given the motivation, people can overcome these problems. Of greater apparent significance is the reported lack of awareness of the need for these programs and the feeling that other agencies already provide such programs. These perceptions on the part of administrators of park and recreation systems allow them to remove themselves entirely from the responsibility of providing recreation for special populations.

Halberg et al. (1986) also report that resources (budget and staff) devoted to programs for people with disabilities were limited in departments which provided these services. The proportion of the total departmental budget devoted to services for individuals with disabilities was small, with 70 percent of departments allocating from 1 to 5 percent of the department budget and 19 percent expending from 6 to 10 percent of the budget. The number of full-time staff involved directly with individuals with disabilities was also small with 37 percent having no full-time staff and 38 percent having one full-time employee.

The nature of the programs which are provided by municipal park and recreation departments is apparent when the results are examined in terms of planning components, procedures for working with clients, and available services.

Table 1
Program Characteristics of Municipal Park and Recreation Department Services to Individuals with Disabilities

Characteristic	Number	Percent
Planning components		
Policy or philosophy (written or verbal)	120	37.7
Long-term objectives	120	37.3
General plan to upgrade services	158	49.8
Consumer or parent involvement in planning	220	69.4
Evaluation procedures	173	54.6
Procedures for working with clients		
Referral system (agencies refer clients to you)	181	56.6
Method of obtaining background information on clients	190	59.2
Method of developing an individualized program plan	107	33.5
Method of helping a client implement a plan	136	42.6
Rreferral system from department to other agencies	192	59.8
Services available to clients		
Leisure counseling	108	34.1
Leisure education	129	39.5
Community leisure resource guidance	199	63.2

Table 1 cont.

Characteristic	Number	Percent
Leisure exploration (chance to try out activities)	227	71.4
Program to upgrade recreation and leisure skills	205	64.5

The information presented in Table 1 indicates that a relatively small percentage of departments engage in systematic or long-term planning of programs for individuals with disabilities.

Respondents were asked if they had available a variety of procedures for working individually with clients. An examination of Table 1 reveals that around half of the departments had most of these procedures (42.6-59.8 percent), although only one third employed a specific method of developing an individualized program plan with a participant.

Respondents were also asked to indicate whether specific services which are important to mainstreaming and integration were available to clients. From Table 1 it is clear that programs tend to focus on participation and skill-building, with a smaller percentage of the departments offering leisure counseling and leisure education (34.1-39.5 percent).

Major Issues in Community-Based Therapeutic Recreation Practice

Based upon this most recent study, two major issues in community-based therapeutic recreation practice are apparent. First, less than half of all municipal park and recreation departments provide services to citizens with disabilities, and over 30 percent neither provide nor perceive a responsibility to provide these services. Unfortunately, data are not available which evaluate the extent and nature of community-based therapeutic recreation service in nonprofit and for-profit agencies and organizations which provide leisure services to the general population. However, it seems likely that comparable or even smaller proportions of these types of agencies provide services to individuals with disabilities. Thus, it can be assumed that a large number of people with disabilities are not receiving the community-based therapeutic recreation services to which they have a right. "It is estimated that 90 percent of ill and handicapped in the United States are underserved and inadequately served in recreation" (Checklist of Special Recreation Advocacy Functions, 1986).

The second issue is a lack of resources and a limited orientation toward mainstreaming and integration. Of those departments which provide services, financial and staff resources are small, programs and services are not systematically planned, and programs are directed toward participation and skill-building in group settings. Community-based therapeutic recreation specialists need to examine their primary role to determine whether their major responsibility is to provide segregated leisure services or to serve as facilitators and advocates for mainstreaming and integration.

Issues in implementing mainstreaming and integration

Some community-based agencies have made substantial efforts to implement an integration-oriented philosophy. Based upon the specific experiences of two of these agencies (Halberg, Earle, and Turpel, 1985), as well as others (see Hutchison, 1983, for a summary of research), some of the very real and difficult issues which must be addressed to effectively mainstream and integrate participants have become apparent. The most basic issues are to recognize that integration efforts must be individualized (Lord, 1983) and that "true integration is not an easy process; it is complex, multifaceted and challenging. The process tends to take more time and resources than one originally anticipates, and is slow and at times frustrating" (Halberg, Earle, & Turpel, 1985, p. 29). The lack of staff and financial resources devoted to community-based therapeutic recreation services, as well as the limited individualized services necessary for mainstreaming and integration in municipal park and recreation departments (Halberg, Mitchell, Hendrick, Breshears, & Hillman, 1986) and other agencies makes this a difficult issue with which to deal.

Another issue is concerned with the breadth and depth of integration efforts. In some cases, community-based therapeutic recreation staff have reported that participants indicate a preference for segregated activities. This apparent preference is in need of further examination.

The participant may not have been thoroughly prepared for integrated activities. While an adequate activity skill level for participation in specific activities may not have been developed, a more likely reason for preference for segregated activities may be that the focus of the integration effort may have been narrow, directed toward the necessary activity skills, rather than focusing more broadly to also address the social skills and support necessary to participate in integrated activities. The participant's friends may be participating in segregated activities, with no social support having been developed for participation in integrated activities. A special issue of *Leisurability*, "Friendship & Integration" (Hutchison, 1986), focuses on this issue. Another deficit related to the inadequate preparation of the participant for integration may be a failure to facilitate the development of the self-advocacy skills necessary for initial, but more important, continuing participation in integrated activities.

Another reason that participants report a preference for segregated activities may be that the therapeutic recreation specialist in community practice may not have worked specifically enough with the managers, staff, and other participants in the activities and agencies to which integration is planned to facilitate successful integration. Work with these agencies may include in-service training with managers and staff; individual consultation to the participant with a disability and to managers, staff, and volunteers; and continuing to facilitate social support and advocacy as needed.

These issues related to the actual mainstreaming and integration of individuals with disabilities suggest that therapeutic recreation specialists in community-based practice need to examine the nature and scope of their programs carefully. Participants need to be thoroughly and realistically prepared for integrated experiences, a social support system needs to be facilitated, and the agencies in which integration is to occur also need to be well-prepared. If these challenging issues are not addressed, integration is likely to fail.

The Implications of Issues in Therapeutic Recreation to Community-Based Practice

As has been discussed earlier in this chapter and in other chapters in this book, critical issues face the therapeutic recreation profession as a whole. These issues also obviously have impact on community practice. Perhaps the greatest issue with which the profession must deal is accountability, the need to be able to specifically document the effects of therapeutic recreation services. While this issue is obviously apparent in clinical practice as increasingly stringent regulatory and legislative mandates appear, it is also true in community practice as budgets for human services, including leisure services, become smaller.

As part of the need for accountability, another issue with which the total profession must deal is changing regulatory requirements, especially the prospective payment system for third-party reimbursement of health care services. While this issue affects more centrally clinical practice, implications are also apparent for community practice. Primarily because of the prospective payment system, more functionally limited clients, who formerly would have been served in clinical settings for a longer period of time, are now back in the community at an earlier stage of the rehabilitation process. This suggests that community-based therapeutic recreation practice must now reevaluate its role and purpose in order to provide needed services for these more limited participants. If the needs of more limited participants are to be met, some services may need to be more intervention-oriented, similar to what has typically been provided in clinical settings, prior to providing services which more specifically address mainstreaming and integration.

A related issue of concern to the total profession is found in the suggestion of some that therapeutic recreation is actually two entities:

> We believe that therapeutic recreation and special recreation (or recreation for persons with disabilities) stand as two separate entities that occasionally overlap. Overlap occurs when a therapeutic recreation program (directed primarily toward a specific therapeutic outcome through a planned intervention) offers the client an accompanying benefit of a recreative experience, or when a special recreation program (aimed primarily toward the provision of a recreative experience) serves as an intervention, bringing about a desired therapeutic benefit. (Kennedy, Austin, & Smith, 1987, p.14)

While some specialization is necessary, the degree of "overlap" between clinical and community practice may be greater than suggested and may become even greater as more limited clients leave clinical settings to return to the community, as discussed above. This situation requires that community practice provide services which are directed toward therapeutic intervention if it is to meet the needs of clients currently being released from clinical programs. It may even suggest that traditional clinical practice may have to occur to a greater extent in transitional and community-based programs if clients are to obtain the types of services they need. Although Kennedy, Austin, and

Smith (1987) suggest that the primary orientation of community-based programs will remain toward recreation participation, they also suggest that a trend in community practice is toward providing therapeutically oriented programs which offer "purposeful interventions for clients needing goal-directed programming" (p. 324).

Clinical and community-based practitioners must reexamine what have been their traditional roles. It seems likely that clinical practitioners will be providing services to clients earlier in the rehabilitation process when more basic issues may be the major concerns of the client, and that community-based practitioners will be providing services to clients who are in need of more specific therapeutic interventions. This will not only require a reexamination of traditional roles but also closer communication and cooperation between clinical and community-based specialists if clients are to obtain optimal leisure independence and the leisure lifestyles which they desire.

Conclusions and Summary

A variety of critical issues currently severely challenge the practice of therapeutic recreation. All of these issues, whether they are more generally issues in therapeutic recreation or issues of more specific concern to community practice, spring from two basic roots: the specific goals and approaches to providing therapeutic recreation services within and across settings, and adequate resources to provide services. Although a variety of issues have been discussed in this chapter, the major issues that community practice in therapeutic recreation must deal with appear to be the following.

A major issue in community practice in therapeutic recreation is the lack of availability of these services.

1.0: *Community-based therapeutic recreation services generally are not available to many individuals with disabilities.*

In order to address the general lack of community-based services, the reasons given for not providing services must be examined.

    1.1: *Some of the reasons given for the lack of community-based services (lack of perception of responsibility and a perception that there is no demand for these services) need to be explored and addressed.*

Additionally, it is apparent that more resources are needed to provide community-based therapeutic recreation services.

1.2:   *Additional resources, especially financial and staff, are needed to expand the availability of community-based therapeutic recreation services.*

The need for accountability, including the ability to document the efficacy of therapeutic recreation in all settings, is another major issue.

2.0:   *The practitioner has difficulty demonstrating in measurable ways that community-based therapeutic recreation services do have specific and positive effects on participants/clients.*

Being able to document the effects of community-based therapeutic recreation services implies providing more specific individualized services and also focusing upon social and environmental barriers in the community. Three areas of concern in community-based practice in therapeutic recreation are apparent. Many community-based programs do not appear to be specifically directed toward mainstreaming and integration.

2.1:   *The currently predominant emphasis in community-based services—participation and skill-building in group settings—needs to shift to more individualized approaches geared toward integration and mainstreaming.*

2.2:   *The social support systems and the attitudinal and environmental barriers found in integrated settings need greater exploration as major components of mainstreaming and integration efforts.*

Because of the prospective payment system for third-party reimbursement for health care services, clients are leaving clinical settings earlier in the rehabilitation process.

2.3:   *A major shift in orientation for many community-based programs is needed if more limited clients/participants are to receive the intervention-oriented therapeutic recreation services which they may need.*

An additional and major issue related to some of the above issues, but that also has roots that go back to the beginnings of therapeutic recreation as a profession (see Meyer, 1980), is the degree of relationship between clinical and community practice in therapeutic recreation. This issue may have greater importance if the profession becomes essentially two professions.

3.0:   *The critical need for effective communication and coordina-*
        tion between clinical and community-based specialists in as-
        sisting the client/participant to reach optimal leisure inde-
        pendence and transition back into the community may become
        a major issue.

Although the total therapeutic recreation profession and those who practice in community-based programs have major issues with which to deal, the ultimate result of how these issues are addressed and resolved will be found with the clients/participants to whom services are provided. These clients/participants have the right to a desired leisure lifestyle and optimal leisure independence through the highest quality of coordinated therapeutic recreation services possible. This can occur   only if therapeutic recreation specialists from both the clinical and the community sectors work together to address the issues critical to the future of the profession.

Study Questions

1.   What are the implications to the mainstreaming and integration of individuals with disabilities if therapeutic recreation becomes two separate entities (therapeutic recreation and special recreation) with a small degree of overlap?

2   List innovative and realistic ways that resources could be increased for the provision of community-based therapeutic recreation services, given that government support is unlikely to increase in the near future.

3.   Defend or refute the following statement: Individuals with disabilities should adapt to leisure programs for all citizens, because adapting these programs to the disabled will violate the rights of nondisabled participants.

4.   Discuss the implications of the adoption of DRGs and third-party reimbursement of health care services to community practice in therapeutic recreation.

5.   Why do you feel that services to individuals with disabilities by municipal park and recreation departments have not significantly increased over the years?

6.   Why do you feel that services to individuals with disabilities by municipal park and recreation departments tend to be oriented toward participation and skill-building in group settings?

7.   Why do some participants in community-based therapeutic recreation programs express a preference for segregated activities?

References

Abrahams, J. (1971). 1970 Report to the Members of the NTRS-APRS Community Liaison Committee. *Therapeutic Recreation Journal, 5* (1), 9-10.

Andres, C. (1970). The Status of Municipal Recreation for the Mentally Retarded. *Therapeutic Recreation Journal, 4* (1), 30.

Austin, D.R., Peterson, J.A., & Peccarelli, L.M. (1978). The Status of Services for Special Populations in Park and Recreation Departments in the State of Indiana. *Therapeutic Recreation Journal, 12* (1), 50-56.

Bernheim,S. (1975). Don Quixote—Therapeutic Recreation in the Community. *Therapeutic Recreation Journal, 9* (3), 95-98.

Brown, R.C.(1975). If You're Not Part of the Solution, You're Part of the Problem. *Therapeutic Recreation Journal, 9* (1), 7-10.

Bullock, C.C. (1979). Mainstreaming—in Recreation Too? *Therapeutic Recreation Journal, 13* (2), 5-11.

Cappel, M.L. (1974). Providing Community Recreation Services to Special Populations. *Therapeutic Recreation Journal, 8* (2), 72-77.

Certo, N., Schleien, S., & Hunter, D. (1983). An Ecological Assessment Inventory to Facilitate Community Recreation Participation by Severely Disabled Individuals. *Therapeutic Recreation Journal, 17* (3), 29-38.

Chapman, F.M. (1975). Leisure and Special Community Populations. *Therapeutic Recreation Journal, 9* (1), 11-17.

Checklist of Special Recreation Advocacy Functions. (1986). *Special Recreation Digest, 3* (1), 15-18.

Chinn, K.A., & Joswiak, K.F. (1981). Leisure Education and Leisure Counseling. *Therapeutic Recreation Journal, 15* (4), 4-7.

Collard, K. (1981). Leisure Education in Schools: Why, Who, and the Need for Advocacy. *Therapeutic Recreation Journal, 15* (4), 8-16.

Crawford, M.E. (1986). Development of Generalization of Lifetime Leisure Skills for Multi-handicapped Participants. *Therapeutic Recreation Journal, 20* (4), 48-60.

DeJong, G., & Lifchez, R. (1983). Physical Disability and Public Policy. *Scientific American, 248* (6), 40-48.

Dixon, J. (1978). Expanding Individual Control in Leisure Participation While Enlarging the Concept of Normalcy. *Therapeutic Recreation Journal, 12* (3), 20-24.

Dixon, J. (1980). Mainstreaming and Leisure Education for the Mentally Retarded. *Therapeutic Recreation Journal, 14* (1), 30-35.

Dunham, C. (1971). Community Recreation for the Psychiatric Rehabilitant. *Therapeutic Recreation Journal, 5* (3), 113-118.

Dunn, J.K. (1981). Leisure Education: Meeting the Challenge of Increasing Leisure Independence of Residents of Psychiatric Transitional Facilities. *Therapeutic Recreation Journal, 15* (4), 17-23.

Edginton, C.R. & Compton, D.M. (1975). Consumerism and Advocacy: A Conceptual Framework for the Therapeutic Recreator. *Therapeutic Recreation Journal, 9* (1), 26-31.

Edginton, C.R., Compton, D.M., Ritchie, A.J. d& Vederman, R.K. (1975). The Status of Services for Special Populations in Park and Recreation Departments in the State of Iowa. *Therapeutic Recreation Journal, 9* (3), 109-116.

Goldman, C.E. (1984). Advocacy in the 80s. *Disabled USA 1,* 21-23.

Halberg, K.J., Earle, P. & Turpel, L.T. (1985). Implementing Recreation Integration, Specific Issues and Practical Solutions. *Journal of Physical Education, Recreation and Dance, 56* (5), 29-31.

Halberg, K.J., Mitchell, N.Z., Hendrick, F., Breshears, W., & Hillman, W. (1986). The Status of Services to Special Populations by Municipal Park and Recreation Departments in the United States. Manuscript submitted for publication.

Hayes, G.A. (1969). Recreation services for the mentally retarded in the state of Kansas. *Therapeutic Recreation Journal, 3* (3), 13-19.

Hayes, G.A. & Smith, D. (1973). Municipal Recreation Services for Special Populations in Texas. *Therapeutic Recreation Journal, 7* (1), 23-30.

Hitzhusen, G. (Ed.). (1979). Mainstreaming Handicapped Individuals in the Community(Special issue). *Therapeutic Recreation Journal, 13* (4).

Hoenk, A.H. & Mobily, K.E. (1987). Mainstreaming the Play Environment: Effects of Previous Exposure and Salience of Disability. *Therapeutic Recreation Journal, 21* (4), 23-31.

Hoffman C.A. & Ely, B.D. (1973). Providing Recreation Counseling in a Psychiatric Hospital: A Vital Community Link. *Therapeutic Recreation Journal, 7* (3), 3-7.

Howe-Murphy, R. & Charboneau, B.G. (1987). *Therapeutic Recreation Intervention, an Ecological Approach.* Englewood Cliffs, NJ: Prentice Hall.

Hutchison, P. (1980). Perceptions of Disabled Persons Regarding Barriers to Community Involvement. *Journal of Leisurability, 7* (3), 4-16.

Hutchison, P. (1983). The Status of Recreation Integration Research. *Journal of Leisurability, 10* (3), 26-35.

Hutchison, P. (Ed.). (1986). Friendship and Integration (Special issue). *Journal of Leisurability, 13* (1).

Hutchison, P. & Lord, J. (1979). Recreation Integration. Ottawa, Ontario: *Leisurability.*

Kennedy, D.W., Auston, D.R. & Smith,R.W. (1987). *Special Recreation: Opportunities for Persons with Disabilities,* Philadelphia: Saunders.

Kinney, W.B., Edginton, C.E.,& Granek, M. (1977). Rules for Radical Recreation Workers. *Therapeutic Recreation Journal, 11* (3), 105-111.

Lindley, D.D. (1972). Problems of Integrating Therapeutic Recreation Programs into the Community. *Therapeutic Recreation Journal, 6* (1), 8-10, 34-35.

Lord, J. (1983). Reflections on a Decade of Integration. *Journal of Leisurability, 10* (4), 4-11.

Mathews, P.R. (1977). Recreation and the Normalization of the Mentally Retarded. *Therapeutic Recreation Journal, 11* (3), 112-114.

McDonald, J.M. (1985). Special Adaptive Recreation as Intervention in Vocational and Transitional Services for Handicapped Youth. *Therapeutic Recreation Journal,19* (3), 17-27.

Meyer, L.E. (1980). *Philosophical Alternatives and the Professionalization of Therapeutic Recreation.* Arlington, VA: National Recreation and Park Association.

Mitchell, H.J. (1971). A Community Recreation Program for the Mentally Retarded. *Therapeutic Recreation Journal, 5* (1), 3-8.

Mitchell, H.J. & Hillman, W.A. (1969). The Municipal Recreation Department and Recreation Services for the Mentally Retarded. *Therapeutic Recreation Journal, 3* (4), 32-40.

Nesbitt, J.A. (1970). The Handicapped Child: Therapeutic Recreation Service Needs in Program, Manpower and Research. *Therapeutic Recreation Journal, 4* (2), 33-40.

Nolan, K. (1978). A Comparison of Two Surveys Concerning the Relationship Between the Therapeutic Recreator and the Community Recreator *Therapeutic Recreation Journal, 12* (1), 40-49.

Polingue, A.B. & Cobb, H.B. (1986). Leisure Education; A Model for Facilitating Community Integration for Moderately/Severely Mentally Retarded Adults. *Therapeutic Recreation Journal, 20* (3), 54-62.

Pomeroy, J. (1974). The Handicapped are Out of Hiding; Implications for Community Recreation. *Therapeutic Recreation Journal, 8* (3), 120-128.

Reynolds, R.P. (1979). What is Normalization and How Can You Do It? *Parks and Recreation, 14* (8), 33-34, 51.

Reynolds, R.P. & O'Morrow, G.S. (1985). *Problems, Issues and Concepts in Therapeutic Recreation.* Englewood Cliffs, NJ: Prentice Hall.

Richardson, D., Wilson, B., Wetherald, L., & Peters, J. (1987). Mainstreaming Initiative: An Innovative Approach to Recreation and Leisure Services in a Community Setting. *Therapeutic Recreation Journal, 21* (2), 9-19.

Robb, G.M. (1975). Therapeutic Recreation: Stagnation in a Time of Change. *Therapeutic Recreation Journal, 9* (2), 47-53.

Rowthorn, A.W. (1978). An open letter to Peter Witt: a response to his article "Therapeutic Recreation: the Outmoded Model." *Therapeutic Recreation Journal, 12* (1), 7-9.

Rusalem, H. (1973). An Alternative to the Therapeutic Model in Therapeutic Recreation. *Therapeutic Recreation Journal, 7* (1), 8-15.

Schleien, S.J., Krotee, M.L., Mustonen, T., Kelterborn, B., & Schermer, A.D. (1987). The Effect of Integrating Children with Autism into a Physical Activity and Recreation Setting. *Therapeutic Recreation Journal, 21* (4), 52-62.

Schleien, S.J., & Werder, J.K. 1985. Perceived Responsibilities of Special Recreation Services in Minnesota. *Therapeutic Recreation Journal, 19* (3),51-62.

Schleien, S., Olson,K., Rogers, N. & McLafferty, M. (1985) Integrating Children with Severe Handicaps into Recreation and Physical Education Programs. *Journal of Park and Recreation Administration, 3* (3), 50-66.

Stevens, A. (1971). Recreation in Community Mental Health. *Therapeutic Recreation Journal, 5 (1),* 13-18.

Stracke, D. (1969). The Role of the Therapeutic Recreator in Relation to the Community Recreator. *Therapeutic Recreation Journal, 3* (1), 26-29.

Thompson,M. (1969). The Status of Recreation for the Handicapped as Related to Community and Voluntary Agencies. *Therapeutic Recreation Journal, 3* (2), 20-23.

Vaughan, J.L. & Winslow, R. (Eds.). (1979). *Guidelines for Community Based Recreation Programs for Special Populations.* Arlington,VA: National Recreation and Park Association.

Voeltz, L.M. & Wuerch,B.B. (1981). A Comprehensive Approach to Leisure Education and Leisure Counseling for the Severely Handicapped Person. *Therapeutic Recreation Journal, 15* (4), 24-35.

Weiner, A. (1975). The Recreation Advocate: Your Leisure Insurance Agent. *Therapeutic Recreation Journal, 9* (2), 63-67.

West, P.C. (1982). Organizational Stigma in Metropolitan Park and Recreation Agencies. *Therapeutic Recreation Journal, 16* (4), 35-41.

Wilkinson, P. (1983). Disabled Children and Integrated Play Environments. *Recreation Research Review, 10* (1), 20-28.

Williams, B.J. (1979). The Status of Recreation for Individuals with Handicaps in Oregon Park and Recreation Agencies. *Therapeutic Recreation Journal, 13* (3), 44-48.

Witt, P.A. (1977). Therapeutic Recreation: The Outmoded Label. *Therapeutic Recreation Journal, 11* (2), 39041.

Wolfensburger, W. (1972). *The Principle of Normalization in Human Services.* Toronto, Ontario: National Institute on Mental Retardation.

Woods, M.L. (1971). Integration of the Handicapped into Community Recreation Centers. *Therapeutic Recreation Journal, 5* (3), 108-112.

CLINICAL ISSUES IN THERAPEUTIC RECREATION

Terry Kinney
John Shank

Introduction

Clinical practice has become a much-used term lately. Discussion with a variety of practitioners has revealed, however, that the term carries different connotations, and subsequent implications, from setting to setting and even from practitioner to practitioner. As the discipline of therapeutic recreation is being moved towards a new era of definition—that is, the recognition of "special recreation" as different from "therapeutic" or "therapy" (Kennedy, Austin, & Smith, 1986)—the understanding of the meaning and issues surrounding clinical practice will take on profound importance. A strained relationship exists between various proponents of elements of therapeutic recreation (such as those who are pushing very hard for TR to achieve clinical status) and those who are attempting to hold onto a solitary, unified frame of reference for the entire discipline. Subjective observation would suggest that semantic differences have contributed to that perceived strain.

In whatever manner the discipline is to progress, it is clear that the issues involving clinical practice must be defined and discussed to the point of some agreement. Failure to do so may result in a state of discordance, whereby our terminology will become confounding and meaningless and certain claims to professional status impotent.

In an attempt to guide discussion, we suggest that the following issues are foremost in such an examination:

1. There is question as to why *clinical practice* is such a popular term at this point in time.
2. The discipline has not defined *clinical practice* and explained how it is related to other aspects of therapeutic recreation.
3. The rationale for conducting clinical practice within the context of human achievement and the continuum of human functioning has not been defined.

4. There is confusion as to where clinical practice occurs.
5. There are no standards as to who should do clinical practice and what skills are required.
6. There is question as to whether university curricula can provide the proper education for conducting clinical practice.

We raise and discuss these issues in the ensuing chapter. While at times we have come close to providing our own perception of the answers to the issues, we have attempted to avoid that because discussion and consideration of alternative solutions is required. However, it is our opinion that such debate needs to be undertaken quickly. As a discipline, we have waited long to address these issues, and those regulatory bodies and influential policymakers that affect our services are growing restless.

Issues Involving Clinical Application

*Issue 1: There is question as to why **clinical practice** is such a popular term at this point in time.*

There has been an apparent desire among many therapeutic recreation specialists to be associated with "clinical practice." This may reflect a perception of greater prestige and credibility—an important issue for young professionals in particular. It may also reflect a growing concern over the difficulty in obtaining third-party reimbursement for therapeutic recreation services, a fact that affects both credibility and security.

Evidence of this desire for clinical association can be found in the clamor for licensure, even though state legislators are resistant to the licensing of new professional groups. A critical factor in licensure consideration is whether delivery of service has the potential for harming the public in some way, a consideration in which the therapeutic recreation discipline lacks substantive data. Further indications of this desire for clinical association can be found in the aspiration among some practitioners to distinguish themselves from those who place greatest emphasis on the *recreation* in the term *therapeutic recreation*, choosing instead to emphasize therapeutic.

The popularity of the term *clinical*, is an interesting phenomenon since very little support can be found in legal mandates for therapeutic recreation. For instance, the Allied Health Professions Act, being considered for reauthorization in 1988, does not mention therapeutic recreation, although physical therapy, occupational therapy, speech—language pathology, and audiology are named. This act provides for the training of allied health professionals where there is considered a shortage and a need to retain those currently serving the public. In other pieces of legislation and regulation affecting public health care, therapeutic recreation is typically nonexistent. In short, it is a discipline that is not usually associated with health care or rehabilitation in a clinical context.

The popularity for clinical association is also intriguing when we consider other significant forces that would work against such an association. For example, the health care industry has indicated for some time now that the future of health care will be characterized by "super-sick" hospitals where critically ill patients would stay for shorter periods while undergoing rigorous treatments. These hospitalizations would be characterized by very sophisticated and highly technical medical treatments, leaving patients little time and energy to address much else. Another significant force against a clinical association is the frequent indication that the future of health care and rehabilitation will be in home health care, including hospice and life care communities where the emphasis of service shifts to a more general "quality of life" service as opposed to specific physical or behavioral interventions.

This is not to say that therapeutic recreation has no place in clinical practice; the point is that what that place is has not been clearly identified or articulated to those who influence the status quo. If therapeutic recreation is to survive as a component of the health care scenario of the future, it needs to move beyond the rhetoric and trendy proclamations of "we are clinical," and define and develop its assets into clear and relevant contributions to health care and human services.

*Issue 2: The discipline has not defined **clinical practice** and explained how it is related to other aspects of therapeutic recreation.*

Although many would contend that writing a recreation treatment plan with measurable goals and objectives constitutes clinical practice, intervention approaches require certain skills and insights manifested in timely judgments. What happens when the program plan or the individualized treatment plan does not go as planned? What happens when there is a marked decrease in compliance or cooperation, and the indicators of progress are no longer there? What happens when an unexpected turn in the health status results in the client's being admitted to intensive care?

Clinical work is rarely simple and linear; therapy is frequently marked with ups and downs. Consequently, there is a need to make judgments that are sensitive, insightful, and at times risky. A characteristic of good clinical practice is knowing when a chosen intervention approach is working and when a goal is unrealistic.

There is some evidence of recent attempts to think through the intervention process in an effort to assist practitioners with clinical intervention. Recent conferences have included significant and promising work in the area of treatment protocols. Protocols outline specific interventions and supports that are believed to be appropriate and effective with specific problems or needs of clients. They generally include specific actions associated with assessment of needs, intervention processes, and evaluation of predetermined outcomes. According to Keogh-Hoss (1988), protocols enable continuity, consistency, expediency, and effectiveness.

It is also essential to good clinical practice to know when evidence of change should come from or be seen in the client. That is, identifying the sources of problems or handicapping conditions within the environment (e.g., a physical threat or a lack of safety, a limited social network, or a dysfunctional family) is an important process for the therapeutic recreation specialist to undertake (Howe-Murphy & Charboneau, 1987).

There has been a great deal of debate, especially recently, over the philosophical relationship of recreation, leisure, and therapy (see *Philosophy of Therapeutic Recreation Ideas and Issues*, published 1987 by NRPA). Recent editions of the *Therapeutic Recreation Journal* have carried a plethora of well-written articles on the subject as well. However, few of such publications have thoroughly defined what therapy is or what constitutes clinical practice. The phrase that comes closest to maintaining any systematic meaning appears to be "recreation as a means to an end."

The central context of this literature seems to focus on recreation activity, and it is activity done for some specific purpose, presumably therapy. Remember, the central context has been activity. It is within the realm of reason that it is exactly this preoccupation with activity as a predominate factor that has led to a morass of confusion. Have we been so preoccupied with recreation activity that we have failed to recognize what constitutes therapy?

An example, admittedly extreme, may help to clarify this point. What would happen if we took away the activities of some hypothetical therapeutic recreation specialist? No activities, no game room, no community reintegration excursions, no craft supplies, no movies, no table tennis, and so on — all that would be left is the person. Although it would be difficult, that person could still provide recreation oriented therapy. When you give back those activities and resources, just what that person does is probably what constitutes clinical practice.

The notion that recreation activity must be defined as involving physical motion is a critical factor in clarifying this issue. Recreation activity can be, on an observable surface, entirely cognitive, as with mental imagery, relaxation, and some kinds of sensory stimulation. Further, as Shank and Kinney (1987) make clear, the basis of therapy is the relationship that is established between the therapist and the client. The activity is only the vehicle through which the therapist interacts with the client and helps the client change or progress toward previously identified goals (Mobily, 1985a).

As a discipline, we need to discover, learn, and practice those clinical interactions that allow us to utilize activity as a means to achieve a specific and defined end for the client. What those clinical interactions are, as opposed to activity interactions, appears to be an elusive element of our understanding and services.

Issue 3: The rationale for conducting clinical practice within the context of human achievement and the continuum of human functioning has not been defined.

As evidenced by recent articles in the *Therapeutic Recreation Journal* (Sylvester, 1985; Mobily 1985; Halberg & Howe-Murphy, 1985), there is logical argument that the indiscriminate use of clinical practice may constrain freedom and subsequently impair attainment of a leisure state of mind. The obvious conflict between recreation as leisure and recreation as clinical treatment is a semantic division that threatens the unity of the discipline. Supporters of the use of recreation as clinical treatment argue that there exists a whole host of intra- and interpersonal concerns that are preliminary to and necessary for the attainment of leisure. The strict emphasis on leisure with certain clients could well encourage the internalizing of maladaptive thoughts or behaviors. For example, Shank and Kinney (1987) state the following:

> Trying to preserve the element of choice in a clinical context can present serious dilemmas. Expecting or insisting that persons exercise choice or perhaps demonstrate this freedom in their "leisure" can be unfair and irresponsible action on the part of the recreation therapist. For some clients, the task of choosing and "being free" can be difficult, is not possible, and expecting it can easily heighten anxiety. Mobily (1985a) has examined this issue from an ethical per-

spective and makes it quite clear that the practitioner's clinical judgment of the client's "ableness" is critically important in minimizing and resolving such dilemmas. (p. 68)

The concept of "pre-leisure" behavior becomes preeminent here. It should be obvious that a certain level of intrapersonal and interpersonal competence is preliminary to any use of leisure, regardless of the definition of leisure. For example, it would be ethically irresponsible to assume that an individual who has serious and unresolved issues of early sibling rivalry should be allowed to be in a setting that encourages competitive peer interactions, unless the situation has been specifically chosen to clinically address such issues or unless the therapist has been prepared in advance for such issues being a team concern and possibly surfacing in peer interactions. The concept of pre-leisure behavior is presented only as an example here to demonstrate the realm of clinical concern as opposed to recreational, or diversional, concern.

This realm of pre-leisure behaviors needs intense scrutiny if it is to be used as one criterion for deciding the relevance of a clinical, as opposed to a more purely recreational, approach. At what level of human functioning is a person likely to experience functional difficulty and then to benefit from clinically insightful support? Where in the continuum of functioning is it appropriate to provide clinical intervention—that point where the individual is in such a state of crisis that responses are dangerous or deleterious to maintenance?

Figure 1 (adapted from Blocher, 1966) presents in a fairly simplistic manner a continuum for understanding the great range of human functioning. It summarizes much of what social scientists tell us about human functioning. At the very top of the range is the ideal. The bottom of the range is panic or gross disorganization. In the continuum of human functioning, individuals may be characterized as operating at any given point for any given period of time, even a lifetime. More likely, however, individuals will function for some length of time at one point and for some length of time at another point and so on, depending on the mix of environmental supports and personal strengths available. It is also very likely that some individuals will operate at one level of the continuum for one domain such as play or work, or even for one situation, and at another level for another domain or situation, again depending on the mix of supports and strengths. Likewise, it can be assumed that individuals can move in either direction on the continuum, that is, either regress or improve.

The mastery level of the continuum approaches the level of ideal functioning. It is the world of Maslow's "self-actualizing person" and Roger's "fully functioning person." This is the individual who is consistent in behavior because of a sound personal identity, commitment to goals and purposes, and willingness to take reasonable risks; ability to control emotions and deal with ambiguous situations; a person who is competent, creative, and all those wonderful things. This is the level, according to many of the pioneers of recreation and leisure services, that is the goal of leisure. While the attributes that make up this level of functioning are impressive, the question must be addressed as to the immediate relevance of those attributes for the many clients who are struggling with a health or situational crisis.

The striving level is where much of the population appears to exist. It is the standard for most people, where the individual has control over most of the things that happen, and where there is a laudable effort to set long-term goals and stick to tasks to reach those goals. For the most part, the individual here aspires to many of the characteristics of the mastery level and frequently demonstrates them but never fully escapes that sense of insecurity—that fear of being overwhelmed, or having goals just "slip away." Individuals at the striving level are generally contented with life, but there are moments of resignation, even despair. This is when long-term goals fade into the background and life becomes dominated by some perceived crisis. The great positive characteristic of this level is the ability of the individual to keep long-term personal and professional goals somewhere in mind, cope and weather the occasional crises, and continue on track. An example is a person recently disabled and involved in vocational rehabilitation who is experiencing a personal or social life that is so unfulfilling that it occasionally disrupts meaningful progress.

The coping level is similar to striving, but less so. This level is also characteristic of much of the population. The individual is capable of making long-term goals, but easily strays from the necessary tasks to achieve those goals and frequently finds it easier to change long-term goals rather than stick to the arduous task of goal attainment. The result is wide swings in contentment and satisfaction—being happy at one point about the new effort, and in despair the next because of personal inability or desire to continue the effort. Much individual activity appears to be planned and meaningful, but it is highly inconsistent. A great deal of life may be perceived as being crisis-to-crisis existence, whereas those crises could be easily avoided if strengths were better utilized. An example is the client who leaves hospitalization with great plans for leisure activity involvement but never realizes those plans, or realizes only a small amount of those plans, because of being so caught up in day-to-day existence.

At the inertia level there is some attempt and some success to control aspects of the individual's short-term environment; however, there is little serious attempt to approach long-term goal planning. The individual tends to exhibit "failure-avoidance" behavior rather than "success-striving" behavior. There is a strong tendency to seek immediate gratification experiences and likewise, an inability to tolerate delayed gratification experiences. At this level, the individual tends to be more externally located in control, perceiving that he or she is at the hands of external circumstance and people; consequently, behavior becomes projected onto others with little conception of self-responsible behavior. An example is a client engaged in recreation discharge planning who appears highly resistant to suggestions; further inquiry reveals a tremendous degree of fear and anxiety regarding the freedom (lack of hospital routine), with subsequent fear of failure. A concern of regression exists if discharge issues are pressed too strongly.

Panic or gross disorientation is the level showing incapacity to control short-term emotions and behavior. The individual may well be out of touch with realistic and logical thinking and perceiving. Many individuals at the panic level are terrified by the degree to which they are out of control and react in manners ranging from a total inability to mobilize psychological strength to unpredictable and seeming irrational behavior that may be interpreted as being dangerous to self or others. An example is the individual who, following traumatic injury, refuses to participate in any kind of therapy whatsoever and exhibits an extreme case of denial, saying, "I'm not concerned—God will cure me."

A continuum such as this provides a rather theoretical framework from which levels of therapeutic recreation service can be envisioned. Individuals functioning at the highest extreme most likely do not require therapy. In actuality, they represent the ideal long-term goal or outcome of therapy. There also should be little argument that individuals operating at the lowest extreme most likely do require therapy. The low-end individuals require assistance in developing pre-leisure behaviors because the issues of leisure are largely irrelevant here.

Extremes, however, tend to be fairly clear-cut and fairly infrequent. An important issue, then, concerns that very large area of the continuum that lies between the extremes. At what point should interventions become less clinically oriented and more recreation or leisure oriented? Clinically oriented practitioners need to recognize that the delivery of

Figure 1
Levels of Effective Human Functioning

Mastery	Highest level of human functioning. Efficient and effective use of personal strengths. Organized, responsible, ethical, consistent, competent, creative, in control of self & environment. Capable of long range planning, & active environmental interactions.
Striving	Effectively uses strengths to interact with environment. Makes long term plans; sets goals, priorities for tasks. Generally in control of self & emotions. Characterized by typically positive behaviors butnot using strengths in most efficient manner. While usually in control of environment and emotions, there are times when control slips & there is indication of compensating to regain control.
Coping	Can make long term goals, but frequently does not. Easier to change goals. Wide swings in contentment. Acts appear meaningful, but inconsistent. Crisis to crisis existence.
Inertia	Can control short term environment but no serious try at long term planning. "Failure avoiding" behaviors. Seeks immediate gratification. Cannot tolerate delayed gratification experiences. External locus of control. Projects own negative behaviors onto others.
Panic	Unable to control even short term emotions & behaviors. Exhibits unrealistic & illogical thinking. Distorted perceptions. Appears & may feel "out of control." Poor concentration & interaction skills. Extreme defenses: withdrawal or aggressive acting out.

leisure opportunities can be a very valuable, even "therapeutic," experience for clients. The last thing a conscientious clinician would want to do is deprive a client of that opportunity (when the client is able) to construct and utilize the experience positively. Independence is the preferred outcome; dependence should rarely be encouraged. There is a place to be clinical and a place not to be clinical. How we determine, and who determines, when to be clinical is extremely important.

Issue 4: There is confusion as to where clinical practice occurs.

There appears to be widespread confusion regarding a fundamental semantic definition of clinical practice. The importance of this semantic confusion reflects the misunderstanding that tends to blur the distinctions between "special recreation" and "recreation as therapy." This confusion in terminology has equated a process with a place, that is, that "clinical" is a place where certain applications occur (the implication being an institution). This is reflected in the semantic categories of "community" versus "clinical" that are inherent in much of the literature. Note that "community" is a clearly definable geographic entity; "clinical," on the other hand, is certainly not a geographic entity.

It has already been discussed at some length that clinical procedures are a process, a scientific application of certain knowledge, techniques, and skills to enable or facilitate a change to occur in specific attitudes, feelings, or behaviors of an individual. As such, this process could presumably be applied anywhere that there exists a need for it—in the community at large or in a specialized treatment environment. Indeed, the community at large provides an excellent stage for clinical applications. Where can you better find reality?

Attempting to define clinical as a place is not logical and serves to perpetuate the confusion between different types of services. Only recently has the literature started exploring and clarifying in any depth the uniqueness of the various types of services. For example, Carter, Van Andel, and Robb (1985) and Kennedy, Austin, and Smith (1986) have provided excellent contexts for an understanding of special recreation.

Peterson and Gunn (1984), in their description of the "leisure ability" model, clearly differentiate treatment as a unique element of service. Though they do not adequately define treatment, it is clear that it is part of a process model and not tied to any location or place. The notion that deriving services in a particular setting automatically defines the nature of those services is extremely fallible. Shank and Kinney (1987) make the point that "simply providing services in a hospital (a traditional clinical setting) does not necessarily mean that those services are treatment" (p. 66). A hospital or another institution may very likely provide only special recreation services, as opposed to clinical or treatment recreation services. Conversely, a community health center may provide clinical or treatment recreation services, as opposed to special recreation. Clearly, it is the process and intended outcomes, not the setting, that define what occurs within the framework of service.

Issue 5: There are no standards as to who should do clinical practice and what skills are required.

Assuming that we accept the description of clinical practice as offered in this chapter, then it is apparent that such practice requires very specific knowledge, understanding, and skills. It is highly unlikely that many, if any, university curricula are adequately preparing clinicians in therapeutic recreation. It is only conjecture as to how those real therapeutic recreation clinicians who exist gained their expertise. One can assume that they

1. have some inherent qualities that allow them to naturally develop clinical skills, much as artists or musicians have inherent artistic or musical qualities;
2. have found themselves in a work setting that either places clinical expectations on them or at least accepts and encourages the development of clinical knowledge and skills; and
3. have found sources for the development of knowledge, either through formal means (education) or informal means (clinical supervision).

We can also assume that among those individuals who are practicing clinical therapeutic recreation, there is a range of knowledge and expertise from none or very little to a great deal. Keeping in mind the proverb that "a little knowledge can be a dangerous thing," it is discomforting to think of a lack of any yardstick by which we can determine who ought and who ought not to be allowed to attempt to provide clinical interventions.

Other disciplines, such as psychology, nursing, and social work, have various educational and professional criteria that allow one the privilege of engaging in clinical practice. This is in response to JCAH standards that require that quality of care be better assured through the delineation of personnel who should be granted clinical privileges. Apostoles and Naschinski (1987) state the following:

> The emphasis on quality assurance through the granting of clinical privileges. . . state that clinical privileges be delineated for each member of the professional staff; be based on verified information; and be granted based on demonstrated current competence. (p. 33)

The nursing model which Apostoles and Naschinski describe identifies five areas for clinical privileging: individual, group, and family psychotherapy; clinical supervision; and consultation.

While such criteria are far from infallible, they arguably provide some attempt to predict an individual's competence for clinical practice. The discipline of therapeutic recreation has initiated some attempts to define clinical privileging, but the issue is in an extremely preliminary stage of address. Furthermore, the issue of privileging in the practice of therapeutic recreation does not garner strong support from other, more accepted areas of treatment and credentialing, such as medicine and nursing, which reinforces the idea that therapeutic recreation is not a clinical service.

Issue 6: There is question as to whether university curricula can provide the proper education and training for conducting clinical practice.

A general assumption made in this discipline is that a new graduate has sufficient preparation to practice therapeutic recreation in virtually any capacity. New graduates are hired to assume roles as diverse as a coordinator of a special recreation program in a large metropolitan city, a director of services in a long-term care facility, a therapist on a locked unit in a psychiatric hospital, or a therapist on a spinal cord injury or head trauma unit in a teaching hospital. It is a sign of our lack of clinical understanding that we assume students can be adequately prepared for this vast diversity of positions in the same curriculum!

Currently, curricula preparing therapeutic recreation practitioners are usually housed in a department of recreation and leisure studies, or some variation thereof. It is extremely unusual to find a separate department of therapeutic recreation in a university or to find therapeutic recreation associated with other departments such as health, special education, social work, or social administration.

Consequently, therapeutic recreation curricula is strongly influenced by the generic recreation and leisure studies philosophy. Nowhere is this more apparent than in the National Recreation and Park Association's Council on Accreditation, which is influencing the development and maintenance of those curricula for which accreditation is desired. The standards for this accreditation dictate a heavy professional core that emphasizes the history, theory, and practice of traditional recreation and park services. Given this strong general core requirement, people with therapeutic recreation specializations or options are left with extremely little room to add new courses that could address concerns of specialization within therapeutic recreation. If new courses are added that could potentially better prepare students for clinical placement, it is likely that professional core courses would have to be dropped. Since it is the Council on Accreditation's view that the professional core courses are the most important, such a move by the curriculum would seriously jeopardize its accreditation.

Consequently, educators are left asking, "How can we prepare students for clinical placements in so few specialty courses?" At the same time, weary practitioners are starting to ask, "Can we afford to hire such poorly prepared graduates?"

Adding to this predicament of inadequate educational preparation is the current therapeutic recreation certification standard that accepts a minimum of three therapeutic recreation content courses and nearly any type of field placement (for professional-level certification). A perusal of various college catalogs will show that the content of these three courses can vary tremendously. There is virtually no quality assurance monitoring of therapeutic recreation content to which students are being exposed, as far as certification is concerned. In an attempt to address this issue, the National Council on Therapeutic Recreation Certification is developing a certification examination that will be based on knowledge and skills that newly practicing specialists are expected to have. Any conscientious therapeutic recreation curriculum must consider how graduates could possibly be prepared for such an examination in only three courses.

The field practicum experience is clearly an important component in professional preparation, and various studies have indicated that recent graduates believe the most worthwhile learning experiences occurred in the field placement. Given the critical importance of this component, it is disconcerting that our discipline has no guidelines for the content of these field placements or for the frequency and type of supervision provided. Learning to differentiate clinical practice from the routine provision of recreation service requires the student to experience intense client interaction guided by qualified, dedicated, and competent practitioners. The extent and nature of this clinical experience and the supervision that accompanies it are currently not standardized. It is primarily the degree of professional integrity and responsibility held by the agency and practitioners that influences supervision. Under such conditions, it is to be expected that the quality of clinical field experiences varies widely.

These problems surrounding professional preparation seriously implicate education and the personnel providing that education. If we are to address such issues effectively, many current educators will have to significantly "re-tool" in order to provide clinically oriented education. The fact is that clinical service was not much of a concern when most educators were getting their education or involved in professional practice. Opportunities will need to be created to allow educators to join practitioners in situations where the educators can learn or relearn clinical skills and knowledge. Without such opportunities, there is little hope that educators will be able to anchor their classroom instruction in accurate and up-to- date information.

Summary

The discipline of therapeutic recreation is at a critical juncture in its evolution. Examination and questioning as to the value and role of therapeutic recreation is occurring both inside and outside the discipline. Such questioning can be a very healthy process that serves to strengthen a discipline and define direction for future growth, or it can become unhealthy and result in disillusionment and disenfranchisement.

The recent emphasis on clinical applications of therapeutic recreation is one example of such questioning. While special recreation has received much attention in recent texts and articles—with the subsequent outcome that it is relatively well defined—clinical aspects have been only superficially discussed. This has resulted in a varied definition of what constitutes clinical practice. Evidence of this is shown by the wide variety of programs and services that claim to be clinically oriented.

External questioning is forcing the discipline to come to grips with its own issues. The health care and rehabilitation system, concerned with bottom-line figures and accountability, is looking to trim irrelevant services. In many cases, this has been translated into reducing or eliminating therapeutic recreation. Therapeutic recreation does have its ardent supporters who argue passionately and eloquently for inclusion in the process of active treatment. Unfortunately, the discipline has done little to provide resources, in the way of research, for example, to aid supporters with their arguments.

The U.S. Department of Education's National Institute on Disability and Rehabilitation Research, recognizing this dilemma, recently held a research competition in which they called for proposals designed to "definitively determine the efficacy of therapeutic recreation within active treatment." The significance of this topic as a research priority by such a high-level, respected federal agency reveals the extent to which concern exists about the structure and value of therapeutic recreation.

Practitioners, however, cannot wait for research to come along and prove that they deserve to be a part of the clinical team. The nature of the problem and the research process is such that efficacy of therapeutic recreation can never be definitively proven. Rather, the discipline needs to focus on resolving its own issues regarding clinical practice and prove its value through excellent practice.

Study Questions

1. Why is the term "clinical" so popular right now in therapeutic recreation. Wha forces exist that make this somewhat difficult to understand?

2. Why is the determination of an individualized treatment plan not enough, in and of itself, to constitute clinical practice? What is needed, in addition to the plan, to make practice more clinical? What is the relationship of clinical practice to special recreation?

3. How can free choice in recreation, at times, be potentially harmful? What is pre-leisure behavior and why would a recreation therapist want to be concerned about it? How does clinical practice address elements of total human functioning?

4. Is it incorrect to refer to "clinical" as a place as in "clinical concerns versus community concerns"? When may therapetic recreation provided in a medical setting not be an example of clinical practice?

5. Who should be allowed to do clinical practice? How can we provide assurance that clinical services are indeed quality clinical services?

6. How does NRPA's Council on Accreditation curriculum standards impact university curricula in attempting to provide quality therapeutic recreation education? Can current curricula legitimately produce graduates qualified to take the variety of jobs in which recreation therapists are employed? What can be done to improve the situation?

7. What are some illustrations that can be drawn from practice of therapeutic recreation that represent the clinical issues associated with the continuum of human functioning?

References

Apostoles, E., & Naschinski, C. (1987). Instituting a Clinical Privileging Process for Nurses. *Journal of Nursing Administration, 17*(1), 33—38.

Blocher, D.H. (1966). *Developmental Counseling.* New York: The Ronald Press.

Carter, M.J., Van Andel, G.E., & Robb, G.M. *Therapeutic Recreation: A Practical Approach.* St. Louis: Times Mirror/Mosby College Publishing.

Halberg, K., & Howe-Murphy, R. (1985). The Dilemma of an Unresolved Philosophy in Therapeutic Recreation, *Therapeutic Recreation Journal ,19*(3), 7—16.

Howe-Murphy, R. and Charboneau, B. (1987). *Therapeutic Recreation Intervention; An Ecological Perspective.* Englewood Cliffs, New Jersey: Prentice-Hall.

Kennedy, D., Austin, D. , & Smith, R. (1986). *Special Recreation.* Philadelphia: W.B. Saunders.

Keogh-Hoss, M.A. (1988). *The Development and Use of Program Protocols in Therapeutic Recreation.* Paper presented at Quality Assurance III, Montclair, NJ.

Mobily, K. (1985a). A Philosophical Analysis of Therapeutic Recreation: What Does It Mean to Say "We Can Be Therapeutic?" *Therapeutic Recreation Journal, 18*(1), 14—27.

_____. (1985b). The Ethical Dilemma of Freedom in Therapeutic Recreation. *Therapeutic Recreation Journal ,19*(4), 22—30.

Peterson, C.A., & Gunn., S.L. (1984). *Therapeutic Recreation Program Design: Principles and Procedures* (2nd Ed.). Englewood Cliffs, NJ: Prentice-Hall.

Shank, J., & Kinney, T. (1987). On the Neglect of Clinical Practice. *Philosophy of Therapeutic Recreation Ideas and Issues.* Alexandria, VA: National Therapeutic Recreation Society of the National Recreation and Park Association.

Sylvester, C. (1985). Freedom, Leisure, and Therapeutic Recreation: A Philosophical View. *Therapeutic Recreation Journal, 18*(1),6—13.

*photo courtesy of San Francisco Recreation Center for
the Handicapped*

Traditional clinical practice may have to occur to a greater
extent in transitional and community-based programs if
clients are to obtain the types of services they need.
—Kathleen J. Halberg

PART III

Issues Related to Practice

Summary

Every profession must inevitably address issues which are essential to its credibility. Fain provides the reader with an understanding of the basic elements of moral philosophy. Ethics is a branch of philosophy and is referred to as moral philosophy. Knowing right from wrong is central to the moral philosopher and the practitioner. In each profession the members develop a set of moral and ethical tenets which serve as the basis for collective action.

Recreation is presented as a moral imperative which is rooted in the values accepted and advanced by a democratic society. Play, recreation and leisure are examined as they relate to social and professional expectations. Fain calls to our attention the abandonment of two major moral imperatives—human rights and community based services. Each, he suggests, is not a platform of the modern era. While the NTRS adopted a Code of Ethics in 1966 when it was formed, it still lacks cases to prove particular points or modify codes and standards. The moral basis of practice is presented in such a manner as to create clearer understanding of the mission of therapeurtic recreation. Eliminating discrimination and promoting healthy lifestyles are but two examples of the power associated with such moral imperatives. While ethical standards and codes of ethics may abound, it is the moral imperative that guides the therapeutic recreator in his/her daily practice. There are often ethical dilemmas which the therapeutic recreator faces daily. Many can be resolved but some provide the most difficult scenario possible. Making decisions on what is right or wrong is central to daily practice—and will be so into the future.

Another practice issue is our ability to assess leisure behavior and human functioning. It is the first step in coming to know the client or consumer.

Howe suggests that the therapeutic recreation professional must develop some leisure literacy if they are to be in a position to assess functioning. She suggests that we must know the parts of the model before we leap into practice. Leisure well being may be approached from different perspectives but must be clear and rooted in theory. The validity, reliability and practicality of leisure assessment is discussed by Howe at some length. Extensive discussions of validity and reliability are offered to provide insight into the type of instrumentation and process required in assessment.

Numerous suggestions are offered to address the practical issues in assessment to be reminded of the issues (eg) availability, ease of administration, etc. The Leisure Diagnostic Battery (LDB) is discussed as a model for assessment instrument development. The LDB manual, forms, etc. serve as excellent materials from which to develop new assessment materials as they meet the rigor of national organizations who govern test development. Howe does suggest that the profession has much work to do in the immediate future in the area of assessment instrumentation. Little valid and reliable materials are available at present. Few are engaged in the process and even fewer know how to develop acceptable instruments. Howe suggests that "Assessments are tools that guide inquiry." It is clear that the status of assessment in therapeutic recreation is anything but complete.

Sneegas presents another point of view in the critical area of assessment. She suggests that the question of whether we can measure leisure behavior of individuals with disabilities and special populations is questionable. It is pointed out that the definition of variables is often problematic. This is further confounded by the issues surrounding the conceptualization of leisure. Numerous methodilogical difficulties are articulated. While a number of qualitative studies are used to measure leisure behavior they are strewn with questions of reliability, generalizability, etc. While not discounted entirely, qualitative research may be used as a parallel or corroborative approach to more rigorous and controlled studies. Sneegas also cites numerous problems with individuals with disabilities because of physical anomalies, imprecision in responses which may affect reliability, sufficient numbers in a particular group, maintaining control in the testing or assessment environment, etc. Considerable discussion is given to the possible similarities or differences between normal and special populations and individuals with disabilities. Attitudinal, architectural and a host of other barriers may serve to accentuate one situation over another.

Reitter and Wilson discuss issues related to the financing of therapeutic recreation from sources other than the base budget of a given agency. In both chapters the issue of diversification of sources of funding is made clear. The changing nature of health care financing is requiring the therapeutic recreator to become more knowledgeable about processes of reimbursement as well as the requirements to be authorized for reimbursement. In an age of accountability, it is clear that we will have to prove that our interventions work—that they prevent, restore, rehabilitate and/or cure and add to an improved quality of life. It is clear that unless we can meet the strictures of other regulatory agencies, third-party payors and can become innovative in securing financial resources for our services, we will be shut out of the clinical arena.

Over the past two decades no issue has received more attention, and yet lip service in some respects, as that of standards. While they have been desired by all, few concerted efforts have been made to insure their institutionalization and compliance. Robertson addresses the matter by asking if there is a gap between standards and practice. The standards that guide practice are difficult to bring into focus. The primary reasons are the diversification of settings, the variety of regulatory agencies and differing populations of clients. Berryman's work in both institutional and community settings served to set voluntary guidelines for the profession. While these first efforts were important, recent developments have utilized standards as a way of determining who was funded or credentialled. Four scenarios for the future are discussed. The bottom line is there is no data to show that even if we meet standards of practice, no harm or help will result to the client or consumer. Again, the empirical evidence is not available!

Halberg, Kinney and Shank focus their attention on the practice of therapeutic recreation in the community and clinical settings respectively. In the community setting it appears as though the momentum gained in the 1960s and 70s and the height of the human rights movement, has been lost in a sea of other issues. The focus on the nations health care, and a fervish desire to be accepted in this arena, has detracted from the critical needs for leisure services to special populations in the communities. With the majority of individuals with disabilities and special populations residing in the community, one ceases to wonder why our national professional organizations place so much importance on clinical issues. Mainstreaming, normalization and integration were terms that offered promise to those who were denied leisure services. Today they are terms that have little actual support in the public arena. Little progress has been made in the provision of leisure services from the public sector. While physical access has been provided in many instances, the issue of programmatic access remains. Less than half of the municipal or public recreation agencies across the nation offer leisure services to special populations. Halberg identifies the lack of available services as a major issue facing the profession. Another major issue is the inability to document the efficacy of therapeutic recreation on the lives of special populations or individuals with disability. A third major issue is the lack of coordination between the community based specialist and the clinically based therapist on matters of mutual interest—the well being and full integration of the client/consumer.

In the clinical arena the issues seem to center around the lack of essential protocols to intervene in the lives of clients. Much of our clinical approach appears to be ad hoc or at best the result of some historically based programmatic success. Additionally, there seems to be an absence of a clear definition of clinical practice. Kinney and Shank suggest that the term "clinical practice" may be alluring but there seems to be no legal mandate for the clinical practice of therapeutic recreation. They also point out the potential problems in trying to achieve "freedom of choice" in a clinical relationship— in some instances it is virtually impossible as an outcome, goal or behavioral objective. The continuing problem of where clinical practice occurs is discussed. It is suggested that it occurs in many settings or venues. Confusing geographic and procedural terms adds to the professional schism which exists between those who purport to be in the more elitist clinical group and those who serve the masses. The authors also imply that the leisure ability model, adopted by NTRS, and advanced by Peterson and Gunn, does not clearly define its clinical or treatment aspects. Finally, they contend that there are no standards for clinical practice. University curricula are ill prepared to provide the necessary knowledge and clinical training essential to carrying out the duties of a clinician. The curricula are diverse, lack essential scientific and medical information, and rely on philosophy rooted in recreation, play and leisure rather than rehabilitation, medicine, human development, psychology, etc. Recent efforts by the National Council for Therapeutic Recreation Certification (NCTRC) to create a national test will almost certainly bring into question the existing standards of the Council on Accreditation (COA) for the therapeutic recreation specialization curriculum. In sum, it appears we are headed for a major difficulty in the near future if the credentialling and the accreditation proponents do not put their heads together and work out inevitable problems.

Federal Agency Issues

photo courtesy of City of Las Vegas

The challenge for our field is to make parents and teachers more aware of the role of recreation and its contributions to the educational process.

—Charles C. Bullock

PUBLIC POLICY: THE ROLE OF THE FEDERAL GOVERNMENT

George Patrick
William Hillman, Jr.
David Park

Overview

For the therapeutic recreation professional, knowledge and understanding of the federal role provides the necessary foundation for today's clinical practice. In fact, the expanding role of the federal government in health care policy is mirrored by the growth of the therapeutic recreation profession—no mere coincidence. Concern for adequate and appropriate recreation opportunities for handicapped individuals has been growing due to demand on the part of handicapped individuals for equal access and equal opportunity, based on the right of "the pursuit of happiness" and the societal mandate of fairness extended to all citizens.

In order to comprehend the role of the federal government in relation to the therapeutic recreation profession, three aspects of our government's health-rehabilitation-education policy must be understood. This chapter is divided into sections on legislation, education and demonstration, and employment of therapeutic recreators in patient/client care. Each of these is actually interrelated with the others, but for heuristic purposes, separation allows for better understanding of the issues as related to the impact of the federal government upon the therapeutic recreation profession.

Legislation

While the first federal laws assisting disabled citizens date back to the early years of the Republic, prior to World War II the statute books contained relatively few acts authorizing special benefits for handicapped persons other than disabled war veterans. However, in recent years — particularly since the early 1960s — there has been a veritable avalanche of federal legislation affecting handicapped persons (Churton, 1987).

In one sense, the federal government does all of its business through legislation, and its subsequent funding and implementation. Certainly public health policy is a result of both legislative efforts as well as contribution of duly designated branches of government that affect the health of United States citizens.

This section summarizes the relevant federal laws concerned with the legal rights and benefits of mentally and physically disabled citizens, as well as initiatives affecting acute, rehabilitative, and long-term care.

Historical perspective

Federal law pertaining to handicapped persons can be traced to 1827, when PL 19-8 created a parcel of land for a "Deaf and Dumb Asylum" in Kentucky. The federal government advanced little beyond vocational rehabilitation and specialized, segregated education until 1973. Significant legislation pertinent to the preparation of physical education and recreation professionals and the conduct of research was enacted in Title V of PL 90-170. This law became the basis for PL 94-142, the Education for All Handicapped Children Act, the first comprehensive legislation that provided "related services" access to the public schools as part of the overall education program. During the 1970s, PL 90-170 was the primary legislation that enabled the advanced training of specialists in physical education and recreation for handicapped children.

Federal support of medical care began July 16, 1798 with the establishment of the Marine Hospital Service, when President John Adams signed an act for the relief of sick and disabled seamen. Soon after, the National Library of Medicine was established (1836) and the federal government began to sponsor biomedical research. The National Institutes of Health (NIH) began as a one-room Laboratory of Hygiene in 1887. Today its parent organization, the Department of Health and Human Services (HHS), oversees the nation's health efforts.

Legislative overview

Therapeutic recreation, both hospital- and community-based, has its present status inextricably linked to federal legislation. Knowledge of the acts and respective sections of those acts allows advocacy groups and professionals the information necessary to participate in the change process. An informed profession provides for effective advocacy. Although the provision for recreation services and opportunity is addressed in these statutes, during the review process these citations can be changed (emphasized or de-emphasized) or deleted, depending on the hearing process. Legislative acumen is the TR professional's responsibility.

The Congress of the United States has been responsible for three major pieces of legislation that play a role in the delivery of therapeutic recreation services: Rehabilitation Act, Developmental Disabilities Act, and Education of Handicapped Children Act. These laws are now explained in nontechnical language and using a common format. A brief overview of each law's legislative history, its basic purpose and structure, the major programs authorized under the statute that affect the provision of recreation for handicapped persons, and the assessment of the impact of the statute on the therapeutic recreation and recreation profession are offered. Federal legislation is numbered in such a way as to recognize the congressional session during which the public law (or PL) was enacted. Thus, PL 100-38 took place during the 100th Congress, in 1987 and 1988.

Rehabilitation act

The Rehabilitation Act (RHA), enacted in 1973, emanated from the Vocational Rehabilitation Act of 1954—and perhaps even further back to 1920, when Congress enacted the first civilian program for assisting disabled persons to regain work skills. In 1963 revisions included training and research funds in the area of recreation for the ill and handicapped. This was the first recognition by a federal agency of the importance of recreation services for handicapped individuals. Initially, 7 colleges and universities were identified and funded to provide TR education. In 1973 more than a billion dollars in federal support was spent in order to place mentally and physically handicapped persons into remunerative employment. To assist this basic goal, a wide variety of service, demonstration, training, and research grant programs (which included recreation), were established including a major federally-funded, state grant-in-aid program.

The RHA of 1973 attempted to provide equal opportunity for the disabled to learn vocational skills and gain employment. The title change from "Vocational Rehabilitation Act" to "Rehabilitation Act" signaled the broadening concept of this legislation. The 1973 act continued authorization of recreation services in both training and research, but added new sections that have had impact on recreation services for persons with disabilities. Selected segments of RHA follow:

1. Title II — Research and Training. This title continued to authorize funds for training recreation personnel to work with handicapped persons and for research monies for projects in recreation.

2. Title III - Section 304 — Special Projects and Demonstrations. This section made monies available for grants for "operating programs to demonstrate methods of making recreational activities fully accessible to handicapped individuals." Several projects in recreation have had impact on the delivery of recreation services.

3. Title V - Section 502 — Architectural and Transportation Barriers Compliance Board. Section 502 created the Architectural and Transportation Barriers Compliance Board (A&TBCB), whose main function is to seek compliance with PL 90-480. Any citizen may file a complaint with this agency if a barrier is confronted in a public building or facility, particularly with respect to monuments, parks and parklands covered by the Architectural Barriers Act of 1968, PL 90-480. Many of the A&TBCB provisions were adopted from the American National Standards Institute (ANSI).

4. Title V - Section 504 — Nondiscrimination Under Federal Grants. Section 504 is acknowledged to be landmark legislation for disabled Americans. It is commonly referred to as the Civil Rights for the Handicapped Act. The Department of Health and Human Services (formerly the Department of Health, Education, and Welfare) was the lead agency for Section 504 compliance until 1980, when those functions requiring compliance were shifted to the Department of Justice. The Department of HHS published "Nondiscrimination on the Basis of Handicap: Programs and Activities Receiving or Benefiting from Federal Financial Assistance." This section states, "No otherwise qualified handicapped individual shall, solely by reason of his handicap, be excluded from the participation in, be denied the benefits of, or be subjected to discrimination under, any program or activity conducted by an executive agency or by the United States Postal Service." Failure to comply with the law can result in the withholding and/or withdrawal of federal financial assistance. Essentially, any parks and recreation department receiving Land and Water Conservation Funds (LWCF) had to comply with the Rehabilitation Act of 1973. Since LWCF money was widely distributed, most parks and recreation departments were required to comply with both facility and program

accessibility. Recently LWCF monies have been reduced to one-tenth of the $300 million per annum spent in the early 1970s. However, inaccessible recreation facilities built anytime since 1968 by agencies receiving federal funds are still grievable under these laws.

The Rehabilitation Act Amendment of 1974, PL 93-516, authorized the planning and implementation of the White House Conference on Handicapped Individuals, which was convened in May of 1977. Recreation was 1 of the 16 major areas of concern at the White House Conference. The final report noted the importance of recreation for individuals with disabilities and called for the expansion of recreation services, as well as an increase in the number of professionally trained individuals employed in the field of recreation.

Recreation and leisure services, outdoor recreation for disabled persons, and recreation programs and facilities are mentioned in the report. Generally, the main points of the report included funding incentives, accessibility, community-based recreation programs, and employment and training of recreation professionals. In addition, under the heading of "social concerns," recreation was listed. The following is an abbreviated list of concerns dealing with the design of recreational services:

•Accessibility	• Transportation
•Program Variety	• Program Integration
•Leisure Skill	• Funding for Recreation
Development	• Public Awareness
	• Handicapped Lobby

As with many federal programs, the 1973 Rehabilitation Act and the programs it authorized expired at the end of 5 years. In 1978 legislation was introduced to extend and amend the 1973 act. The 1978 Act, PL 95-602, contained six separate sections that called for recreation and leisure services as part of the rehabilitation process. The act included recreation as a service to be provided in rehabilitation facilities as well as in special public projects and demonstration programs.

The 1978 Senate Committee on Human Resources, in introducing the Senate Bill to amend and extend the 1973 Rehabilitation Act, stated the following:

• In recognition of the recreational and social needs of handicapped individuals, the committee bill amends Section 304 to authorize the

Secretary to make grants to states and public non-profit agencies and organizations for the purpose of initiating recreational programs for handicapped individuals.

• Recreation programs for handicapped individuals are greatly needed to assist them in developing their capacity for mobility and socialization. Unfortunately, existing programming for this purpose is limited; therefore, it is the committee's intent that this authority stimulate the development and utilization of more community-based recreation programs.

• It is the committee's intent that handicapped individuals participate in existing regularly scheduled recreation programs to the maximum extent feasible; the committee realizes, however, that the specialized needs of handicapped individuals may necessitate adaptive equipment and programming and specially trained personnel. The committee therefore expects that such adaptive equipment and programming, as well as specialized personnel attuned to the needs of handicapped persons, will be an integral part of any recreation program initiated under this authority. It is further expected that such recreation programs should be coordinated with other recreational activities offered in the community. (Public Law 95-602, 110)

From a legislative funding perspective, the provision of recreation services to special populations has fared quite well. As a result of the amendments to the RHA of 1978 (PL 95-602), with reference to Sections 311 and 316, approximately $17 million has been allocated through the two Sections to various agencies to make recreation facilities and programs accessible to disabled individuals.

Section 311 provides grants to public and nonprofit agencies and organizations to pay part or all of the costs of special projects and demonstrations for operating programs and, where applicable, renovating and constructing facilities to demonstrate methods of making recreational activities fully accessible to handicapped individuals. Section 311 was funded in 1981 for $1 million. It was funded for 1 year only and is mentioned here as an object lesson that shows the need for continuing Congressional education and lobbying for even the most positive legislation to survive competing interests for funds.

Section 316 is a most significant part of the RHA. It provides grants to states and public nonprofit agencies and organizations for paying part or all of the cost of initiating recreation programs to provide handicapped individuals with recreation. It also provides for personnel preparation and research in therapeutic recreation. Section 316 requires and receives greater amplification in the next part of this chapter.

Finally, a major new section added to the 1978 Act expanded the number of persons with disabilities eligible to receive services and "recreational and leisure time activities." Title VII, entitled Comprehensive Services for Independent Living, made funds available for the development of comprehensive services to persons with disabilities (Kennedy, Austin, & Smith, 1987).

In 1986 under the reauthorization proceedings, 10 titles or sections to the act were approved in PL 99-507, addressing such key issues as vocational rehabilitation, research and training services and facilities, employment opportunities, independent living, and others (U.S. Congress, 1986). As stated, Section 311 was not one of them.

For the past 20 years, the RHA has addressed not only employment of disabled persons, but also factors that allow a person to be employed and maintain employment. Services other than vocational training have been included as viable parts of the total rehabilitation picture. Thus, recreation services are now considered important and necessary services in the lives of disabled persons.

Title I: Amendments to the General Provisions, Section 103, Evaluation of Rehabilitation Potential: Recreation factors have been included in the definition of rehabilitation potential. Section 103(g), Rehabilitation Facility, includes recreation therapy as a service available in facilities. Section 103(f), Rehabilitation Engineering, cites recreation among other services included within this definition.

Title III: Research and Training, Section 205, Research: supports the study and analysis of recreation factors affecting rehabilitation.

Title IV: Supplementary Services and Facilities, Section 403, Training: includes the training of physical education and therapeutic recreation personnel.

Section 407, Special Recreation Programs: Formerly noted as 316, this grant competition expands the language and includes physical education and sports among other leisure and recreation opportunities. Also, this program has been expanded to a 3-year funding authorization.

Title VIII: Services for Independent Living, Section 801: The language for eligible services was changed from "recreational activities" to "recreational services." Section 804, Grants for Centers for Independent Living: includes recreation as an applicable service.

Title III: Research and Training, Section 303: National Institute on Disability and Rehabilitation Research (NIDRR), formerly the National Institute on Handicapped Research, offers a variety of funding competitions for which recreational personnel can compete. Authorized under the RHA, NIDRR addresses programmatic, technological, and innovative programs related to rehabilitation of persons with disabilities (Churton,1987).

The impact of RHA over the last 20 years has yielded trained therapeutic recreational specialists via educational grants. It has encouraged accessibility in new public facilities and retrofitting, where possible, of older facilities. RHA has brought accessible transportation, deaf interpreters, research and demonstration projects, rehabilitation centers, centers for independent living, accessible nature trails, and massive public awareness of the civil rights of disabled persons for full participation in society.

The Developmental Disabilities Assistance and Bill of Rights Act

The Developmental Disabilities Services and Facilities Construction Amendments of 1970 (PL 91-517) were the first Congressional effort to ensure that the needs of the developmentally disabled (DD) would be addressed. PL 100-146 amended the Mental Retardation Facilities and Community Health Centers Construction Act of 1963. This Act (1970) defines the DD as a person with mental retardation, cerebral palsy, epilepsy, or other neurological conditions closely related to mental retardation which originate prior to age 18 and constitute a handicap. Revisions in 1978 replaced categorical references with functional disabilities and defined DD as severe, chronic disability (a) is attributed to a mental or physical impairment or combination of both; (b) manifested before the person attains the age of 22; (c) likely to continue indefinitely and results in substantial functional limitations in three or more of the major life activities: (i) self-care, (ii) receptive and expressive language, (iii) learning, (iv) mobility, (v) self-direction, (vi) capacity of independent living, (vii) economic self-sufficiency; and (d) reflects the person's need for a combination and sequence of special, interdisciplinary or generic care, treatment, or other services that are lifelong or of extended duration and are individually planned and coordinated.

The DD program does not provide direct services to individuals. Rather, it is oriented toward the provision of grant funds to a grantee, who in turn provides the direct service to a population as a result of the acquired funds. Monies are awarded according to priorities established in the annual state plan.

These grants are for planning, administration, services, and construction of facilities, and are awarded through Titles I and II of the Developmental Disabilities Act. Title I provides funding under a formula grant, in which money is allocated to the states on a formula basis and is to be distributed by state agencies. Recreation as a fundable activity is mentioned in the law as one of the specific supportive services under the formula grants. Recreation services are aimed at providing opportunities for recreation, physical education, and open-space acquisition and development.

The mechanism for delivering DD services has come through University Affiliated Programs (UAP). These facilities offer outpatient services, provide training for service personnel, and improve the move toward integration and appropriate community services to developmentally disabled individuals.

In 1978 the DD Act was amended through passage of the Rehabilitation Comprehensive Services and Developmental Disabilities Amendments. This had an impact on the expansion of services for individuals with disabilities. The overall purposes of the act were these:

1. to assist in the provision of comprehensive services to persons with developmental disabilities, with priority to those persons whose needs cannot be covered or otherwise met under the Education for All Handicapped Children Act, the Rehabilitation Act of 1973, or other health, education, or welfare programs;
2. to assist states in appropriate planning activities;
3. to make grants to states and public and private nonprofit agencies to establish model programs, to demonstrate innovative rehabilitation techniques, and to train professional and paraprofessional personnel with respect to providing services to persons with developmental disabilities;
4. to make grants to university-affiliated facilities to assist them in administering and operating demonstration facilities for the provision of services to persons with developmental disabilities and

interdisciplinary training programs for personnel needed to provide specialized services for these persons; and,
5. to make grants to support a system in each state to protect the legal
and human rights of all persons with developmental disabilities.

The implications of these amendments to the recreation field are
numerous. They allow recreation professionals opportunities to develop and implement special services, training, and research projects in
the area of developmental disabilities, especially in rural and otherwise
nonserviced areas. Some of the possibilities include (a) services
necessary for community adjustment, such as counseling and educating
the individual regarding leisure habits and resources for involvement in
the community; (b) public awareness and education programs to assist
in the integration of handicapped individuals into the mainstream of
society; (c) coordination of all available community resources; (d)
training of specialized personnel needed for service delivery or for
research related to developmental disabilities; (e) development of demonstration techniques and/or projects to serve as pilots for the expansion and continuation of innovative and successful programs; and (f)
gathering and dissemination of information related to developmental
disabilities (Kennedy, Austin, & Smith, 1987).

The qualified recreation professional, through grant writing, can
be actively involved in the provision of quality services following acquisition of federal monies. This law addresses the areas of facilities,
research and training, demonstration projects, and special recreation
programs.

The Education of the Handicapped Act

The Education of the Handicapped Act (EHA) was first signed
into law in 1967. Since 1977 the EHA has been reauthorized three
times. It currently consists of Parts A—H, with H (handicapped infants
and toddlers) being added during the 1986 revisions. Part B is permanent legislation while A, C—H remain discretionary. No other piece
of legislation has done more for handicapped children than the EHA,
and it is considered an international landmark for the disabled (Department of Education, 1987). It provided a considerable amount of federal
funds for the professional preparation of recreation personnel working
with children with disabilities. In 1967 Senator Edward Kennedy (D-
Mass.) introduced an amendment that created specific authorization for

funds in the areas of physical education and recreation. More specifically, Title V, Section 501(a) stated:

It is authorized to make grants to public and other non-profit institutions of higher learning to assist them in providing professional or advanced training for personnel engaged or preparing to engage in employment as physical educators or recreation personnel for mentally retarded and other handicapped children ... or engaged or preparing to engage in research or teaching in fields relative to the physical education or recreation of such children.

Over the past 15 years, this legislation enabled many colleges and universities to educate hundreds of students to work with children with disabling conditions in a variety of recreational settings. (Kennedy, Austin, & Smith, 1987).

The Education for Handicapped Children Act was amended by PL 94-142 (1975). The amended act was titled the "Education for All Handicapped Children Act." It read, in part:

It is the purpose of this act to assure that all handicapped children have available to them, within the time periods specified in Section 612 (2)(b), a free appropriate public education (FAPE), which emphasizes special education and related services designed to meet their unique needs, to assure that the rights of handicapped children and their parents or guardians are protected, to assist states and localities to provide for the education of all handicapped children, and to assess and assure the effectiveness of efforts to educate handicapped children.

The term "related services" means transportation, and such development, corrective and other supportive services (including ... recreation . . .) as may be required to assist a handicapped child to benefit from special education.

The regulations governing implementation of the law define recreation as including
1.   assessment of leisure functioning,
2.   therapeutic recreation,
3.   recreation in schools and communities, and
4.   leisure education.

The inclusion of recreation as a related service provided a rationale for the inclusion of recreation as part of the individualized education plan (IEP) and suggested a framework for the delivery of recreation services.

The EHA promotes leisure and recreation as a significant aspect of the total education of handicapped persons. Some school systems have hired therapeutic recreators either as system employees or as contracted services or shared services in cooperative agreements with community recreation agencies, but these have been rare.

In 1986 during the reauthorization of the EHA, recreation is found within two sections:

Part C: Secondary Education and Transitional Services for Handicapped Youth, Section 626 (10), includes specially designed physical education and therapeutic recreation programs to increase the potential of handicapped youth for community participation.

Part E: Research and Demonstration in Physical Education and Recreation for the Handicapped, Section 642, authorizes the Secretary to make grants to states or local education agencies, institutions of higher education, and other public or nonprofit private educational or research agencies and organizations, and to make contracts with states, state or local educational agencies, institutions of higher education, and other public or private educational or research agencies and organizations, for research and other purposes related to physical education or recreation for handicapped children, and to conduct research, surveys or demonstrations relating to physical education or recreation for handicapped children.

In retrospect of the last 13 years, so little has been done by the recreation profession to capitalize on the opportunities presented by being designated as a "related service." If more professionals had been willing to press for inclusion of recreation services under the provisions of this act, entree to handicapped children in the public schools would be routine now, rather than the exception.

Education and Demonstration

The legislative history of the last 20 years has left the RHA and the EHA and all of their additions (DD), deletions (311), changes in enforcement agencies (to DOJ), and, not the least, allocation changes. This section focuses on how these allocations affected therapeutic recreation through professional preparation, research, and demonstration projects.

Congress has allocated millions of dollars over the last 20 years in order to improve the leisure wellness of handicapped individuals. Graduate-level training of therapeutic recreators, curriculum development, innovative recreation programs, outdoor education, leisure education, community recreation services and mainstreaming in recreation have been financially supported.

The Rehabilitation Act created the Rehabilitation Services Administration (RSA) in 1965. From the beginning, RSA recognized the role of recreation in rehabilitation through authorization of money for personnel preparation in therapeutic recreation. Initially 15 agencies and institutions were awarded funds, seven were awarded to the following colleges and universities: Indiana State University, New York University, San Jose University, University of Illinois, University of Kentucky, University of North Carolina, and University of Oregon. The latter used these funds to develop and implement master's level training programs in TR. This early rehabilitation legislation also authorized research related to recreation services for disabled populations. The initial efforts were a catalyst for the growth and development of recreation opportunities for disabled persons.

The RSA has been involved in four major activities which brought together consumers, rehabilitation professionals, recreation specialists, therapeutic recreation specialists, and others to identify problems and seek solutions. These national efforts were concerned with the availability of opportunities for disabled persons to participate in recreation activities in the community as a part of regular living patterns.

1.The National Forum on Recreation and Handicapped Individuals was convened in 1974 by the President's Committee on Employment of the Handicapped and the National Recreation and Park Association (NTRS's parent organization) to identify problems and issues involved in providing recreation and park services for disabled persons and to devise feasible, practical approaches to resolve and/or respond to those problems and issues.

2.The National Hearing on Recreation for Handicapped Persons, held by the Architectural and Transportation Barriers Compliance Board, offered an opportunity to explore how to improve the public's understanding of the issues and to bring about more appropriate options for recreation participation for disabled persons. Testimony was taken from individuals representing consumer and advocacy groups; national, state, and local recreation service providers; and other professionals in recreation and rehabilitation. Witnesses included the National Park Service, the Bureau of Outdoor Recreation, the Rehabilitation Services Administration, the National Rehabilitation Association, and the National Recreation and Park Association. Three of the specific recommendations emerging from the testimony were (a) initiation and implementation of national policies that demand compliance with existing laws; (b) development of appropriate recreation resources, including the establishment of a national public policy; and (c) stimulation of research in recreation for disabled persons.

3. The 1977 National White House Conference on Handicapped Individuals was the culmination of a series of state conferences held during 1976. Recreation and leisure needs of disabled persons was one of the specific topics addressed. Recommendations and specific implementation plans for service delivery, consumer involvement, information dissemination, education, accessibility, enforcement, job opportunities, and research and demonstration evolved from the discussions. Again, a strong influence was exerted by NRPA.

4. By 1980, generic state-of-the-art conferences began to develop greater focus. An example of the more directed conference was held at the George Washington University, a 3-day conference to determine priority research topics in recreation for disabled individuals, which was sponsored by a grant from the National Institute of Handicapped Research. The outcome of this conference was published as *Focus on Research: Recreation for Disabled Individuals* (Park,1980) by the School of Education and Human Development, The George Washington University. Priority topics were specified for consumer involvement, attitudes, treatment implications, personnel preparation, and accessibility. NTRS members presented a majority of the papers and reactions published.

As was mentioned in the previous section of this chapter, the Rehabilitation Act, especially Sections 316 and 311, paved the way for demonstration projects directly enabling recreation participation for disabled individuals. Section 316 of the 1978 Act reads:

> The Secretary . . . shall make grants to state and public non-profit agencies and organizations for paying part or all of the cost of initiation of recreation programs to provide handicapped individuals with recreational activities to aid in the mobility and socialization

of such individuals. The activities authorized to be assisted under this subsection may include, but are not limited to, scouting and camping, 4-H activities, sports, music, dancing, handicrafts, art and homemaking . . . and that with respect to children the activities for which the grant is to be made will be conducted after school.

Comprehensive services are defined as those necessary to enhance the ability of a severely handicapped individual to live independently or to function in society, and if appropriate, secure and maintain appropriate employment. Included in such services are "recreational and leisure time activities." Recreation is also included as one of the services that should be provided within independent living centers.

Thus, it seems clear that the 1978 Rehabilitation Act has greatly expanded the concept of comprehensive rehabilitation to include all services that assist the disabled not only to obtain employment but also to live a complete, well-balanced life. In this context, recreation services are perceived as vital.

The 1978 Amendments to the Rehabilitation Act of 1973 authorized programs of Special Projects and Demonstration under Title III, Section 311 (a)(2), for making recreation activities accessible to handicapped individuals. Eight 1-year projects were funded in September of 1981 within the total amount of $1,000,000. This section was unfunded in subsequent years due to the political climate and lack of support. Section 316 was similarly slated by the RSA for nonfunding, but due to a concerted and effective lobbying process of professional recreation organizations, consumers, and dedicated therapeutic recreators who testified to the importance of recreation in total rehabilitation, Section 316 survived; it continued in 1988 with total expended funds of over $17 million.

Section 316 authorized grants to the states and to public or nonprofit agencies and organizations "to demonstrate methods of making recreational activities fully accessible to handicapped individuals . . . and to evaluate methods of community out-reach for individuals . . . in areas such as housing, transportation, employment, and community activities."

Most recently, these funds have been put on a 3-year funding cycle to provide greater stability to the program. According to Frank Caracciolo (1987) about 90,000 handicapped individuals have participated in 162 projects funded under recreation-specific programs from FY 1981 through FY 1986. In FY 1987 $2,300,000 was available.

Section 316 funds have diminished for professional preparation of therapeutic recreators as EHA monies have "provided support for some of the most singular and vital methods used by the recreation and leisure profession in meeting the leisure challenges being confronted by the nation's handicapped citizens" (Hillman, 1984). Several conferences were sponsored by the Bureau of Education for the Handicapped (BEH/HEW) through EHA funding. Of special note was the 1969 Study Conference on Research and Demonstration Needs in Physical Education for Handicapped Children, which the American Association for Health, Physical Education, Recreation and Dance and the National Recreation and Park Association (NRPA) jointly managed. Similarly, the 1974 conference entitled "Leisure Activity Participation and Handicapped Populations: Assessment of Research Needs" was conducted by NRPA.

Curriculum development has greatly benefitted from BEH funding. The *Guidelines for Professional Preparation Programs for Persons Involved in Physical Education and Recreation for the Handicapped* (Stein, Burnette, Park, & Hillman, 1970) was to set the standard for curricula for at least 7 years. Thereafter, competency-based curriculum projects were funded at the University of Illinois (published as *Therapeutic Recreation Education: Developing a Competency-Based Entry-Level Curriculum*) and at Temple University (published as *Theory and Design of Competency-Based Education in Therapeutic Recreation* and *Master's Degree Competency-Based Curriculum in Therapeutic Recreation*) Postdoctoral training has been offered by Indiana University and the University of Maryland, funded by BEH to continue to upgrade therapeutic recreation faculty skills.

Outdoor education and camping received attention through BEH funding of several research and demonstration projects. Notable among these were Project REACH, Project TORCH, and the many projects run at Bradford Woods (Indiana University). Much of this information went to the American Camping Association and came out in awareness of camp standards for accessibility throughout the country.

A bold move to infuse the community schools with the concept of using leisure education to assist in the integration of handicapped youth came from BEH funding. Similarly, mainstreaming through leisure was supported by numerous BEH grants. The University of Iowa developed many models for community-based recreation services aimed at integrating handicapped children and youth in the mid-1970s. In New Jersey, an elaborate in-service project was developed and implemented to optimize the recreation component of PL 94-142 for handicapped children aged 3—21.

The YMCA developed and implemented a mainstreaming initiative and trained not only its own staff, but also national youth serving other agencies, in the use of recreation to bring handicapped youth in positive contact with nonhandicapped youth.

The total impact of innovative projects in personnel preparation, research, and demonstration is yet to be quantitatively assessed. Large numbers of handicapped individuals have been served. These and many other projects have provided what appears to be a strong foundation for the improvement of leisure and recreation services for the handicapped. Our knowledge base has been significantly improved, and many have received professional preparation due to funding from the federal government (Hillman, 1984).

Certainly, public awareness is an ongoing issue. The most recent example of awareness enhancement has been the President's Commission on Americans Outdoors (PCAO). The PCAO was created in 1985 to "make recommendations to the President concerning the outdoor recreation resources, programs, and opportunities that will ensure the future availability of outdoor recreation for the American people." To complete its work, the commission solicited a series of concept paper and literature reviews, held public hearings, and commissioned several studies. The Commission solicited papers under several major subheadings, including special populations. These papers were published in the *Therapeutic Recreation Journal*,(1987) and were particularly important because they became a major vehicle for reminding the Commission of their responsibility to address the needs of *all* Americans.

> "Overall, the papers reveal many recommendations that could be of use in developing a national recreation policy that would include all Americans. It is not surprising that overcoming architectural, ability, economic, or attitudinal barriers (depending on the special population in question) emerges as a critical need. From the collective reviews it is clear that we have sufficient knowledge about what needs to be done to develop an outdoor (or "indoor," etc.) service system that would be accessible and affordable to all Americans" (Witt, 1987).

These forums, hearings, conferences, and commissions did much to create awareness of the need for therapeutic recreation intervention in rehabilitation and in the community. They highlighted the need for public policy and funding to support such programs. Thus, the cycle of legislation, funding allocation, grants for research and demonstration, awareness, lobbying, and more legislation is all related in the public policy impact on therapeutic recreation.

Direct Patient Care

The federal role in providing direct patient care comes by way of the Veterans Administration (VA) hospital system, the National Institutes of Health (NIH), and military hospitals such as Walter Reed Army Medical Center. These government-operated hospitals have various purposes (acute care, rehabilitation, long-term care, and research) and employ over 700 therapeutic recreators (Krueger, 1988).

The VA system is the "founder" and largest user of the recreation therapy occupation in the federal system. The VA has the largest rehabilitation program in the Western Hemisphere, operating in 172 medical centers. Over 400 recreation therapists are employed in the VA system. As of January 1989, the Veterans Administration will be elevated to the President's cabinet. Such a move will be watched with interest. It provides an opportunity for therapeutic recreation concerns to be heard at the executive level.

NIH is the world's largest hospital devoted exclusively to clinical research. Although only 550 patient beds are available in the Clinical Center (Bethesda, MD), over 1,700 laboratories exist to support the research effort. According to Arnold Sperling, chief (1988), the mission of the Patient Activities Department is "to provide a patient-centered program of therapeutic recreation and library services, supporting the biomedical and clinical research, and aiding in the comfort and health of the Clinical Center patients." TR has been developing a greater clinical emphasis in the last six years through staff education and quality assurance efforts.

NIH spends $22 million getting advice from some 3,000 scientists about how to use its annual $6.7 billion budget. But it is Congress that often makes the decisions (Marwick, 1988). This information is presented in order to alert the reader that special interests, lobbying intensively, do have a direct influence on brokering the research agenda of the nation's premier biomedical research facility.

The VA, NIH, and other federal government medical centers share the same personnel (government service, or GS) guidelines. Almost a decade has passed since the Office of Personnel Management (OPM) determined the hiring qualifications for a recreation therapist

(GS 638) as being different from a recreation specialist (institutional) (GS 188). Essentially, the GS 638 position requires a therapeutic recreation degree or option, and in many settings requires that the incumbent be certified (National Council on Therapeutic Recreation Certification) within 6 months of employment as part of the hospital's credentialing requirements. Interestingly, GS 188s still exist, and at the same pay grade as GS 638s. In spite of that, the strong message for federal employees is to upgrade the requirements, either through hiring or programmatically, to reflect the changes in the profession, such as the shift from hospital recreation in the 1950s to recreation therapy in the 1980s.

At NIH, functions are split between 188 and 638 staff. The 188s run an adult recreation program and playrooms, serving ambulatory patients with recreational opportunities on a drop-in basis. These activities include arts and crafts; group activities, such as bingo, cards, and movies; physical activities, such as volleyball, and exercises; special events, such as holiday parties; and community outings. The 638s are given responsibility for specific patient care units. They do their work with the benefit of physician referral, using the therapeutic recreation clinical process of assessment, treatment planning, and thorough documentation. Both 188s and 638s work together for the benefit of the same patient in different ways, representing the continuum of services suggested by the National Therapeutic Recreation Society's Philosophical Position Statement (1982).

The inception of the 638 series put the federal personnel system on notice to hire appropriately trained personnel for therapist positions by distinguishing them from recreation specialists (188). Insofar as federal hiring system guidelines are perused by state personnel departments, the 638 series may have set the precedent for nationwide change. Certainly, with NIH a major employer, professional preparation curricula are sensitive to the personnel requirements of the 638 series. Presently both 638 and 188 series are paid the same. However, Title 38 may allow increased compensation for the 638 series in the near future if sufficient rationale can be offered.

Both the VA and NIH have made major strides in monitoring and analyzing therapeutic recreation services. A major trend toward quality assurance in therapeutic recreation is being piloted in the federal system (Patrick, 1988, Riley, 1987). The federal system strongly supports program accountability and is among the leaders of the therapeutic recreation profession in studying outcomes (efficacy) of its own services.

Summary

The increased federal role in expanding recreational opportunities for disabled individuals has led to the strengthening of the therapeutic recreation profession by legislative recognition; funding or professional preparation by legislative recognition; funding of professional preparation, demonstration projects, and research; and direct service provision in federal medical centers. Federal legislation dealing with accessibility has made the public more aware of the need to eliminate architectural barriers. Buildings, both new and remodeled, have been made more accessible to and usable by persons who are physically challenged. RHA and EHA have provided monies and opportunities for hundreds of therapeutic recreation students to become professionally prepared to work in a variety of clinical and community settings. The federal medical centers, most notably the VA and NIH, provide leadership in setting the standards of care in TR by their efforts in more rigorous personnel description and monitoring for quality assurance.

Public policy in the health care industry has been shaped by the federal government in ways that affect the kinds, amount and quality of care. The therapeutic recreation profession is now being required (externally) to (a) improve patients' physical and emotional status as quickly as possible; (b) promote leisure well-being both during acute treatment, rehabilitation, and extended care, and on community reintegration; (c) involve patients in the treatment decision-making process with sensitivity to illness-related anxiety; (d) base such treatment on accepted protocols appropriate for diagnostically related groups; and (e) sufficiently document these actions in medical (or client care) records.

How therapeutic recreators respond to the clamor for accountable, quality therapeutic recreation will be crucial for the very existence of the profession during the 1990s. The profession must consider an activist role in the shaping of public policy. This will undoubtedly mean a professional lobbying effort firmly knowledgeable in the workings of the federal systems which affect therapeutic recreation.

Study Questions

1. What is the relationship of the federal government to TR credentialing? What should it be? Why?

2. What are some of the identifiable problems in health and human services in the United States? How do they relate to the therapeutic recreation profession's concerns?

3. Describe the key human service legislation enacted in the last 30 years. Discuss its effect on TR service.

4. What is the role of TR professional organization in legislative lobbying? What do you want your professional organization to do? What are you willing to do?

5. Do planners and politicians, that is, those who make policy and resource allocation decisions, really want all Americans to be included in the system of opportunities and services that result from their efforts? How can they be influenced?

6. Is there a role for the GS 188 classification (recreation specialist— institutional) in the 1990s? Should GS 188 continue to receive the same salary as GS 638 (Recreation Therapist)?

7. How will the elevation of the Veteran's Administration to the President's cabinet affect therapeutic recreation?

References

Architectural and Transportation Barriers Compliance Board. (1977). *Access to Recreation*. Washington, DC. Government Printing Office.

Caracciolo, F.S. (1984). Special Recreation Programs for Handicapped Individuals: Program Review FY 1981—1984. Washington, DC: RSA, OSERS, Department of Education.

Caracciolo, F.S. (1987). Memorandum: Priority FY 1987 Special Recreation Programs. Washington, DC: RSA, OSERS, Department of Education.

Churton, M.W. (1988). Federal Law and Adapted Physical Education. *Adapted Physical Activity Quarterly, 5*, 278—284.

Compton, D.M. (1985). The Status of Recreation Participation by Disabled Persons in America. In J.D. Kelley (Ed.), *International Forum: Leisure, Sports, Cultural Arts and Employment for Persons with Disability*. Washington, DC: Inspire '85, 11-19.

Dunn, D.R. (Ed.) (1971). *Guidelines for Action: Developing Opportunities for the Handicapped in Recreation, Parks and Leisure Services.* Washington, DC: National Recreation and Park Association.

Hillman, W.A. (1984). Innovative Approaches to Recreation and Leisure for the Handicapped. *Special Perceptions,* Summer (3), 19-22.

Kennedy, D.W., Austin, D.R., & Smith, R.W. (1987). *Special Recreation: Opportunities for Persons with Disabilities.* Philadelphia: Saunders College Publishing.

Krueger, D.B. (October, 1988). *Personal communication.*

Marwick, C. (1988). When It Comes to Advice, Congress Offers Some of the Most Needed to NIH. *Journal of American Medical Association, 260,* 1199.

National Therapeutic Recreation Society. (1982). Philosophical Position Statement of the National Therapeutic Recreation Society. Arlington, VA: National Recreation and Parks Association.

Park, D.C. (1980). *Legislation Affecting Park Services and Recreation for Handicapped Individuals.* Washington, DC: Hawkins & Associates.

Park, D.C. (Ed.) (1980). *Focus on Research: Recreation for Disabled Individuals.* Washington, DC: The George Washington University.

Patrick, G.D. (1988). Quality Assurance Plan for the Patient Activities Department. Bethesda, MD: National Institutes of Health.

President's Committee on Employment of the Handicapped. (1974). *Recreation and Handicapped People.* Washington, DC:Government Printing Office.

Public Law 95-602. (1978). *Rehabilitation Act Amendments of 1978* (95th Congress, 2nd Session, Senate Report 100-112.)

Public Law 99-457. (October 8, 1986). *Education for the Handicapped Act Amendments of 1986* (99th Congress, 2nd session, House of Representatives Report 99-860).

Public Law 99-507. (October 2, 1986). *Rehabilitation Act Amendments of 1986* (99th Congress, 2nd session, House of Representatives Report 99-995).

Public Law 100-146. (July 17, 1987). *The Developmental Disabilities Assistance and Bill of Rights Act Amendments of 1987* (100th Congress, 1st session, Senate Report 100-113).

Reynolds, R.P., & O'Morrow, G.S. (1985). *Problems, Issues and Concepts in Therapeutic Recreation.* Englewood Cliffs, NJ: Prentice-Hall.

Riley, R. (1987). *Evaluation of Therapeutic Recreation Through Quality Assurance.* State College, VA: Venture Publishing.

Sessoms, H.D. (1970). The Impact of the RSA Recreation Trainee Program, 1963—1968. *Therapeutic Recreation Journal, 14* (1), 23—29.

Sperling, A. (1988). *Mission Statement.* Bethesda, MD: Patient Activities Department, National Institutes of Health.

Stein, J.W., Burnette, W., Park, D., & Hillman, W.A., (1970). *Guidelines for Professional Preparation Programs for Personnel Involved in Physical Education and Recreation for the Handicapped.* Washington, DC: American Association for Health, Physical Education and Recreation.

Subcommittee on the Handicapped. (1985). *A Compilation of Federal Laws for Disabled Children, Youth, and Adults.* U.S. Government Printing Office: Washington, DC.

The White House Conference on Handicapped Individuals. (1977). *Final Report.*

U.S. Department of Education. (1980). *Summary of Existing Legislation Relating to the Handicapped.* Washington, DC: Office of Special Education and Rehabilitation Services.

Veterans Administration. (May, 1987). *The VA Today.* Washington, DC.

Veterans Administration. (1984). *Professional Services: Recreation Service.* Washington, DC: Department of Medicine and Surgery.

Witt, P.A. (1987). Editor's Comments. *Therapeutic Recreation Journal, 21*(1), 7-8.

NONTRADITIONAL PRACTICE ISSUES:
Therapeutic Recreation in Special Education

Charles C. Bullock

Introduction

Since 1975, Public Law 94-142, the Education for all Handicapped Children's Act (EHA), has become the most powerful piece of civil rights legislation in this country. In subsequent reauthorizations it has been strengthened to be even more responsive to the needs of students with handicapping conditions. The mandate as guaranteed under the law is for all children to receive a "free and appropriate education."

But what is an appropriate education? Parents, teachers, administrators, and researchers have been asking that question since long before the 1975 statute. Among other things, one area that continues to emerge is the importance of recreation and leisure in the overall education of a child. "The Cardinal Principles of Education" (1912) included "worthy use of leisure" as one of its objectives. John Dewey (1916), the dean of modern education, repeatedly upheld the importance of play in the educational process. More recently, the National Advisory Committee on the Handicapped, in its 1977 annual report stated, "It seems clear that no IEP can be considered complete unless it takes into consideration the handicapped child's special need for training and guidance in . . . recreation, and the constructive use of leisure time." Yet the inclusion of those elements is hardly more of a reality today than it was in the early part of this century.

One thing that should make the inclusion of these elements a reality is that PL 94-142 includes a provision for therapeutic recreation services as one of several related services. Even though the federal statute contains "recreation as a related service," recreation, let alone therapeutic recreation has seldom been implemented as a part of special education. This paper will explain the "recreation as a related service" provision and discuss issues related to implementation of therapeutic recreation in this nontraditional setting of special education.

What is Recreation as a Related Service?

In PL 94-142, recreation is included as a "related service" to assist a handicapped student to benefit from special education. As such, recreation, as a supportive service, and special education are legislatively bound in an interdependent relationship. Recreation as a related service provides assistance, instruction, and intervention to enhance and expand the quality of the educational process provided to handicapped students. Within the "related services" provision, recreation consists of four components:

- Assessment of recreation and leisure functioning: a procedure to determine current functional strengths of the handicapped student in recreation and leisure as the basis for IEP prescription and subsequent remediation.

- Leisure education: instruction to improve the leisure participation and leisure lifestyle of handicapped students through the development of positive attitudes toward leisure, the development of skills necessary for recreation participation, knowledge of recreational resources, and recognition of the benefits of recreation involvement.

- Therapeutic recreation: the purposive use of recreation activities and experiences to ameliorate deficits in social, cognitive, and physical functioning of handicapped students.

- Recreation in school and community agencies: the provision of recreation services to handicapped students in the least restrictive environment.

Is Recreation as a Related Service the Same as Physical Education?

Recreation and physical education are not the same from a legislative or programmatic perspective. Unlike physical education, recreation is by definition, an addition to regular special and physical education. As a related service, recreation assists, augments, and enhances the education process. Recreation and leisure are essential parts of a total education. Recreation personnel, identified in Subpart B of the rules and regulations as "Therapeutic Recreation Specialists," must work with traditional service personnel such as special educators and physical educators to provide recreation services that assist and augment rather than duplicate. This is accomplished through cooperative working relationships that provide the highest quality and most comprehensive educational experiences.

Recreation as a related service for students with handicaps must be administered in a manner consistent with other related educational services. That is, services are provided to those children who need it to benefit from their special education. The focus of recreation for handicapped students is to serve children whose recreation and leisure skills, abilities, attitudes, and knowledge are significantly below average and are affecting learning, classroom performance, and present and future life style. Therapeutic recreation personnel direct their energies toward analyzing and identifying students' strengths and weaknesses, and determining the appropriate programmatic responses. Specific interventions and strategies are then developed to improve performance.

How Does Recreation as a Related Service Fit into Special Education?

The need for recreation has long been seen as a universal need. Recreation participation has a significant impact on the social and psychological adjustment of an individual. Recreation activity is instrumental in the individual's development of a sense of personal identity and self-worth and the ability to interact with others and one's environment. Recreation assists in the learning process. Recreation as an educational tool can be used to achieve cognitive, social, emotional, and physical objectives identified in the IEP. Recreation activities and experiences are an important aspect of community adjustment and have an impact on total adjustment, especially in the transition from school to work and/or independent living. Therefore, recreation as a related service is an important part of a child's education.

Yet handicapped children are not provided the recreation services and opportunities needed to assist them in their adjustment and subsequent transition from school to adult life. Through recreation, handicapped students explore their own attitudes and values regarding leisure and recreational involvement and plan ways to utilize recreation to assist in their adjustment to school, community, and ultimately independent living. Recreation services for students with handicapping conditions should include assessment of leisure functioning, leisure education, therapeutic recreation, and recreation in school and community agencies. Although handicapped students should be afforded these services as referred, the content of instruction will vary according to the ages and abilities of students.

At all levels, emphasis is upon the assessment and subsequent remediation of recreation and play skills. Following assessment, remediation is accomplished through (1) treatment-oriented recreation services, (2) leisure education, and (3) recreation participation in the least restrictive environment. Early in a child's education, the student may receive therapeutic recreation to ameliorate cognitive, social, and physical deficits, thereby assisting in the educational process. Later, special emphasis is placed on initial exploration of recreation and leisure skills, values, and attitudes and on participation in activities consistent with their nonhandicapped peers.

At the secondary school level the emphasis may still be on assessment, remediation, and participation; however, the greatest emphasis at this level is leisure education to help in the preparation of the student to assume adult roles. Leisure education is crucial to the pretransitional and transitional phases of the handicapped student's life. At the time when the student is preparing for exit from school, there is an increasing emphasis on preparation for work. It is essential also that he or she understand the importance of recreation and leisure to a well-balanced adult life. As such, leisure education on an individual or group basis

1. clarifies leisure values;
2. fosters changes in leisure attitudes, appreciations, knowledge, skills, and behavior patterns;
3. reexamines time use patterns;
4. develops motivation and skills to participate in leisure experiences;
5. formulates new perspectives about the environment in which discretionary time may be spent;
6. relates the influence of leisure upon health, well-being, and satisfaction;
7. interrelates the creative and individual use of leisure and the quality of life;
8. serves as a tool to create a life of involvement and self-directed participation; and
9. discovers new talents and forms of expression.

Who May Receive "Recreation as a Related Service?"

All children with handicapping conditions as defined by federal mandate (PL 94-142) may receive recreation services. However, only those students whose IEPs include recreation as a related service receive assessment and subsequent remediation. Students are referred for recreation services by regular or special education teachers, child study teams, or other related services personnel. The students referred are ones who need a comprehensive recreation and leisure assessment or have been identified by other assessment procedures as needing recreation services to assist in the completion of regular education goals or IEP objectives. Whatever the reason, any student with a handicapping condition who is referred for recreation services will receive recreation services as appropriate to extend and enhance the student's education in the least restrictive environment.

Where are These Related Services Received?

Depending on the services prescribed in the IEP, recreation services for students with handicaps are delivered in a variety of settings. These environments include self-contained developmental or remedial education classes, mainstreamed classes, resource programs, and other places such as institutions and treatment facilities. IEP- prescribed services need not be restricted to school hours.

The therapeutic recreation specialist could work within a single educational setting (for example, regular school); itinerant service to more than one school, resource room, special school, or center; in a shared service arrangement; or outside the traditional instructional setting. With the present emphasis in secondary education on transition from school to work and community living, therapeutic recreation specialists may begin to work closely with vocational education, vocational rehabilitation, and community service agencies in order to enhance the student's education and, consequently, potential for successful transition.

Who Provides Recreation as a Related Service?

The Education of All Handicapped Children Act, PL 94-142, clearly identifies recreation as a related service that enhances the educational goals of a handicapped child. If recreation is included in a child's IEP, it cannot be completed by a curricular service such as special education or physical education. The person who provides this array of recreation services is called a therapeutic recreation specialist (TRS). "Therapeutic recreation specialists" are specifically identified in Subpart B of the rules and regulations for P.L. 94-142 , in sections 121a. 126 (b) and 121a.382 (a) 3, as the personnel to be identified and used to meet the goals of the act. The precise role of the therapeutic recreation specialist is dependent upon the size of the school system, the number and type of handicapped students, and the extent to which regular educators are available and prepared to provide programs for students with special needs.

The actual role of the therapeutic recreation specialist may be one or both of the following:

Direct service delivery: The therapeutic recreation specialist works directly with students in an educational environment as designated by an IEP. Usually the direct service delivery occurs in special, segregated schools serving more severely disabled students; however, it may occur in other school settings. Also, this type of service may be provided in nontraditional school settings within institutions and other treatment facilities.

Consultant: The therapeutic recreation specialist consults with teachers, parents, community, and other agencies on strategies for providing appropriate recreation services and programs for handicapped persons. This most often occurs in regular school environments, particularly mainstreamed settings, but may occur in myriad other settings.

Responsibilities vary depending upon the role or roles assumed. The duties of the TRS are dependent upon the referral and generally include

- assessing the recreation and leisure abilities, skills, knowledge, and attitudes of students with handicapping conditions;
- planning an appropriate implementation/remediation strategy based upon the assessment of the student with handicapping conditions;
- implementing and conducting leisure education programs to assist in the transition from school to work and independent living;
- providing resource/consultative assistance to regular and special education teachers to infuse leisure education concepts into their ongoing curricula;
- providing opportunities for recreation participation in the least restrictive environments in schools and community agencies;

- providing supportive/resources services to special education teachers who incorporate recreation and play into the curriculum to enhance cognitive, affective, and motor behavior; and
- interacting and working with professionals and paraprofessionals from other disciplines, parents, and community members who are concerned with handicapped students.

The therapeutic recreation specialist is not a teacher, but rather a supportive member of the educational team who consults with physical education and special education personnel, other related services personnel, and other educators to extend and enhance the students' total education.

Does Therapeutic Recreation Fit into the Current Trends in Special Education?

There are three major thrusts in special education today: childhood (0-3 years) identification and education, education in the least restrictive environment, and transition from secondary school to work and adult life.

The major issue by far, and the one that relates most directly with therapeutic recreation in the last 5 years, has been transition. The successful transition of youth with disabilities from school to adult, community-based employment and living environments has become a critical concern for parents, professionals, and policymakers. Many reasons exist for placing increased emphasis on transition services. Presently, youth with disabilities face an uncertain future when they leave public school programs. Follow-up studies of youth with disabilities who have left school report that high unemployment exists for the total population, even for those persons who have participated in special education programs tailored to their individual needs (Hasazi, Gordon, & Roe, 1985).

The current emphasis on transition by the Office of Special Education and Rehabilitation Services, U.S. Department of Education (Will, 1984) has defined the critical components of transition planning which help bridge the gap between school and employment. These critical components include

1. effective high school programs that prepare students to work and live in the community;
2. a broad range of adult service programs that can meet the various

support needs of individuals with disabilities in employment and community settings; and

3. comprehensive and cooperative transition planning between educational and adult service agencies for the purpose of developing needed services for graduates and dropouts.

Transition from secondary school to adult life should be perceived as a "right of passage" for all youth with disabilities leaving public school programs. If we believe it is a right, we must continue to advocate a major change in the focus of educational practices for youth with disabilities. The goal of special education programs should be to prepare individuals with disabilities to live and work in their communities (Halloran & Ward, 1987).

What is the Status of Implementation of Recreation as a Related Service?

Few state and local education agencies include recreation as a related service in their Comprehensive System of Personnel Development administrative codes or training objectives, or on a student's IEP form. Without the need for recreation services being addressed through these processes, it is impossible for children with handicapping conditions to receive appropriate and necessary recreation services as part of their education. Studies by Ellis (1978), Coyne (1981), Stanley (1981), Coyne (1984), and Bullock (1985) indicate conclusively that recreation as a related service is seldom being used to enhance the total education of handicapped children.

Bedini and Morris (1987) surveyed a sample of teachers of exceptional children in North Carolina regarding recreation as a related service. Only 10 % of the 270 respondents indicated that they requested recreation as a related service on the IEPs of their students. Recreation as a related service is rarely made available because many education and related services personnel are not aware of the role of recreation and its contributions in the educational process for students with handicapping conditions. It is often seen as a frill and unaffordable. The challenge for our field is to make parents and teachers more aware of the role of recreation and its contributions to the educational process.

No one denies that recreation has an enhancing effect on all the major domains of development—psychomotor, social/affective, and higher order cognitive processes. There is little question that all students can benefit from the availability of these services. In fact, the National Advisory Committee on the Handicapped noted in its 1977 annual report, "It seems clear that no IEP can be considered complete unless it takes into consideration the handicapped child's special need for training and guidance in physical education and recreation, and the constructive use of leisure time. Few classroom teachers are equipped, however, even to evaluate such components, much less to help formulate them. The apparent alternative is to seek counsel from members of the school staff who have had professional training in these areas." The same principle was reaffirmed by Certo, Haring, and York (1984, p. 247): "No IEP should be considered even minimally acceptable unless it contains an ILP (individualized leisure program) component that addresses both immediate and longitudinal, comprehensive recreation and leisure needs in representative proportions. In a survey (Halloran, et al., 1986) well over 60% of the respondents indicated that greater emphasis should be placed on recreational and leisure service needs as an integral component of community life. In a recent discussion (October 1987), Ms. Patti Smith, deputy assistant secretary of the Office of Special Education and Rehabilitation Services, and parent of a disabled child, stated "Recreation is often a parent's number 1 issue."

Yet, despite repeated affirmations of the importance of this related service, recreation or therapeutic recreation is not being implemented as a related service to enhance special education. As a result, the issue was taken to the courts. In 1980 the first due process hearing establishing therapeutic recreation services as an allowable and appropriate inclusion in an IEP, Sandra T. vs. Old Rochester Regional School District (Massachusetts), could have paved the way for increased inclusion of recreation as a related service. It didn't! The decision *was* positive and allowed the previously denied therapeutic recreation services. However, the decision did not lead other school systems in Massachusetts or any other state to push harder for the inclusion of recreation as a related service into IEPs. Presently, nearly eight years later, a resurgence of similar litigation and threats of litigation are being pursued in Ohio, Georgia, and other states to include this often overlooked related service provision. The outcomes are still unknown as of this writing.

What Must be Done?

In order to deliver recreation and leisure services to special education students, a series of interrelated processes must be accomplished:

1. Increasing educators' and parents' awareness of the potential con- tributions of recreation by providing in-service training.
2. Bridging assessment for recreation with already existing compre- hensive pupil assessment procedures in order to determine which special students need which specific recreation services.
3. Implementing recreation and leisure services through the vehicle of the Individualized Education Program.
4. Identifying and employing certified therapeutic recreation special- ists as the "qualified personnel" to deliver recreation as a related service and/or to assist school personnel (as consultants) in the delivery of services.
5. The Office of Special Education and Rehabilitation Services, U.S. Department of Education, and state education agencies must monitor recreation as a related service to ensure that it is being implemented adequately and appropriately.

The time is ripe for therapeutic recreation to respond to this immense need to fill the void in this non-traditional practice area. No longer can our field sit back and ignore the growing and increasingly acknowledged need. Our college and university curricula, our institu- tions, our state and national organizations, and our practitioners must respond. If we do not respond, we may find ourselves complaining (not unlike many practitioners in more traditional settings today) that someone else is doing our job. Legislatively, if for no other reason, therapeutic recreation is a part of special education. It is our job. The question is whether or not we will fully embrace this ripe nontraditional service area and whether we will respond quickly enough.

Study Questions

1. How will therapeutic recreation respond to this available nontradi- tional setting? Answer in terms of the philosophical and operational understandings of therapeutic recreation presented in earlier chapters in this book.
2. Who is likely to be most supportive of the inclusion of recreation as an integral part of the education process--parents, school ad- ministrators, teachers, employers, therapeutic recreators? Why? How will the others respond?
3. Much common wisdom among teachers and parents holds that there is no difference in physical education and recreation. Legis-

latively they have been defined differently, however. Should there be both physical education and therapeutic recreation in school as part of special education? Why or why not?

4. Why is it so hard to get recreation as a related service written into students' IEPs and subsequently implemented?

5. You are the chair of an ad hoc committee of your state or national therapeutic recreation professional organization. Outline your plan of action for the upcoming year.

References

Bedini, L.A., & Morris, L. (in preparation). Teachers' Perceptions of the Implementation of Recreation as a Related Service.

Bender, M., Brannan, S.A., & Verhoven, P.J. (1984). *Leisure Education for the Handicapped.* San Diego: College Hill Press.

Brightbill, Charles K., 1961. *Man and Leisure: A Philosophy of Recreation.* Englewood Cliffs, NJ: Prentice Hall.

Bullock, C.C. (1985) *Implementation of Recreation as a Related Service.* Unpublished manuscript, University of North Carolina at Chapel Hill.

Dewey, John (1916). *Democracy and Education.* New York: Macmillan.

Ford, A., Brown, L., Pumpian, I., Baumgart, D., Nisbet, J., Schroeder, J., & Loomis, R. (1984). Strategies for Developing Individualized Recreation and Leisure Programs for Severely Handicapped Students. In N. Certo, N. Haring, and R. York (Eds.), *Public School Integration of Severely Handicapped Students.* Baltimore MD: Paul H. Brookes.

Halloran, William D., & Ward, Michael J. (1987) *Improving Transition Programming: Changing Special Education's Focus.* Unpublished manuscript, U.S. Office of Special Education and Rehabilitative Services.

Halloran, W., Engleke, S., Donehey, A., Lewis, L., & Walsh, S. (1986). *Severely Handicapped Youth Exiting Public Education: Issues and Concerns.* Washington, DC: National Association of State Directors of Special Education.

Hasazi, S.B., Gordon, L.P., & Roe, C.A. (1985). Factors Associated with the Employment Status of Handicapped Youth Exiting From High School From 1979 to 1983. *Exceptional Children, 51.*

McConnell, J., Wilcox, B., Boles, S., & Bellamy, G.T. (1985) Transition Issues Facing Youth With Severe Disabilities: Parent's Perspective. *Journal of the Associaton of Persons with Severe Handicaps, 10*(1).

National Advisory Committee of the Handicapped (1977). *Annual Report.* Washington, DC: Author.

Putnam, J. Werder, J,. & Schleien, S. (1985) Leisure and Recreation Services for Handicapped Persons. pp 253-275 In K.C. Lakin and R.H. Bruininks (Eds.), *Strategies for Achieving Community Integration of Developmentally Disabled Citizens.* Baltimore, MD: Paul H. Brookes.

Stanley, J.B. (1985) *Recreation as a Related Service: A Decade of Decadence.* Trenton, NJ: Department of Community Affairs.

U.S. Office of Special Education and Rehabilitative Services. (1986). *Eighth Annual Report to Congress on the Implementation of Education of the Handicapped Act: Vol. 1.* Washington, DC: Author.

Voeltz, L.M., Weurch, B.B., & Wilcox, B. (1982) Leisure/Recreation: Preparation for Independence, Integration and Self- fulfillment. In B. Wilcox and G.T. Bellamy (Eds.), *Design for High School Programs for Severely Handicapped Students.* Baltimore, MD: Paul H. Brookes

Wilcox, B., & Bellamy, G.T. (Eds.). (1982). *Design of High School Programs for Severely Handicapped Students.* Baltimore, MD: Paul H. Brookes.

Will, M. (1984). *OSERS Programming for the Transition of Youth with Disabilities: Bridges from School to Working Life.* Washington, DC: U.S. Department of Education, Office of Special Education and Rehabilitative Services.

Legislative and Political Issues

photo courtesy of San Francisco Recreation Center for the Handicapped

The moral test of government is what it does with those in the dawn of life, those in the shadow of life and those in the twilight of life.

—Hubert H. Humphrey

POLITICAL IMPERATIVES FOR THERAPEUTIC RECREATION

David M. Compton

Introduction

Webster defines the word imperative as "absolutely necessary; urgent; compelling." It is with this orientation in mind that I challenge the therapeutic recreation profession to become more politically astute and aggressive. Several years ago I addressed a large assembly of therapeutic recreation practitioners, challenging them to "legislate, litigate, or abdicate." The message was one of deep concern over our profession's relative naivete in the political and legal arenas. The game of survival in the health care arena and also in the structure of public recreation had become one predicated on the ability of professionals to politically influence law, regulations, and systems about the importance of therapeutic recreation. Without a concerted effort aimed at politically influencing selected individuals and agencies, one could stand by and watch the erosion or eventual demise of our profession. While the therapeutic recreation profession is not down for the count, it is essential to be aggressive in the establishment of a political position in the health care and human service arenas. This chapter attempts to address several political imperatives facing the profession. These imperatives are the result of the authors discussion with professionals from therapeutic recreation and other allied health disciplines, trends in health care and human services, and personal convictions about the direction the profession must take to survive the next decade of emerging regulations, economic swings and human needs.

Health and Human Services:
A Role for Therapeutic Recreation

Dr. C. Everett Koop, Surgeon General, the top public health official in the United States, has on numerous occasions pointed to the preventable health dilemmas facing the nation. Lung cancer, substance abuse, AIDS, accidents resulting in traumatic injury, and heart disease are all preventable conditions (Committee for the Study of the Future of Public Health, 1988). Today, more than at any time in our history, there is widespread information about achieving a healthy lifestyle, and preventing disease, injury, or deterioration of bodily systems. Yet we see more than a million people currently infected with the AIDS virus, 140,000 Americans die annually from injuries and another 70 million sustain nonfatal injuries. Additionally, 60 million people are affected by high blood pressure, and thirty percent of the public is addicted to cigarettes—resulting in the single greatest cause of premature death (Committee for the Study of the Future of Public Health, 1988), and the list goes on. The implications for therapeutic recreation are great. There are many individuals who could benefit from a healthy lifestyle ... one deeply rooted in the belief that leisure is not only a worthy aspect of life but holds much promise to prevent debilitating or life threatening conditions. While one would not want to overstate the case for leisure or therapeutic recreation as it relates to health status, it is clear from much of our own literature and that of the health promotion movement, that an active lifestyle is essential to a sense of well being and a high quality of life.

Several categories of disease and disability are growing rapidly, and require careful attention by the medical, rehabilitation, and human services professions. According to Katzman (1986), "As many as 2 million Americans are suffering from Alzheimer's disease, resulting in severe, disabling intellectual impairment. The exact causes of Alzheimer's are unknown, but it is clearly associated with age." While a relatively small percentage of those under 60 have Alzheimer's, there is a sharp increase in the incidence of the disease in those over 80, according to federal sources. More than 20 percent of this segment of the population is estimated to have the disease (Secretary's Task Force on Alzheimer's Disease, 1984). Of considerable concern is the prediction that the disease will increase dramatically over the next several decades as the population ages significantly. While this situation may seem tangential to therapeutic recreation at first, I submit it is at the core of some political imperatives for the profession.

If therapeutic recreation is to have a significant impact on the lives of the elderly, and in particular, the Alzheimer's patient, then we must carefully position ourselves to have a more significant role in home health care and the nursing home industry than we currently possess. It will be necessary for us to seek research funding to address critical issues facing the care and leisure needs of the Alzheimer patient. We will need to drastically increase the number of credentialled therapeutic recreation specialists employed in the long-term care industry if we are to gain credibility in the industry and with federal regulators. This will certainly require changes or amendments to the current federal regulations governing the operation of nursing homes. Further, we will need to embark on training professionals, administrators, and relevant others about the role that therapeutic recreation can and must assume in the care and support of the patient throughout the course or stages of the disease. There is a need to know what, if any, treatment protocols work with this type of patient. Do these approaches differ at various stages of the disease? These and numerous other questions must be systematically addressed by the profession if it wants to be included in the care and delivery of services to the Alzheimer patient of the future. Instead of a small band of individuals assembling at a conference after a presentation on the subject of Alzheimer's, we need to establish and fund a standing committee on the subject.

A similar approach could be taken for several other groups of citizens who have acute needs for health and human services. The plight of America's millions of homeless individuals and families is one example of a major human dilemma rarely discussed or addressed by therapeutic recreation. Does the profession recognize the problem? Are we concerned? What is the public recreation sector, and the many therapeutic recreation specialists employed in the public sector doing about this dilemma?

Another nationwide health care crisis is the matter of chemical dependence.

"Alcohol and drug abuse are major factors in much illness, disability, and death in the United States. Some problems are immediate, and some evolve over time. Ten percent of all deaths in the United States are related to alcohol use. Cirrhosis of the liver, which is largely attributable to alcohol use, caused 10.7 deaths per 100,000 population in 1984. Alcohol abuse is also frequently related to motor vehicle injuries and deaths. In 1984, the death rate from alcohol-related motor vehicle accidents was 9.5 per 100,000, and from other alcohol-related accidents, 4.3 per 100,000. Drug abuse has also been related to premature death, severe physical disability, psychological disability, homicides, suicides, and injuries. In 1984, it was estimated that there were more than 3,500 drug-related deaths in 26 major metropolitan areas in the United States. Drug use causes some 100,000 to 350,000 hospital admissions per year" (Office of Disease Prevention and Health Promotion, 1986).

What role has therapeutic recreation or recreation in general taken in addressing this health care dilemma? To the best of my knowledge setting national policy, securing research or training funds, or developing innovative and widely acclaimed approaches to the problem. Billions of dollars have been made available in the Reagan and Bush administrations to combat the chemical dependence problem, and yet the therapeutic recreation profession could hardly be called a role player in the game. Again, this calls for a more well-defined approach by the profession to a specific human condition or social issue. While we grope with problems of defining terms, the health care needs mount. When will we take a stand? What strategies will we develop?

These examples are merely a microcosm of the challenges facing the profession if it is to assume a more viable posture in the health care arena in the future. Politically positioning ourselves in regard to these and other matters may have significant consequences for the profession. If we are at the forefront of creating legislation, it is more likely that we will be included in language authorizing our services. If we are not involved at the front end, we must assume a posture of reacting to pieces of legislation that either limit our roles or exclude us from participation. An example of this is the recent proposal to amend the language of the "Medicaid Home and Community Quality Services Act of 1987." Early drafts of the bill omitted "recreation therapy" (note the term used here) from the proposed legislation. Through a concerted effort of the Consortium of Citizens with Disabilities, the Legislative Coalition of NTRS and ATRA and others, the point was made that this was unacceptable (Washington, 1987). Still the pattern is strikingly similar. In the early preparation of PL94-142, therapeutic recreation was excluded from formal participation in the drafting of language of this vital piece of legislation. Only through some skilled political maneuvering, were individuals such as David Park, William Hillman, John Nesbitt, and others able to ensure that therapeutic recreation became part of the related service language in PL 94-142. Recent efforts by the venerable John Shank, Chair, Legislative Coalition, have protected our position in numerous pieces of legislation in health and human services. For the most part, however, we operate from a reactive rather than a proactive position. We have no "war chest" to battle other organizations, interest groups or professions. Further, the lack of full-time lobbying personnel seriously limits our timeliness and effectiveness. The National Recreation and Park Association's efforts in the political arena have been admirable but matters of specific interest to therapeutic recreation are rarely of high priority. Their focus has, and will continue to be, legislation that affects public parks and recreation.

There is a vital role for therapeutic recreation in the health and human services of this nation. Almost all of the health care problems facing the nation require addressing the leisure time, leisurability, habilitation, or rehabilitation goals through some form of intervention to achieve a higher quality of life. We are lacking the depth of focus on selected health care issues. There is no concentrated lobbying effort to proactively shape legislation. It is politically imperative that we change course and begin to address these issues in a manner that will be beneficial to the profession in the long run. The following section presents several political imperatives for the profession.

Restructuring of Organizations: Federating for Maximum Power

The current arrangement of professional organizations either directly or tangentially involved in the promotion of therapeutic recreation is not working. Much has been said about the difficulties of the National Therapeutic Recreation Society representing the clinical interests of the profession. Peterson (1984), in a poignant article, states

"The overall mission of NRPA has little to do with the nature of the work that takes place in clinical and treatment centers. The knowledge and expertise needed in the clinical setting is significantly different than that required in the public park and recreation arena. Thus, the nature and type of professional organization that the clinical therapeutic recreation recreator needs is quite different than what the current NRPA can provide." Further she indicates "Clinical therapeutic recreation is in a tenuous position within the current health care system. The complexity of service delivery, the high costs of health care, the increasing and changing nature of regulations and standards impacting service, and the overall sophistication of medical and psychiatric services make survival as well as impact in this arena of human service difficult. The individual delivering therapeutic recreation services in clinical settings needs a strong professional organization to provide support, technical assistance, legislative action, information on the latest regulatory and procedural advancement, as well as professional development opportunities and continuous flow of information." (pp.15-16)

It was suggested that the needs of the profession had changed and that a new organization was needed to meet the clinically-oriented therapeutic recreation professionals' needs.

The formation of the American Therapeutic Recreation Association appears to have filled a need expressed by many leading professionals. The problem is that its creation appears to have divided the collective energy and leadership of the profession and created unnecessary philosophical, logistical, and political dilemmas. This is not to suggest that ATRA is the root of the problems—it may have crystallized thinking to the point where action can take place. The point should also be made that the problems have existed for some twenty-five years, and few people were bold enough to suggest that the house in which therapeutic recreation resided was the wrong address.

Several other organizations also operate under the aegis of therapeutic recreation. Most notable is the National Association of Activity Professionals (NAAP). Its membership is primarily composed of individuals working in the long-term care industry. They represent a large cadre of health care workers, many with minimal training and credentials. Other specialty organizations in such areas as horticulture therapy, pet therapy, disabled sports of all types, art therapy, and music therapy all ply a similar trade under similar philosophical banners.

As past president of the NTRS, I addressed the issue of the organizational structure of that body in a letter and presentation to the President (Michal Ann Lord) and Board of Directors. The tenor of my commentary was to invite the organization to address its structure. In my opinion, it was outmoded. I believe the same observations are applicable today. The following are some excerpts from that letter.

Much has been said about the wisdom of NTRS staying in the NRPA family. Over the past few years, many rather pioneering people in therapeutic recreation, and involved in NTRS from its very beginnings, became disillusioned with the NRPA structure as well as some personnel. What evolved into serious confrontation eventually birthed a competing organization (ATRA). In retrospect, different managerial approaches may have led the NRPA to have been a bit more flexible and the advocates for change less demanding and confronting. I think it may have been inevitable that a new organization would emerge. There were some who had long standing differences with NRPA. It is interesting that a philosophical difference emerged over the "clinical vs. community" issue and became a convenient rationale for some who had argued in exactly the opposite direction only a few years before. That is water under the bridge now. Not only does ATRA exist but a host of other organizations exist who do some of the very things that NTRS assumes it alone does.

What remains is the clarification of what NTRS will stand for as a professional organization. Who will it represent? What are its goals? How will it represent its constituency? This, I believe, is not complete at this time. The rather amorphous constituency is still not understood or defined. While the effort to align the goals of the NTRS with those of the NRPA was noteworthy, it may have represented a strategy of convenience rather than a critical examination of the profession, constituency, consumers or needs of the nation. Merely aligning NTRS with the NRPA agenda will not insure NTRS' viability, continuance or credibility.

Closely aligned with the issues of knowing who you are and what you stand for, are the issues of where you belong and how you should be governed. Again, much has been said about the relative merits and demerits of NTRS within the NRPA structure. Rather than belabor the background of this issue, I will simply state that it seems to me that there is a need for an organization within the NRPA structure who represents professionals delivering "therapeutic recreation" to special populations or individuals with disabilities. It is essential that this voice not be lost in an organization where there are numerous and seemingly tangential agendas.

I am convinced that the NRPA will inevitably have to realign or reorganize itself to meet the needs of its membership. This may ultimately come to pass in the abolition of branches to create a more unified and simplified organization. On the other hand, I tend to believe that a "federation" is a better way to proceed. This is a way in which some of the criticisms of the past from the NTRS could be addressed while attempting to achieve optimal development of specialized interests. This calls for "Big Daddy" (in Orwellian terms), to turn loose of the power grip on the branches. Every futurist who has written on the nature of organizations or who has spoken to an NRPA Congress, has pointed out the inevitable fact of decentralization and smaller organizational units closer to the heart of the member. The centrist organizational structure of NRPA with a few individuals holding power is clearly contradictory to the pluralist notions they hold for a mass professional/consumer coalition of members. It is also the key to suppressing the emergence of specialized efforts that are nearer to the interests and passions of the members. The essence of a federation is "trust" and "autonomy"—and this is precisely what many of our departed colleagues were yearning for in the past. Much has been written on the subject of "a sense of ownership" in the organizational behavior literature. It is clear to me that unless some radical changes take place in the organizational structure of NRPA, there will continue to be an almost cancerous erosion of the very fiber of the organization.

What does all of this mean for the NTRS? I believe that the leadership must begin to understand the frailty of the organizational structure under which they find themselves. I am not advocating taking our "game" elsewhere. I am saying that unless the organizational structure changes, there will be few, if any, major successes for NTRS in the future. It may still exist as an organization, but what will it have achieved? What contributions will it have made to the profession? consumers? society?

Will they be traceable and/or attributable to efforts of the organization? Will it have reached its optimal level of achievement? This issue of organizational structure is at the very root of NTRS' existence as the major organization in therapeutic recreation. It is not a question of affiliation with NRPA; it is a question of how that affiliation should be structured. In my opinion, the current structure mitigates against the organization becoming the powerful force that it should be or must be if it is to call itself the leader in matters pertinent to therapeutic recreation. (Compton, 1987)

One major problem facing the profession is that the individual organizations purporting to represent therapeutic recreation are all small in membership. Collectively they could amass a membership of more than 30,000 professionals and advocates. In this magnitude they could become   powerful players in the professional organization leagues that they must compete in to influence matters for their profession. It is interesting to note that our allied health colleagues in occupational and physical therapy (major players in the clinical arena), each have over 40,000 members. They are able to function in the political arena from a strong base of support not only in sheer numbers but with the necessary funds to finance their efforts. We, on the other hand, are operating on budgets of uncertainty or with minimal capital dedicated to the political process. Our position is weak, and should be recognized as such. One option to correct this situation is the examination of new organizational structures. A federation of organizations is one such option.

A federation is the creation of a league of entities who consent to be full members of an effort to advance their mutual interests. While the members of the federation give power to the elected officials, they usually have veto power over actions deemed not to be in the interest of an established mission statement and goals. One growing problem with the current structure of NRPA, ATRA, and many of the other organizations representing therapeutic recreation is the absence of delegate voting—direct member participation in the affairs of the organization. There is little involvement of members in the affairs of these organizations. The policies and activities are usually derived from the board of directors or trustees agenda—not the memberships! In any new organization that might be formed, I would strongly suggest that it be patterned after the American Speech and Hearing Association (ASHA), the American Physical Therapy Association (APTA) or the American Alliance for Health, Physical Education , Recreation, and

Dance (AAHPERD) where there is a member electoral process to select delegates. These approaches are truly democratic. Our current organizations are operated in an elitist, rigid, and selective manner that runs counter to democratic principles of "one person-one vote" representation.

Several characteristics of a federation make it an attractive alternative for the therapeutic recreation profession. These include:
1. large numbers of members
2. increased revenue to fund various activities
3. autonomy of the special interests is retained
4. critical issues get a single, unified response
5. more efficient day-to-day operations
6. increased awareness of other professionals concerns and problems and increased interdisciplinary communication
7. target political action
8. expand the fund raising potential and other sources of extramural funding

The problems associated in creating a federation should also be pointed out. These include:

1. securing agreement over a charter, mission, goals, and operations will exponentially become more difficult as the numbers of players is increased.
2. financing the organization will be a delicate issue, given already high costs of membership in existing organizations.
3. political recognition and clout will need to be earned and will not come automatically.
4. the mixture of organizations may compound the strains facing each in their current operations.

While space does not allow for a complete discussion of the positive and negative attributes of creating a federation, this in no way diminishes the importance of exploring organizational alternatives for therapeutic recreation. The current arrangement of professional representation is not only weak but ineffective. We are split into far too many small entities vying for identity. The time has come to consider realigning ourselves under a new banner. What that organization might look like is open to deliberation. What its purpose and outcomes might be are contained in the numerous charters, bylaws and constitutions of the various organizations who should be considered for membership.

Prepare the Profession for Active Roles in the Creation and Oversight of Public Policy

Another political imperative is for the profession to train its members in the art and science of politically shaping public policy. After all, it is public policy in health care, human services and education that authorize the funding of services. Without full participation in the process of creating public laws, regulations and agencies, we accede to the political influence of others. Evidence of our outside role is provided in the recent report by the Committee to Study the Role of Allied Health Personnel of the Institute of Medicine prompted by a congressional mandate contained in Public Law 99-129, the Health Professions Training Act of 1985 (Institute of Medicine, 1989). None of the national organizations in therapeutic recreation was present or represented in this critical policy meeting. Occupational therapy and physical therapy were both represented and secured major positions in the resulting report. Noticeably absent was therapeutic recreation or recreation therapy.

We must adopt a national agenda that clearly focuses on the major issues facing the profession, health care, human services and education. Legislation must be identified in its earliest stages to ensure proper and full input into public policy. Training of young professionals must take place in the colleges and universities. Continuing education efforts must provide indepth training efforts for practitioners so they can influence legislation at local and state levels as well as the national level. Organizations representing the profession should assume major responsibility for this training. Publications, newsletters, telecommunications and other mechanisms should be employed regularly to keep professionals abreast of impending legislation, rules and regulations and extramural funding opportunities.

While the involvement in the formation of public policy is vital to the future of the profession, there is an additional role that our professionals must assume. The responsibility for oversight of current public policy is imperative if we are to receive our fair share of resources. Committees in each of our organizations should constantly monitor the regulatory agencies as well as the agencies who dispense funds for grants and contracts. Subtle changes in the wording of regulations governing a public law could spell disaster for the profession. The constant monitoring by the National Consortium for Physical Education and Recreation for the Handicapped averted on numerous occasions sharp reductions in funding levels for personnel preparation and research funds from the former Bureau of Education for the Handicapped, (BEH) now called the Office of Special Education and Rehabilitative Services in the Department of Education. There were several times, however, when the profession was caught unaware, and funding dropped significantly (Sherrill, 1988). Tables 1 and 2 illustrate the relative nature of funding of therapeutic recreation and adapted physical education from 1982-88. These figures do not include the year 1981 when the Reagan administration nearly wiped out the Department of Education and important funding programs that supported therapeutic recreation.

Central to accomplishing the aforementioned is having a full-time lobbying staff. Piecemeal efforts of the past were not effective. Asking professionals to volunteer large segments of their time is also ludicrous. In addition, we must have representatives in the federal bureaucracy. The advocacy roles played by individuals such as Mel Appell (OS-

Table 1
Funding Analysis for Adapted Physical Education and Therapeutic Recreation Projects Supported by the Division of Personnel Preparation - Office of Special Education Programs

Fiscal Years 1982 through 1988

Fiscal year	Number of projects	Funding	Percentage of division appropriation
1982	63	$1,642,284	3.3
1983	80	3,239,632	6.5
1984	71	3,445,717	6.0
1985	71	3,676,758	6.0
1986	55	3,237,014	5.2
1987	46	3,044,695	4.4
1988	49	3,233,545	4.8

(Bokee, 1988)

Table 2
Funding Analysis for Therapeutic Recreation Projects Supported by the Division of Personnel Preparation - Office of Special Education Programs

Fiscal Years 1982 through 1988

Fiscal year	Number of states	Number of projects	Estimated no. of students trained	Funding
1982	18	24	12,317 (2,778 preservice) (9, 539 inservice)	$ 653,442
1983	18	31	9,672 (2,796 preservice) (6,876 inservice)	1,242,880
1984	18 District of Columbia	29	294*	1,473,217
1985	14 District of Columbia	27	264	1,496,658
1986	15 District of Columbia	23	252	1,329,016
1987	9 District of Columbia	12	132	752,161
1988	12 District of Columbia	14	156	839,375
Totals:		160	23,087 (6,672 preservice) (16,415 inservice)	$7,786,749

*Beginning in fiscal year 1984, the estimated number of students trained is based only upon preservice training: training that leads toward a degree or certification. (Source: Bokee, 1988)

ERS), Bill Hillman (OSERS), David Park, (National Park Service) and others were instrumental in ensuring funding for therapeutic recreation. The loss of internal advocates results in critical policies, rules and reviews being shaped by those unfamiliar with the discipline. Obviously the process of having our proposals funded diminishes significantly.   The successful organizations in allied health and human services pay for the qualified lobbyist to advance their cause. We should expect nothing less from our organizations.

Seek Funding to Support a National Research Agenda

Over the past two decades, there has been increasing attention paid to the need to corroborate our platitudes about the importance of therapeutic recreation. In 1969, The American Association for Health, Physical Education, and Recreation, and the National Recreation and Park Association jointly sponsored a conference aimed at identifying the "immediate and future needs for research and demonstration projects." These included the following:

- Leisure concepts and implications for handicapped children and youth
- Leisure participation as it relates to human growth and development
- Inhibitors/facilitators of leisure participation
- Activity analysis
- Leisure counseling /development of leisure profile
- Leisure education/career education for leisure occupations
- Information resources and research techniques
- Education, training and development of personnel
- Mobilization and full utilization of institutional and community resources.

These items were then condensed into five categories as follows:

- Leisure concepts
- Attitudinal barriers
- Activity analysis
- Design/Adaptation considerations
- Education/Counseling

In 1974, a similar conference was held to "conduct a research needs assessment conference in the area of leisure time activity for handicapped populations" (primarily children and youth) (Verhoven and Goldstein, 1976). This conference also produced a list of research topics for the profession. Several other attempts to articulate the research needs of the profession have been undertaken at various symposia, conferences and institutes. The problem is that we have rarely been able to execute the agenda.

The state of research in therapeutic recreation is seriously weak. Austin (1982), Lewko and Crandall (1980), Compton (1984), Iso-Ahola (1988), and Witt (1988) all express concern for the status of research in therapeutic recreation. In the past few years there has been increased attention to several priorities I described in an issue of the *Therapeutic Recreation Journal* dedicated to research (Compton, 1984). These priorities included:

1. Plan and conduct a national conference on research priorities in recreation for special populations for the next decade.
2. Establish specialized laboratories that conduct research on recreation for special populations.
3. Establish a clinical consortium to examine the therapeutic process, results, techniques and interactions under controlled environments.
4. Establish endowed chairs for the study of leisure with special populations at selected universities.
5. Conduct annual nationwide training in applied and basic research.
6. Establish a national research fund for the study of recreation for special populations.
7. Encourage the expansion of current periodicals to include a full section on research in recreation for special populations.
8. Prepare and publish a biannual compendium of researching recreation for special populations.
9. Continue the study of certain issues, problems and developments over time to ensure completeness and quality.

While there are signs of change in therapeutic recreation, there are also some deep concerns on the horizon. First, we have fewer Ph.D faculty entering the profession than ever before. We are in a crisis mode with a serious lack of qualified faculty to fill available positions. Further, few of these individuals are in a position to conduct high quality research. Recent tenure decisions at a number of institutions attest to the fact that we are not measuring up to rigorous standards of scholarly productivity. In addition, we are experiencing a drought in federal funding for research projects. Only a handful of research grants are submitted annually and even fewer are funded. Couple this with low faculty salaries, high teaching loads, increasing numbers of majors and one can readily see why we have problems on the horizon in higher education.

Witt (1988) echoes my call for funding for research from the national organizations. We cannot develop the body of necessary to prove the efficacy of the profession if it must be bootstrapped or piecemealed with limited departmental funds. Organizations such as the Veterans Administration should be sought out to collaborate in the funding of vital research in the discipline. After all, they are the single largest employer of therapeutic recreation personnel in the nation. The private sector should also be courted to provide funds for research into the economic efficiency and effectiveness of therapeutic recreation as a treatment modality. National organizations such as NTRS and ATRA should also invest in research.

Recent efforts by the NTRS Research and Development Committee in this regard are encouraging (Aguilar, 1987).

Third Party Funding: A Key to Survival In Health Care

Reitter aptly presents the case in an earlier chapter for becoming competent and effective in acquiring third party funds for our services. What may not be emphasized enough is the critical nature of this strategy. In many cases, the future of individual jobs, departments, and entire services hang on the ability to secure reimbursement for our services. We must become more astute about the fiscal policies and practices that drive the health care system. The words offered by West and Thorn (1984) should not go unheeded,

1. Therapeutic recreation is not a free service. As long as paid employees have used supplies, equipment, and facilities to provide service, there has been a cost incurred. This cost is passed on to consumers either directly as a specific charge for services provided or indirectly as included in the overhead.
2. Any agency, public or private, must balance the fiscal "bottom line" in order to stay in business. Enough revenue must be generated to cover expenditures, both direct and indirect, and provide for a projected growth.
3. In the health care industry, third-party payments (Medicare, private and commercial insurance) cover the majority of the costs. Third-party payers decide what costs are covered by determining what services are reasonable

and necessary. When services are not covered, it is because third-party payers have determined that the service is not necessary for the treatment of a particular patient or condition and that the services provided are not reasonably expected to improve the client's conditions or contribute to the diagnosis.

4. Considering today's economy and the current dilemma of health care financing to be valued as a health care service by consumers, administrators, physicians, third-party payers, and allied disciplines, one must not only produce a reasonable, necessary, and beneficial outcomd from services provided, but must also produce this outcome at the lowest reasonable cost and determine how this cost will be financed.

5. Concern about the quality and quantity of services must include concern about the financing of services. When we are successful, a reasonable quality of services can be available to more clients. When we ar unsuccessful, services will be reduced or eliminated and may not be available to clients who need them.

Touchstone (1984), Reitter (1984) West (1984) and Ollson (1986) all point to the need for therapeutic recreation to examine carefully the critical dimensions of the health care system that dictate who will be around in the 1990s. Olsson clearly outlines the problems and potentials of the prospective payment system that all health care providers are having to cope with today and in the future. Touchstone addresses the issue of risk management that many organizations fail to confront in planning and wind up dealing with in court. West introduces the notion of "productivity analysis" in attempting to focus in on measures of performance by the therapeutic recreation unit or professional. Reitter suggests that it may be too late for the profession to enter the third party reimbursement arena. Yet today, more than ever before, therapeutic recreation specialists and managers are seeking to become more like their allied health care partners. Preparation and retraining programs in marketing, accounting, legal and management matters are critical to their survival. Conferences, institutes, workshops and symposia should pay careful attention to the emerging needs of the profession. Shaping the future of the profession will require maximizing our ability to learn new systems, approaches and skills necessary to compete in a dynamic industry.

Conclusions

It appears that if the therapeutic recreation profession is to prosper and grow in the future, it must become more politically astute. First, it must reorganize to achieve a base of power that allows it to compete with the major players in allied health and human services. Second, it must develop information through research to prove its efficacy. Third, it must retrain individuals to develop more skills in fiscal matters if it is to survive in an era of fiscal accountability, prospective payments, and third party payments.

Study Questions

1. Examine the role therapeutic recreation could have with preventable health dilemmas such as lung cancer, substance abuse, AIDS, accidents resulting in traumatic injury, and heart disease. Prepare a position paper on the subject and clearly document the case for therapeutic recreation as a preventive, remedial, and restorative agent.

2. One central difficulty in amassing politcal power in therapeutic recreation is the diversity of organizations, people, and movements who in some way operate under the banner of "therapuetic recreation." Study the pros and cons of different organizational structures such as federation, alliance, consortium, affiliate, etc. Which allow various organizations to come together under one banner? List which organizations should be brought together. Debate the issue in a formal seetting.

3. Study the operations of other allied health and human service organizations such as AOTA, APTA, ASHA, etc. How are they different from NTRS, ATRA, and NAAP? How are they similar? What positive aspects of these organizations might we adopt? What should we avoid?

4. What current or proposed legislation affects therapeutic recreation? Make a list of federal and state laws with a synopsis of the law and its relationship to therapeutic recreation. What specific "authorization" language exists?

5. Investigate how voluntary associations and organizations gain "power." What criteria differentiate the weak, ineffective organization from the powerful ones? What structural, financial, and operational elements of the organization affect the power of an organization?

References

Aguilar, T.E., Elliott, L., Kaufman, J., Lucas, M., & Munson, W. (1987). NTRS Research and Development Committee, Final Report (1986-87) (mimeographed copy).

Austin, D.R. (1982). Therapeutic Recreation Research: An Overview. Abstracts from the 1982 symposium on Leisure Research. Alexandria, Virginia, National Recreation and Park Association.

Bokee, M.D. (1988). The 1988 Report by the Division of Personnel Preparation on Adapted Physical Education and Therapeutic Recreation. Washington, D.C. Mimeographed paper.

Committee for the Study of the Future of Public Health, Institute of Medicine (1988). *The Future of Public Health.* Washington, D.C.: National Academy Press, 20-31.

Compton, D. M. (1984). Research Priorities in Recreation for Special Populations. *Therapeutic Recreation Journal, 15*(1), 9-17.

Compton, D.M. (1987). Personal correspondence to Michael Ann Lord, President, National Therapeutic Recreation Society regarding organizational structures, funding, etc. (September 14, 1987).

Institute of Medicine. (1989). *Allied Health Services: Avoiding Crises.* Washington, D.C.: National Academy Press.

Iso-Ahola, S.E. (1988). Research in Therapeutic Recreation. *Therapeutic Recreation Journal, 22*(1) 7-13.

Katzman,R. (1986). Alzheimer's Disease. *New England Journal of Medicine, 314*(15), 964-973.

Lewko, J. & Crandall, R. (1980). Research Trends in Leisure and Special Populations. *Journal of Leisure Research, 12* (4), 9-16.

Office of Disease Prevention and Health Promotion, Public Health Service. (1986). *The 1990 Objectives for the Nation: A Midcourse Review.* Washington: D.C.: U.S. Department of Health and Human Services.

Ollson, R. (1986). The Prospective Payment System: Implications for Therapeutic Recreation. *Therapeutic Recreation Journal, 20*(1), 7-17.

Peterson, C.A. (1984). A Matter of Priorities and Loyalties. *Therapeutic Recreation Journal. 18*(3), 11-16.

Reitter, M. (1984). Third-Party Reimbursement: Is Therapeutic Recreation Too Late? *Therapeutic Recreation Journal 18*(4), 13-19.

Secretary's Task Force on Alzheimer's Disease, U.S. Department of Health and Human Services. (1984). *Alzheimer's Disease.* Washington, D.C.: U.S. Government Printing Office.

Sherrill, C. (1988). *Leadership Training in Adapted Physical Education.* Champaign, IL: Human Kinetics Books.

Touchstone, W. (1984). Fiscal Accountability Through Effective Risk Management. *Therapeutic Recreation Journal, 18*(4), 20-26.

Verhoven, P.J. & Goldstein, J.E. (1976). *Leisure Activity Participation and Handicapped Populations: An Assessment of Research Needs.* Arlington, VA: National Recreation and Park Association.

Washington, Y.A. (1987). Personal Correspondence to the CCDD Task Force on Medicaid Long Term Care from Yvonne A. Washington, Program Manager National Therapeutic Recreation Society (September 2, 1987).

West, R.E. (1984). Productivity Analysis as a Method of Fiscal Accountability for Therapeutic Recreation. *Therapeutic Recreation Journal ,18*(4),27-36.

West, R.E., & Thorne, B.T. (1984). Guest Editorial. *Therapeutic Recreation Journal, 18*(4), 10-12.

Witt, P.A. (1988). *Therapeutic Recreation Research: Past, Present, and Future, 22*(1) 14-23.

LEGISLATIVE AND REGULATORY IMPERATIVES FOR THERAPEUTIC RECREATION

John W. Shank

Introduction

It is expected, perhaps even inevitable, that a professionalizing occupation establishes the ability to seek and maintain legal support for its services. Houle (1980) includes legal support as a distinct characteristic of a profession, suggesting that the worthiness of the profession is deemed by the legal structures that can ensure its continuation by providing support for training these professionals and by providing monies to support the service the profession provides to the public.

In its recent history, therapeutic recreation has garnered this support. Given the resources available to it, therapeutic recreation has an impressive track record in influencing public laws. However, its advocacy action is far from where it should be in terms of continuity and consistency. The ability to increase its legal support and to influence public policy will prove to be one of the most crucial issues determining the advancement of the profession. The purposes of this chapter are to provide a brief overview of therapeutic recreation's involvement in the legislative arena and to accentuate the critical factors challenging our future success in this area.

A 20-Year History

The legislative advocacy action of the therapeutic recreation discipline has occurred in the relatively short span of 20 years, from shortly after the 1966 creation of the National Recreation and Park Association (NRPA), and its branch, the National Therapeutic Recreation Society (NTRS) to the present. The early history of the branch's involvement in legislative advocacy reflected the Association's early and apparent commitment to governmental relations and corresponded with the nation's interest in social policy that would advance the conditions of all persons.

The National Therapeutic Recreation Society's legislative involvement began in 1970 under the presidency of John Nesbitt. Nesbitt declared legislative advocacy to be a priority for the NTRS, and he arranged for E. B. Whitten, then executive director for the National Rehabilitation Association, to provide direction to the board of NTRS on procedures and strategies for becoming involved in governmental affairs.

In 1971, NRPA Executive Director Dwight Rettie made legislative action a reality for the Association. He brought to the Association the former legislative council for Common Cause, a consumer rights lobbying group. For the next 3 years, from 1972 through 1975, NRPA public affairs director John Lagomarcino and a staff of five full-time government affairs specialists drew significant attention to recreation in Washington. The NTRS enjoyed the exclusive efforts of one of these staff members. Loren Frazer worked closely with David Park, the executive secretary of NTRS and its president, Bill Hillman, on matters pertaining to individuals with disabilities. This was a critical time in the history of legislation for disabled persons. The Rehabilitation Act of 1973, considered to be the "civil rights law for disabled persons," contained the original and important references to recreation as an integral part of comprehensive rehabilitation.

This was also the time Congress was studying legislation introduced by Senator Ted Kennedy-- on education for individuals with handicaps. Physical education and recreation professionals officially formed the National Consortium on Physical Education and Recreation for the Handicapped (NCPERH) in 1975. The Consortium focused its energies on the Education for All Handicapped Children Act (PL 94-142). Under the leadership of John Nesbitt, NCPERH president during 1976-77, the Consortium worked closely with the NRPA and the AAHPERD to successfully lobby for federal regulations that defined recreation as a related service for the education of handicapped children. Nesbitt continued his commitment to legislative advocacy by becoming an enduring voice on Capitol Hill through his own organization, Special Recreation, Inc.

In 1975 the economic difficulties of the NRPA peaked, resulting in a major reduction of staff, including those in public affairs. From this point on, all legislative action directed by the NTRS would be coordinated through voluntary action. This began with Dave Park, after he left NRPA and joined the faculty at George Washington University, followed by Andrea Farbman from her position on faculty at GWU, and then by this author, who has voluntarily coordinated the legislative action of the NTRS since 1983. From 1984 to 1985, NTRS had the services of an NRPA staff member assigned to work on legislative affairs. However, this special appointment lasted only 1 year.

Although the NRPA now again has a full complement of public affairs staff and devotes a portion of its time to legislative and regulatory matters of concern to therapeutic recreation, the NTRS continues to depend heavily on voluntary membership action for the coordination and conduct of the branch's governmental affairs. (The relationship between this action and that of the Association staff will be addressed later). Likewise, the American Therapeutic Recreation Association, formed in 1984, and the NCPERH rely on the voluntary services of members to coordinate their legislative advocacy action. In summary, then, the apparently impressive array of Washington-based resources for TR legislative advocacy lasted for a very brief period and has never been adequately replicated by volunteer efforts.

Some Significant Accomplishments

During the past 20 years, we have seen increasing evidence of legal support for the provision of recreation and the training of its providers in a number of laws and their associated regulations. Support can be found for recreation as a form of treatment, rehabilitation, education, and community service for individuals who are ill, disabled, or otherwise in need of specialized support and service (Park, 1980). Certain laws, however, have been the consistent targets of TR legislative action and have had the most influence on advancing the role of recreation and therapeutic recreation.

The original view that rehabilitation pertained only to vocational training and preparation underwent a major conceptual shift with the Rehabilitation Act of 1973 (PL 93-112). Now the federal government embraced the notion that "comprehensive rehabilitation" includes those services that prepared individuals for the fullest participation in life possible, including living independently in the community. This expanded view enabled Congress to be more receptive to considering the role of recreation in rehabilitation and independent living.

In 1977 therapeutic recreation leaders Fred Humphrey and Jerry Kelly gave persuasive testimony to the Senate on the importance of recreation. When the Rehabilitation Act was amended in 1978, it included a new authorization for special recreation demonstration projects (Title III, Section 316), intended to increase the mobility and socialization of disabled persons through such activities as camping, sports, and the arts. When the Rehabilitation Act was reauthorized in 1986 (PL 99-56), it was again amended in ways that extended and expanded the role of recreation in rehabilitation. The law now authorizes research on "recreational factors" associated with the experience of disability, training of "therapeutic recreation" personnel as bona fide rehabilitation personnel, and a broadened scope of recreation services as a means to community integration and living independently. The Congress, by its actions, recognized recreation and therapeutic recreation as not only a specific category of activities but also a means toward desirable goals in the overall rehabilitation process. These significant advances were largely due to persuasive oral testimony, solid written testimony, and many letters from professionals in the field during the creation and enactment of these amendments.

Perhaps the only other piece of federal legislation to receive as much thorough attention from the therapeutic recreation profession has been the Education for All Handicapped Children Act (PL 94-142). This 1975 law mandates a free and appropriate education for all children with disabilities, provided in the least restrictive learning environment possible. The therapeutic recreation profession staged an impressively persuasive argument to Congress, contending that recreation was a vital service to a child's learning and a necessary support to all other education. It is very important to note, however, that this major accomplishment was actively supported by friends of the special recreation movement, such as Harold Russell, the former chairman of the President's Committee on Employment of the Handicapped. He carried the banner of recreation in this testimony to congressional committees when the regulations were being drafted for PL 94-142.

The law was crafted so that recreation would appear as a content area "related" to special education. Thus, if a child's evaluation determined a need, the individualized education plan would include either an assessment of leisure functioning, therapeutic recreation, leisure education, or recreation programs in the school or the community.

The entire professional recreation community worked together to press Congress to recognize the importance of recreation in the complete preparation of handicapped children. This effort involved the combined resources of the NRPA, AAHPERD, and NCPERH. After witnessing an unprecedented level of coordination and cooperation among these major professional organizations in influencing the role of recreation in this law, NCPERH president John Nesbitt (1977) reported the following:

> Recreation is organized, recreation is committed, recreation is ready to move forward with P.L. 94-142. The current state of readiness is a milestone. I would reflect that when various vocational rehabilitation acts have been passed, we have not been ready. When aging legislation and health care legislation have been passed, we have not been ready. When mental health and law enforcement legislation have been passed, we have not been ready. But we are ready now to help handicapped children. (p.54)

Unfortunately, subsequent analyses (Bullock, 1986; Coyne, 1981; Stanley, 1985) indicate that recreation is rarely included in an IEP but is more likely to be found as an after-school extracurricular program. Stanley (1987) has made a strong case for the failure of the profession to follow through on the legislative support for recreation in the education of disabled children. She points to our lack of work with state and local education authorities and the failure of our curricula to address the unique needs and circumstances found in the academic setting, where recreation as a related service would be delivered. Perhaps we applauded ourselves for the legislative success without fully realizing it was up to us to actualize for disabled children what Congress gave us the opportunity to do. In other words, we asked for the chance and have generally failed to follow through.

The Legislative Process

One cannot be critical of or completely objective about the legislative action of the TR profession without a basic understanding of the complexities of the legislative and regulatory processes. Certainly one apparently critical factor is resources: professionals are needed to do the advocacy work in a consistent and on-going manner. However, it is essential that we comprehend the legislative and regulatory process. Without trying to study a condensed overview of Civics 101, it would be to our benefit to examine three of the most fundamental processes related to introducing, passing, and implementing laws in our system of government--authorization, appropriation, and regulation.

Authorization

Authorization is the law under which a program is established (or continued as in "reauthorization") for a stated number of years. An authorization bill specifies the aim and conduct of the program and, unless "open-ended," puts a ceiling on monies that can be used to finance it. An authorization bill gives authority to a federal agency to use federal funds for purposes specified in the act, although it does not mean that the monies will actually be spent for the program.

For example, when the Rehabilitation Act was up for reauthorization in 1986, the Senate Subcommittee on the Handicapped conducted hearings during which the therapeutic recreation profession presented oral and written testimony, including recommendations for changes in the statutory language which authorized special recreation demonstration projects. Subsequently, this section of the law now authorizes the U.S. Department of Education's Rehabilitation Services Administration (RSA) to fund projects related to more than traditional recreational activities, such as leisure education and leisure networking. The new law also sets specific amounts of money (e.g., $2.4 million in fiscal year 1988) that Congress "authorizes" to be used for such projects.

Appropriation

Appropriation is the means by which authorized programs are actually funded by Congress for the particular fiscal year. An appropriations bill is introduced, but it may not necessarily include funding levels consistent with the total permissible under the bill authorizing the program. An appropriations bill originates in the House and is followed by one in the Senate. If there are any differences between the two—and there usually are—the two appropriations committees come together in conference and work out a compromise to be taken back to their respective houses of Congress for passage.

Each year, special recreation programs are in jeopardy of not receiving funds in the fiscal year budget. This was true during the two terms of the Reagan administration because that administration believed that it was inappropriate for the federal government to fund recreation programs. Therefore, a case must be made for members in both the House and the Senate to agree to appropriate monies for discretionary programs such as recreation. This is particularly challenging in times when everyone is uncomfortably aware of the need to reduce the federal deficit. Fortunately, we have been successful in persuading Congress to override the Administration's recommendation for zero funds for special recreation demonstration projects. Because of this, approximately 125 projects throughout the country over the last 7 years have been funded and have been instrumental in increasing the recreational opportunities for more than 200,000 disabled individuals.

Regulation

Finally, regulation is the organization, rules, and procedures whereby a federal agency distributes funding for and monitors the conduct of programs authorized by specific legislation. Regulations govern access to federal monies. They usually describe the purpose of the program, identify the types of activities that are eligible for support, set forth the process for selecting funding priorities, and describe the various weighted criteria for successfully obtaining federal funds.

For example, the RSA was responsible for promulgating new regulations that would reflect the congressional intentions embodied in the 1986 amendments to the Rehabilitation Act. The RSA held hearings during the summer of 1987 to aid in determining the necessary policy and regulatory changes in the administration and monitoring of the Rehabilitation Act due to the major statutory changes contained in the 1986 amendments. This means that the terms *leisure networking* and *leisure education* would need to be defined, and the nature and scope of research on "recreational factors" related to the lives of individuals with disabilities would need to be clarified, so that proposals could be solicited and grants awarded for such special recreation demonstration projects and research. Similarly, in late 1986 and early 1987, the National Institute on Disability and Rehabilitation Research (NIDRR) sought input on setting research funding priorities. Comments were submitted to the NIDRR supporting proposed research priorities on recreation as a component of community integration programs for mentally retarded persons and on the efficacy of therapeutic recreation as a treatment modality. The NIDRR responded to this input by including these topics among the funding priorities for 1988.

Reviewing these three processes is important for illustrating two of the most important points in understanding legislative action. First, the legislative and regulatory process contains these three distinct yet inter-related processes. Even if the therapeutic recreation discipline is successful in lobbying for the inclusion of therapeutic recreation in the language of the law, monies may not be appropriated for the conduct of TR services, and a federal agency, representing the Administration, may not necessarily administer the program in ways consistent with the intentions of Congress.

The second point is that legislative advocacy is a constant, seemingly never-ending task! No one else is going to assume the responsibility for ensuring that the laws are implemented to provide for the recreational needs of all persons, nor will anyone else take the lead in ensuring that there is compliance with the law and its regulations.

The need for such vigilance and perseverance is obviously reflected in the annual appeal that Congress appropriate in its budget the full amount authorized in the law, in spite of the Administration's budget. Another example of this ongoing "watchdogging" occurred in 1985 when the assistant secretary of education decided that approximately 75 percent of the funds appropriated for Sec. 316 special recreation projects be earmarked for the International Special Olympics. This required immediate action to alert members of Congress to this decision and to seek their assistance in preventing such a move by the Administration. Senator Lowell Weicker (R-CT), then chairman of the Senate Subcommittee on the Handicapped, joined with Senator Ted Kennedy to point out to the assistant secretary that such a move was contrary to the intentions of Congress in its authorization of special recreation programs. After the assistant secretary appeared before the Senate Subcommittee on the Handicapped for this reprimand, the monies were reinstated.

Again, the point of this short review is to stress the interactive nature of the authorization, appropriation, and regulation processes and to illustrate the need for consistent, organized, and vigilant lobbying efforts. The obvious question is one of resources. What are the resources for the lobbying efforts of therapeutic recreation? Is it reasonable for TR professionals to expect that their needs and interests in the legislative and regulatory arenas are well tended to? What are the dominating concerns that will guide this action? With the preceding information as a backdrop, the purpose of the remainder of this chapter is to identify and explore some of the most critical issues that now, and will in the future, influence the legal supports for special recreation and therapeutic recreation.

Resources

As indicated earlier, the central focus of legislative advocacy action has been on education and rehabilitation, issues that blend easily with the concerns of public recreation providers and physical educators. However, since the late 1970s there have been significant changes in health care predictably causing changes in the laws and regulations that govern access to and the provision of health care services.

In 1983 the growing discontent within the TR field was making inevitable the creation of a new and independent professional organization representing therapeutic recreation. This was in part due to issues of autonomy, but largely due to the belief that the National Recreation and Park Association could not adequately represent the therapeutic recreators' needs and concerns that emanated from delivering services in health care settings. A particular issue was the emergence of a prospective payment system based on diagnostic related groupings for Medicaid and Medicare services, which called into question the reimbursability of TR services. In response to formidable pressure put on NRPA by the NTRS, new resources were promised. Through the generosity of an NRPA trustee, a new position was created within the NRPA staff complement, one which was to be devoted almost exclusively to NTRS concerns. Among the top-priority duties associated with this position was government affairs. For more than 10 years, the NTRS has had a Legislative Action Committee, which is responsible for interacting with the NRPA public affairs office regarding legislative and regulatory matters, and for planning and initiating membership action on such matters. The plan was for the NRPA in-house TR specialist and the NTRS legislative action coordinator to work together to maximize lobbying efforts on behalf of the branch.

NRPA pledged to represent the NTRS with some of the most important coalitions in Washington, D.C., namely the National Rehabilitation Coalition, the Coalition for Citizens with Developmental Disabilities (CCDD) and the National Association for Pupil Services Organizations (NAPSO). These coalitions represented consumer, provider, and advocacy groups actively involved in lobbying Congress. The in-house NRPA therapeutic recreation specialist and the NTRS branch manager joined these coalitions and signed onto numerous task forces which addressed particular issues such as Medicaid, education, transportation, developmental disabilities, and the budget. In all, the NRPA staff obligated themselves to more than 13 different task forces. By participating in these coalitions, NRPA would gain access to much valuable information for its lobbying purposes. Also, by interacting with other health care and human service consumer and provider groups, it could work to gain the support of these groups for the purposes of NRPA and NTRS.

In 1985, after only 1 year, the TR specialist position at NRPA was eliminated. However, NRPA continues to send the branch manager and a public affairs staff person to these coalition meetings. This connection to powerful, coalesced lobbying groups has given the TR discipline useful visibility and has gained support for some of the issues the discipline was concerned with. Indeed, during the 1970s and early 1980s, recreation and therapeutic recreation received crucial lobbying support from important organizations such as the Kennedy Foundation, the National Easter Seals Society, and the President's Committee on Employment of the Handicapped. Although such support can still be found, it was apparent that we could not count on any other group to take the lead in lobbying for increased legislative provisions for therapeutic recreation.

A Coalition of Our Own

The Rehabilitation Act and the Education for Handicapped Act were both due for reauthorization in 1986. In anticipation of a critical lobbying year, then NTRS president David Compton convened a meeting in Dallas to discuss strategy. He assembled representatives from NTRS, ATRA, NCPERH, AAHPERD, and congressional staff members assigned to the Senate Subcommittee on the Handicapped. It was clear that only through a unified presence would those organizations associated with recreation and therapeutic recreation make an impact on this reauthorization process. As a result of this meeting, a "legislative coalition" for therapeutic recreation was formed, representing NTRS, ATRA, and NCPERH.

This was not the first time a unified approach to lobbying was planned. In 1976 and 1977 there was an unprecedented level of coordination and cooperation surrounding the development of position statements on PL 94-142 and the recommended rules and regulations for this law. A consensus on the role of recreation in the education of handicapped children was reached among the following professional groups: the National Therapeutic Recreation Society of NRPA, the American Park and Recreation Society of NRPA, the National Forum of NRPA, the Council of State Presidents of NRPA, the American Association for Leisure and Recreation of AAHPER, and the National Consortium on Physical Education and Recreation for the Handicapped. This process included assembling a team to work with the Bureau of Education for the Handicapped to advise on draft formulation of rules for PL 94-142 and subsequent professional testimony at public hearings throughout the country, which led to the desirable rules and regulations to support the development of physical education and recreation in the education of handicapped children (Nesbitt, 1977).

Once again it seemed clear that a coalition of professional organizations would be most influential in having impact on the reauthorization process. The American Therapeutic Recreation Association, since its founding in 1984, has recognized the critical need for effective legislative action. Yet, due to its infancy and meager financial resources, it too has been limited in its capacity to conduct significant lobbying efforts. The ATRA has relied on the efforts of one member volunteer to coordinate its lobbying efforts and to stimulate grass roots action. The legislative coordinators for NTRS and ATRA, and to a lesser extent NCPERH, have collaborated on information sharing and submission of testimony related to legislative and regulatory matters. Indeed, since 1985, when this Legislative Coalition for Therapeutic Recreation was formed, numerous alerts, membership reports, and drafts of testimony to congressional committees and federal agencies have been submitted on behalf of the therapeutic recreation profession and the constituency it serves, rather than one or another organization that represents TR professionals.

This is clearly a major issue; the therapeutic recreation profession needs to speak with a unified voice on Capitol Hill. More than any single organization, a coalition of organizations can effectively alter policy. To date there is no evidence to suggest that any particular issue (or statute or rule) generates differing views between and among the three organizations represented by the Legislative Coalition for TR. Yet the appearances of separate TR organizations to consumer and provider groups in Washington, D.C., begs the questions of what's the difference between the groups, and why the need for more than one professional organization? As a discipline, our collective lobbying resources are far too limited to venture into the legislative advocacy arena in a singular fashion.

It is politically naive to think that forming and operating a coalition is simply a matter of desire and earnestness. Operating as a coalition requires a willingness to share resources and to keep the channels of communication open. The political realities of professional organizations inevitably complicate the work. For example, the competition for dues-paying members becomes an issue when the credit for successes is being doled out. Also, there is an organizational concern that the resources of one organization used in a particular lobbying effort will exceed that of the others, and therefore some other organization will "unfairly" benefit from the hard work and perhaps greater financial contributions of that first organization.

Finally, there is the issue of representation. That is, if comments at one of the national coalition meetings, or the oral or written testimony of the Legislative Coalition for TR presented to a congressional body, are to be cleared by all organizations involved, might these positions misrepresent a particular organization's views on an issue? This has been a thorny problem for NRPA since the formation of the TR Legislative Coalition for TR. The NRPA has maintained a policy that only NRPA staff are to represent the Association at national coalition meetings. Since NTRS is only a branch of the NRPA, it is of concern to NRPA that the actions of the NTRS are consistent with the views of the NRPA. Taken a step further, if NTRS is a part of a legislative coalition with ATRA, and the ATRA representative to the coalition meets with a congressional staff person as a representative of the coalition, then this person is in effect representing NRPA. The NRPA has handled this concern by taking its own action on the issue and on behalf of its therapeutic recreation branch, despite the fact that the NTRS is stating its position through testimony under the name of the Legislative Coalition for TR! Who, then, speaks for NTRS?

The political nuances found in coalitions have yet to be addressed by all organizations involved. The expediency of collective representation and the apparent benefits of appearing as a unified whole seemed to carry the early actions of the Legislative Coalition for TR. Now, almost 3 years and many official documents later, many questions remain to be raised and addressed between and among the organizations who appear to be a part of such a coalition. The benefits of lobbying in such a unified manner are rather easy to identify. However, there are many problems and technicalities that need to be sorted out if we are to proceed.

Unfortunately, none of the organizations claiming to represent TR specialists is willing to or actually has the means to support a full-time paid lobbyist. In 1984 there was a very brief contract between the government affairs director of the National Easter Seals Society and NRPA, in response to the demands the NTRS was making for lobbying resources. However, this lasted for a very short period of time and had questionable value to the branch. The NRPA maintained then, and continues to maintain, that it can and will represent the concerns of its professional TR members, relying on its limited staff and finances. The ATRA and the NCPERH must rely on volunteer membership action without the benefits of even a professional consultant lobbyist.

To a large extent, each organization has relied on a government "insider" for information, insight, and guidance. For example, Bill Hillman, a past president of NTRS, had been a recreation and physical education technical advocate within the Department of Education's Office of Special Education and Rehabilitation Services. Andrea Farbman, a past NTRS Legislative Action Committee chairperson, is now the public affairs director for the National Council on the Handicapped. Both of these individuals have access to information that is tremendously important to TR professional organizations and their government relations work and have offered whatever guidance they could. However, the TR discipline does not have a government affairs specialist who can provide ongoing and consistent monitoring on Capitol Hill and the necessary nurturance of relationships with key congressional staff. Without such a knowledgeable and skilled person unencumbered by other responsibilities, the discipline is vulnerable.

For comparison purposes, let's consider the resources of other professional organizations. The American Occupational Therapy Association has three full-time government affairs specialists, and contracted attorneys, to address the issues important to occupational therapists. The National Association of Music Therapy has recently hired a full-time lobbyist, and it provides funding for a half-time person to assist its legislative coordinator, who is a member volunteer. Neither ATRA nor the NTRS legislative coordinators have even had a budget they could count on for their activities! It is fortunate that these volunteers have supportive employers who absorb enormous postage, duplicating, and telephone expenses.

Nesbitt (1986) traces the problems recreation and therapeutic recreation has on Capital Hill to the lack of sufficient numbers of advocates, lobbyists, and spokespersons to convince legislators of the importance of recreation service. He points further to the lack of standards pertaining to recreation; the lack of support for research; and the lack of a national philosophy of recreation, of the process of rehabilitation, and of the experience of disability. "Until there is adequate advocacy focused on the Congress of the United States, special recreation will have a low priority in U.S. Government programs and services" (Nesbitt, 1986, p.38).

The issues that coalitions form around limit the range of potential members in the coalition. Furthermore, the salience of the forming issue affects the extent to which the organizations are willing to coalesce, and also tends to influence the direction of the coalition's activities (Roberts-DeGennaro,1986). Certainly, the forming issue of the Legislative Coalition for TR was clear: to influence the reauthorization of education and rehabilitation laws as they pertained to recreation and physical education.

Now that that has been accomplished, the Coalition has taken on other issues, such as reauthorization of the Older Americans Act and nursing home reform legislation and regulation, without any reconsideration or recommitment of the represented organizations. Perhaps it is time to question the purpose and makeup of this coalition.

Roberts-DeGennaro (1986) points out that as issues change, coalitions can shift, creating new alliances. The original set of organizations might decide to disband, or new linkages could be formed around other issues since the issues may dictate a different structural arrangement. Two considerations related to coalition participation are an organization's legislative priorities and its long-term agenda. For instance, the NCPERH has a majority membership of physical education professionals; their legislative and regulatory agenda is primarily centered on public education, something that has limited bearing on therapeutic recreation (even though recreation is considered a "related" service in a child's education plan). Certainly there is generally little if any priority given to therapeutic recreation as a health care discipline. Many consider the ATRA to be concerned only with "clinical" issues and not very concerned with the special recreation services provided mostly in non-health care settings.

Currently it seems that the NRPA's resources and its proximity to Capitol Hill provide the best potential support for therapeutic recreation. However, this large organization has many other professional branches to serve, and there has been a significant disparity in legislative agendas between the NRPA and the NTRS. Examining the focus of the NRPA's public affairs actions reveals a clear (and necessary) preoccupation with the Land and Water Conservation Fund and other legislation that supports public parks and recreation. This agenda does not automatically include issues related to disadvantaged or disenfranchised groups in the general public. Legislative and regulatory matters associated with such groups are typically considered "TR" concerns.

The NRPA's efforts on the special recreation authorization (Section 316 special demonstration projects) stand to reason; the continued funding of these projects has had major impact on the development and expansion of community-based recreation for disabled individuals. It is on matters related to the provision of therapeutic recreation as a treatment modality or specialized health care service that the NRPA lacks the expertise and real commitment needed to offer adequate lobbying support. It is this focus that is most directly contrary to the mission of the NRPA.

Operating as a coalition with special interest and commitment will require a reaffirmation of the desire for each organization to be part of such a coalition, and a clear agreement on the focus of this collaborative lobbying effort.

Determining a Legislative Agenda

What then is the legislative agenda of therapeutic recreation? There has never been a thorough explication of such an agenda by either the NTRS or the ATRA. Neither organization has put forth such a position, as might emerge from a series of white papers on health care, independent living, education, aging, and so on. These position papers would guide actions of the profession and would be very useful educational materials for state and federal agencies and policymakers. Such papers could also strengthen the foundation and subsequent action of a legislative coalition for TR, and downplay the differences in organizations. Up to this point, the political action of therapeutic recreation professionals has been characterized by "reactive" measures--trying to respond to legislative and regulatory matters as they arise. There is virtually no evidence of the discipline's identifying a long-term focus, establishing strategies for influencing desired changes, and acting in a "proactive" policy-creating manner. As with philosophy, there is an essential need for the TR discipline to clarify its mission in such a way that a certain social policy can be identified as being the basis for its political action. Without such a proactive stance, the therapeutic recreation profession cannot expect to influence the political process that produces social policy.

During the past few years, therapeutic recreation has gained some real, albeit tentative, support from other health care and human service disciplines, including consumer groups. This is largely due to our presence at national coalition meetings in Washington. However, some of these participant groups are wary of us and question our motivations. The therapeutic recreation discipline has been perceived as having very parochial concerns, limited almost exclusively to recreation matters which are addressed in ways unrelated to the total life needs and experiences of persons who are ill, disabled, or otherwise disadvantaged. For instance, what is our position on civil rights, child abuse, homelessness, and welfare reform? What research needs to be conducted on recreation as a treatment modality or as a potential contribution to life quality and independent living? How does the TR discipline want to participate in the social policy debate on life quality, medical technology, and the right to die? These issues have legislation associated with them, and the coalitions TR attempts to participate with are considering them. Although not directly related to recreation, they certainly are issues relevant to life quality and the fundamental supports one typically needs in order to pursue recreation. How then ought therapeutic recreation to conceive its position on these matters, and what can it use to guide its position with the Washington-based coalitions?

A Need for Greater Participation
in Legislative Advocacy

The most predictably successful grass roots action has come in those instances where job security has been in question. Although this is to be expected, a deeper commitment to influencing social policy will determine the character and morality of the profession. Generally, there has been a noticeable lack of involvement in legislative action among TR professionals, and there is apparent lack of knowledge about such action. For the past few years, the presidents and the boards of directors of the NTRS and the ATRA have been urging membership training on this issue. Yet, once again, there are limited resources to conduct sophisticated and thorough training. Any serious and credible degree of advocacy will require extensive and intensive training of professionals.

Assuming that the profession of therapeutic recreation does make a concentrated effort to become a broad-based lobbying force in the area of social policy, legislation, and regulation, certain guidelines will be essential to its success and ought to be included in legislative advocacy training. Given the likelihood that the organizations representing the TR profession will not have full-time paid lobbyists, the future will depend on the energies and efforts of all professionals, not just those who will volunteer to be the designated leaders within the organizations. Successful action will obviously go beyond writing letters to legislators.

Partners as well as providers

The independent living movement is consumer controlled. This means that if we really want to advocate improving the quality of life for disabled persons, we must join forces with consumer boards and state independent living councils, and not as providers but as partners. A simple assessment of our professional conferences and meetings will quickly reveal the conspicuous lack of disabled persons in attendance. The estrangement and alienation seen between other provider groups and their service recipients must not be the future of therapeutic recreation.

State action

Training is crucial if professionals are going to be politically active at the state level, as well as at the national level. In fact, state level action may actually be more critical than action at the federal level. A great deal of federal legislation and regulation is applied at the state level, where state agencies implement the law.   This includes educational, rehabilitation, and developmental disabilities services, all of which are mandated by federal legislation and contain federally determined regulations but are implemented at a state level. Thus, it is the state agencies that TR professionals should be interacting with to set state priorities for services based on state-run needs assessments.

For example, each state must develop a state plan for developmental disabilities services, and each state has the prerogative to identify certain services that it wants to include and thereby obtain federal funds for.   Likewise, each state office of vocational rehabilitation determines its service priorities, which may include recreation. It is up to professionals at the state level to educate these agencies and to advocate state-level attention to the recreational needs of its constituents.

Beyond passionate appeals

As a discipline, we are hampered by the lack of hard data on the nature, scope, and efficacy of therapeutic recreation services. Too much of our advocacy efforts have involved passionate appeals to an intuitive appreciation of recreation's importance in a person's life, especially when one's life circumstances are inadequate. It is rare to find a policy maker opposed to recreation, although he or she may likely see it as much less important than many other things. Influencing social policy will require data on facts, particularly as they emerge from research.

For example, in order to make the case that therapeutic recreation services ought to be reimbursable as a home and community service for Medicaid patients, the Health Care Financing Administration will base its decision on whether these services are cost effective and whether the services will assist a person in avoiding institutionalization. As a discipline, we have virtually no such data to demonstrate cost effectiveness or the impact of TR services on minimizing the need for institutionalization. Such data and similar information from outcome-oriented evaluation and research will have the most significant impact on our success in the legislative advocacy action in the years to come. Again, it is a matter of resources and coordinated leadership to guide the collection of this important and vital information.

Conclusion

In the spring of 1987, Senator Tom Harkin (D-IA) succeeded Senator Lowell Weicker as Chairman of the Senate Committee on Labor and Human Resources Subcommittee on the Handicapped. During his keynote address at a conference titled "Disability Policy: State of the Nation," Harkin attacked the Reagan Adminstration's apparent refusal to concern itself with the health, education, and well-being of all Americans. Harkin stated, "The gross national product measures everything but that which makes life worth living." He went on to implore us all to help make life more rewarding and enjoyable for all 36 million disabled Americans.

Therapeutic recreation professionals represent human experiences that are worth fighting for. The role of advocacy is an important determinant of the success of therapeutic recreation as a legitimate and contributing health care and human service profession. This success will be measured not only by what we can accomplish for the profession directly but by what we can accomplish on behalf of children and adults who need special assistance in accessing recreational opportunties and whose lives can be improved through recreation as a clinical, rehabilitative, educational, and community service. The legislative and regulatory imperatives for these outcomes are clear; it remains to be seen how the therapeutic recreation profession rises to the challenges.

Study Questions

1. What would be the particular benefits and limitations if the therapeutic recreation profession aligned its lobbying efforts with

(a) allied health, (b) public recreation, or (c) special education groups?

2. Select three major services a professional organization ought to provide its members, and compare and contrast legislative advocacy with these three services. How important is legislative advocacy?

3. Construct a position paper on therapeutic recreation and health care, education, independent living, or rehabilitation to be given to a state or federal agency which sets policy or administers these particular services.

4. Identify three state agencies responsible for providing or regulating health care and human services, and assemble a packet of information suitable for informing each agency of the role and function of therapeutic recreation.

5. Prepare a "visitation itinerary" for your state and federal legislators. Include in this plan the specific TR programs that can serve as models and the particular learning experiences you will offer these legislative representatives.

References

Bullock, C. (1986). *Recreation as a Related Service.* Paper submitted to the Select Education Committee, U.S. House of Representatives, Washington, DC.

Coyne, P. (1981). The Status of Recreation as a Related Service in P.L. 94-142. *Therapeutic Recreation Journal, 15*(3), 4-15.

Houle, C. (1980). *Continuing Learning in the Professions.* San Francisco: Jossey Bass.

Nesbitt, J. (1977). *Professional Advocacy at the National Level in Physical Education and Recreation for Handicapped Children: 1976-1977.* Unpublished report to the president of the president of the NCPERH.

Nesbitt, J. (1986). Guide to U.S. Government Special Recreation Resources. *Special Recreation Digest, 3* (2), 27-56.

Park, D. (1980). *Legislation Affecting Park Services and Recreation for Handicapped Individuals.* Washington DC: Hawkins and Associates.

Roberts-DeGennaro, M. (1986).   Building Coalitions for Political Advocacy. *Social Work*, July-August, 308-311.

Stanley, J. (1985). Recreation in P.L. 94-142: Won the Battle and Lost the War?   Unpublished paper presented at the National Recreation and Park Association National Congress, Dallas, TX.

Stanley, J. (1987).   *Recreation in the Education of Handicapped Students*. Trenton, NJ: New Jersey Department of Community Affairs.

Research Issues

photo courtesy of San Francisco Recreation Center for the Handicapped

The purpose of research is not only finding out why, but more importantly, knowing what questions to ask.

—David M. Compton

RESEARCH INITIATIVES IN THERAPEUTIC RECREATION

David M. Compton

Ignorance is of a peculiar nature; once dispelled, it is impossible to reestablish it. It is not originally a thing of itself, but is only the absence of knowledge.

Thomas Paine, *The Rights of Man*

Historical Perspectives of Therapeutic Recreation Research

Therapeutic recreation has struggled to remove itself from the bonds of ignorance. Not knowing what one does, or why one is doing it causes great concern among even the most naive individual or organization. While progress has been made over the past five years, it is as though we have taken our first steps in the search for truth, meaning, and knowledge.

Several years ago I wrote an article for the *Therapeutic Recreation Journal* (Compton, 1984) that identified priorities for therapeutic recreation research. In looking back over the decade 1973-83, it was clear that we had only begun to position ourselves for the difficult battle ahead. The literature during that period reflected our naivete, limited knowledge, and lack of sophistication in conducting research. We placed great emphasis on meeting, studying and prioritizing our needs. Numerous conferences, workshops and other activities positioned us for the anticipated explosion of knowledge about our field.

Our early positioning for a research agenda drew support from the federal government and other sources to carry out the process of planning. They anticipated that their investment in planning would ignite the profession to produce increased quantities of applied and basic research. Apparently it was not taken into consideration that a national research agenda requires a large volume of stable funds over time. The basic sciences, humanities, and medicine have funds set aside for requested and investigator-initiated research. While some research was funded by the former Bureau of Education for the Handicapped and the current Office of Special Education and Rehabilitative Services, the Rehabilitation Services Administration and other federal agencies, the amount and frequency of this funding has always been very small and not responsive to the needs of the profession. In addition, there has been no ongoing or systematic effort to conduct research aimed at demonstrating the efficacy of therapeutic recreation.

Over the past five years, there has been an increase in the quantity and quality of research in therapeutic recreation. This is in stark contrast to the period from 1973-83 (Compton, 1984). Witt (1988b), editor of the *Therapeutic Recreation Journal* indicates that the volume of research published in this refereed journal has increased significantly from 1978 to 1986 when he states that,

> "The percentage of research articles published under each of the last three editors of the *TRJ* has increased from 33 percent (1978-80) to 39 percent (1981-83) to 58 percent (1984-86). In addition, of the research based articles that have been published in each of these periods, the percentage of articles utilizing survey methodology has been declining (68%, 58%, 38%), while the percentage of experimental research has been increasing (21%,39%,47%)."(p.17)

One continues to be amazed at the lack of continuity or longitudinal nature of therapeutic recreation research. Many articles still appear to be the result of singular investigations, and rarely build on previous experiments, clinical trials, or a line of inquiry. One effort that has provided encouragement and an invaluable body of knowledge is the research emanating from the Leisure Diagnostic Battery (LDB). Gary Ellis and Peter Witt, in collaboration with several students and practitioners, have clearly provided the empirical evidence necessary to advance the process of assessment in therapeutic recreation. A summary of the research on the LDB, its present status and its future, is presented in a summative article that appeared in the *Therapeutic Recreation Journal* (Ellis and Witt, 1986). While the efforts of the LDB team are impressive, Iso-Ahola (1988), Mannell (1983), Riddick et al (1984), Schleien and Yermakoff (1983) and Witt (1988a) confirm the notion that research in therapeutic recreation has been dominated in the past by survey methodology, "one-shot" inquiries, and lacks focus on some disability groups. However, there is a change occurring in therapeutic recreation research. Iso-Ahola (1988) states, "Despite problems, the future is promising for research in therapeutic recreation. There are signs that important research questions are being addressed and that the quality of research is improving."

Preparedness for Conducting Research

Therapeutic recreation professionals appear to be more aware of the need to possess basic understanding of research methods and techniques. This is evidenced by the increased number of research sessions at the national meetings, regional and local attention being paid to the subject, and even the hiring of researchers in municipal park and recreation agencies. It is also evidenced in a keen sense by several organizations and agencies that to conduct quality assurance programs, individual assessment of clients and a range of other management duties require: 1) knowing what questions to ask; 2) knowing how to present questions in order to obtain valid, reliable and usable information; 3) knowing how to analyze the data so as to benefit from the information; and 4) knowing how to interpret the data and act upon its message. While at first this may not seem terribly complex, it does suggest that we may be approaching an era of enlightenment and skill acquisition.

It is clear that few professionals actually do research. Fewer conduct research that meets the rigor of peer review. Only a handful are able to conduct research that utilizes widely accepted research design principles or statistical methods. Submissions to refereed journals in the discipline, and outside to related areas, are not of sufficient quantity to warrant a backlog of quality manuscripts. Bullock, McGuire, and Barch (1984) indicate that only 17.9% of 189 responses to a survey of therapeutic recreation professionals in the southeastern United States had conducted research in the past 12 months. It is important to note that of the affirmative responses, 34.5% were educators. While these individuals stated they had conducted research, one must question if the results were published.

Some of the major reasons for not conducting research include a lack of time, inadequate training, cost, lack of support from administrators, and lack of motivation (Bullock, McGuire and Barch, 1984). It appears that practitioners' concerns with research may differ from those of the educator. Practitioners often indicate that there is little time to design the study, collect data, write the results, or follow up on issues. There also seems to be little collaboration between practitioners and educators, although this seems to be a marvelous way to accelerate the productivity and applicability of research in the discipline. A recent research project at Temple University to determine the efficacy of therapeutic recreation, supported the notion of collaboration between clinical sites and the university but this approach has not been adopted nationally for a variety of reasons. Bullock, McGuire and Barch (1984) suggest that, "Research needs to be conducted as a cooperative effort. Faculty at colleges and universities are usually eager to work cooperatively and often only need an open door. Also, other local therapeutic recreators may be interested in working cooperatively on a research project. Research may be more feasible when conducted as a group effort."

National organizations have advocated a research agenda for years but with limited, if not disappointing, results. Aguilar et al. (1987) have aptly described the problems and needs facing the profession in a report for the National Therapeutic Recreation Society. According to the report, if the profession is to "contribute to the development of a sound body of knowledge specific to TR . . . then the procedures, activities, suggestions and recommendations of the committee should be implemented." The following are the major problems identified by the committee:

1. Lack of collaboration among individuals completing and/or utilizing the results of TR research.
2. Poor research preparation of students/practitioners/educators.
3. Lack of communication about research efforts.
4. Deficiency of research on TR effectiveness.
5. Lack of replication and expansion of previous research.
6. Implementation of a variety of research designs and methods.

In order to address these problems the committee recommended the following:

A. NTRS Research and Development Committee:
   1. Coordinate a research agenda
   2. Facilitate TR research
   3. Serve as a clearinghouse for the following information:
      a. research in progress
      b. completed research
      c. funding sources
      d. research guides/resources
   4. Develop a long-range master plan for TR research
   5. Identify available research consultants

B. NTRS Board of Directors
   1. Provide funding for research studies, such as:

       a. competitive small grants
       b. research scholarships/awards
       c. matching funds
    2. Provide assistance for research workshops/in-service training
    3. Support a long-range master plan for TR research activities
    4. Recognize outstanding research contributions by NTRS members
    5. Consider additional publication outlets for research and/ or practice

C. State TR Organizations
    1. Establish a research committee to accomplish the following:
       a. Identify a research network
       b. Sponsor research workshops/in-service training
    2. Provide financial assistance for research
    3. Disseminate information about research
    4. Promote forums on student research (i.e.) at conferences

D. Researchers
    1. Establish a thematic program of research
    2. Collaborate with others in the TR network
    3. Provide research training
    4. Utilize a variety of techniques and/or designs

E. Educators
    1. Collaborate with others in the TR network
    2. Utilize/incorporate research in educational materials
    3. Teach research skills to students, including:
       a. reading research
       b. computer skills
       c. writing research papers/reports
       d. research (implementation) skills

F. Practitioners
    1. Collaborate with others in the TR network
    2. Increase understanding of and skills in research
    3. Develop program protocols to be tested
    4. Test specific intervention techniques

    5. Include evaluation research of program effectiveness
    6. Consider interdisciplinary (team) research

G. Students (Undergraduate and Graduate)
    1. Seek adequate preparation for research activity (see listing under educators- Items 3a-3d)
    2. Design and implement pilot studies
    3. Replicate/expand upon previous research
    4. Present papers on completed research" (Aguilar et al., 1987)

The basic problem with these type of reports is that the national organizations are incapable of fulfilling the mandate. In fact, the organizations are barely able to keep skeletal staff support to meet the everyday needs of the membership. Where is the staff support necessary to mount a research campaign? Where are the funds to seed research efforts? Where is the support for specialized publications to ensure that necessary information about research activity is transmitted to those who critically need the information? Where are the funds to support training practitioners, educators and possibly students in the most up-to-date research methods possible? Certainly these will not come from any of the existing or anticipated national organizations who advance therapeutic recreation as a profession. It is unlikely that the federal government will do more to advance this agenda, given the mounting budget deficit and potential cutbacks in research that is not of the hard science variety or defense-oriented.

Universities may provide seed money for small projects from central research pool funds. These will be inadequate to meet the requirements of researchers for major projects demonstrating theory or the efficacy of therapeutic recreation. Our scientific track record pales when compared to other disciplines and consequently limits our ability to secure funds on campus. The increasing demand for limited funds on campuses also paints a bleak picture for our research agenda. The primary problem is that we have few sources of funds to carry out a monumental campaign to prove that what we do is efficacious.

If universities and colleges are to be looked to as leaders in the research agenda, then much change will have to take place quickly. First, we will need stability in several major research institutions so a longitudinal effort can be mounted by a team of researchers. Qualified, tenurable young professors will need nurturing from more experienced professors. Their research will need to be focused, and clearly meet the retention, promotion and tenure guidelines of the university or college. They will need relief from the awesome teaching and advising responsibilities often loaded on fledgling assistant professors. Before they enter the tenure game, our brightest and most productive future assistant professors should be afforded post-doctoral studies at institutions where research is the main menu item. This will be difficult, but could prove to be an insurance policy well worth investing in. It is standard procedure in the primary disciplines of medicine, science, the humanities, and so on.

Additional change in the universities will be required. We need to have departments that have more than one therapeutic recreation faculty member. How can one survive in a setting where one is constantly trying to interpret one's discipline or sub-discipline to others? In an era of collaboration among faculty, why do we persist in trying to succeed with an "N" of one? At last count, there are less than ten major colleges or research universities where more than two therapeutic recreation faculty exist. Is this any way to run a business or a discipline? Another important factor in the structure of institutions of higher learning is the absence of laboratories where legitimate research can take place in therapeutic recreation. One is hard pressed to identify a single laboratory or clinic where research on therapeutic recreation is the sole agenda. While universities such as Illinois, Indiana, and Utah have leisure or play research laboratories, therapeutic recreation is not the primary activity. Universities need to take a major role in the training of new practitioners in research, even at the undergraduate level. They also need to address the research needs of practitioners through continuing education or extension education efforts. It is clear that unless we upgrade the skills of a large number of potential researchers, we will continue to face the problem of the quantity of our research paling in comparison to our allied professions who are much larger in size. This does not beg the question of quality, but merely points to the fact that we have so little depth in a multitude of research areas, that we may never be able to create the essential body of knowledge to enable us to be called a discipline.

Essential Ingredients for Advancing Research Productivity

While a list of ingredients required to advance therapeutic recreation research would be nice, it seems to me that it would be highly inappropriate. Understanding why we do not have a national effort to create a scientific basis for the discipline might not only be more fruitful but challenging as well. Identifying what seems to mitigate or inhibit our efforts would also be helpful in drawing a bead on the future agenda. While I am reluctant to bring out the crystal ball, there are some observations about the current state of affairs that need to be made to gain a better understanding of our current plight. First, we are a relatively young and emerging discipline when compared to other long-standing disciplines such as biology, medicine, law, or a host of others. Second, we have few doctoral granting institutions where therapeutic recreation researchers are prepared. We have prepared teachers and practitioners, but few researchers. Third, we have been focused on an occupational and professional preparation model in higher education. This model detracts from our ability to advance tenets or knowledge pertinent to the broader social or human agenda, moral and philosophical issues or, for that matter, health care issues. Burdge (1983, 1985) has argued that a separation of leisure studies from the professional preparation program is necessary to gain credibility as a discipline. Fourth, therapeutic recreation has not yet defined itself. Continuing questions over a philosophy, definition of terms, and models of service clamor for answers from the profession, yet none seem immediately forthcoming. Fifth, our base of operation is minimal in higher education, clinics and community settings. We lack the clout to demand major changes or support. On the contrary, we are usually looking to defend our territory. In other words, we are primarily defensive specialists who strive to be a part of the offense (and game plan).

Witt (1988a) suggests that there are several inhibitors to advancing therapeutic recreation research. He states,

> "One of the major inhibitors to research involving special populations is the lack of a clear understanding on the part of both practitioners and academics of the value and necessity of undertaking research. Coupled with the failure to impress on students and practitioners the value of research is the failure of curricula to include adequate educational experiences in research methods and statistics. As a result, both educators and practitioners end up perceiving that they lack the skills to either successfully undertake or apply available research. Lack of perceived competence can lead to feelings of helplessness with regard to research."

There are ten key ingredients that would assure a brighter future for therapeutic recreation research. These include,

1.   creating a pool of funds for research in TR

The inhibitors to research are illustrated in Figure 1.

Figure 1

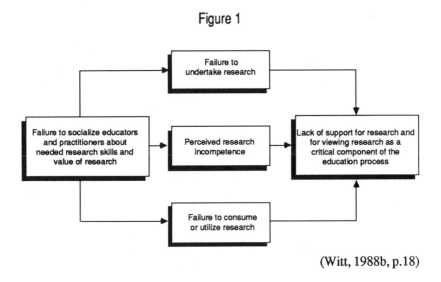

(Witt, 1988b, p.18)

2. training and re-training practitioners and educators in research and statistical methods
3. requiring research competencies at the undergraduate level
4. demanding improvement in the research competence of graduate students with prestigious certification for those able to pass an examination
5. establishing working agreements between universities and clinical and community settings to conduct research
6. articulating a national research agenda and funding those who work on problems identified in the plan
7. encouraging the submission of more grants to federal, state and private entities
8. establishing a national training and dissemination center for research in TR
9. publishing materials that link research findings to practice
10. ensure that each continuing education program offered to therapeutic recreation professionals has a research component (Compton, 1984; Iso-Ahola, 1988; Witt, 1988a)

These ingredients are not new or novel. They merely represent the continued call for action from the profession and its members. While we have made progress, it has been in inches rather than yards or miles. In the past five years, declarations were made on the direction required to accelerate the research agenda (Compton, 1984; Witt, 1988a). They are as relevant and unfulfilled today as they were five years ago. Consequently, they are worth presenting again for viewing, and hopefully, action. While they are discussed at length in both the aforementioned articles, only the salient points are reviewed here.

Therapeutic Recreation's Research Agenda

1. Plan and conduct a national conference on research priorities in recreation for special populations for the next decade.
2. Establish specialized laboratories that conduct research on recreation for special populations.
3. Establish a clinical consortium to examine the therapeutic process, results, techniques, and interactions under controlled environments.
4. Establish endowed chairs for the study of leisure with special populations at selected universities.
5. Conduct annual nationwide training in applied and basic research.
6. Establish a national research fund for the study of recreation for special populations.
7. Encourage the expansion of current periodicals to include a full section on research in recreation for special populations.
8. Prepare and publish a biannual compendium of research in recreation for special populations.
9. Continue the study of certain issues, problems and developments over time to ensure completeness and quality. (Compton, 1984)
10. Endorse the social analysis approach that focuses on the quality of service of the client.
11. Upgrade the research literacy of TR graduates.
12. TR doctoral students should exercise care in selecting a school and mentor for their studies.
13. National and state conferences should emphasize reporting of research findings, developing skills and applying knowledge to practice.
14. Leaders of TR need to serve as role models in advocating for research and actually doing research of their own.

15. Link educators and practitioners together by forming consortia for research.
16. Selected universities should develop post doctoral fellowshps for the most promising young researchers. (Witt, 1988b)

While lists of action items are handy to pull out occasionally, they do little to incite productivity. If the national organizations are serious about promoting a research agenda, then the very first step is to place it in their respective strategic plans. The most important step, in my opinion, is to cultivate research literacy across the profession. The most essential step is to secure funds to support innovation and competitive research in well defined areas.

Emerging Lines of Inquiry

The future of therapeutic recreation research will be constructed by many individuals who are not yet in the profession. With this in mind, it is incumbent on the profession to clearly establish the problems and issues that face the practice of therapeutic recreation. There must also be a rigorous search for theory that can give credence to certain phenomena we do not understand or choose to ignore. Social analysis, in which a systematic process of inquiry takes place, must replace social empiricism (Iso-Ahola, 1980; Witt, 1988a) Further, we need to examine different methods of inquiry such as case study method, historical, empirical, naturalistic, etc. To limit ourselves to a single method is tantamount to hiding our head in the sand.

Our challenges today do not differ radically from those in 1984. It was clear then and it is clear now that,

> "Our challenges now reside in the need to more clearly understand the leisure behavior of special populations. Additionally, we need to seek ways to help increase their competence in order to achieve optimal leisure functioning for every individual. As a profession we have been somewhat enamored with the 'doing' aspect of leisure/recreation services. On the other hand we have somewhat ignored arriving at an understanding of why some individuals are deficient in their leisure endeavors, why their level of satisfaction remains unfulfilled, and how to improve leisure functioning" (Compton, 1984, p.99).

Fundamental questions about the phenomenon of leisure and special populations must be the basis for our future lines of inquiry. The constructs of leisure functioning have been articulated in numerous articles in the leading journals of the discipline, including the *Therapeutic Recreation Journal, Leisure Sciences* and *Journal of Leisure Research.* We must begin to examine these in relation to the various special populations, disability groups, processes, protocols, programs, and settings. We must begin the arduous task of building knowledge around such vital topics as leisure motives and needs, leisure satisfaction, perceived freedom, the general nature and central characteristics of the leisure experience, quality of life, personality factors and leisure lifestyle, attitudes toward leisure (Iso-Ahola, 1988), gender, ethnicity and severity of disability in relation to leisure functioning, to name but a few. The task seems ominous but with careful attention to an agenda, the profession can identify the lines of inquiry and proceed to fill the knowledge gaps.

In the development of lines of inquiry, the profession must be cautious it does not choose to continue fostering studies that are organizational in nature, status-oriented or mere social empiricism. Rickards (1985) suggests that, "Unless well-developed, empirical research is undertaken, efforts at professional development may serve to promote and legitimize the field without helping us understand how and why the procedures we utilize work." The pathway to respectability and distinction does not go through invalid or unreliable data sources or unfounded writings. Other allied health professions have experienced the same problems currently facing therapeutic recreation. Physical and occupational therapy are good examples. While the practice of both disciplines is at an all-time high in terms of demand, there are questions in academic circles related to the scientific basis for each discipline. It is clear that both disciplines enjoy a favorable position politically, but there is not a plethora of theories underlying either. Neither is there a large volume (proportionally) of research of an empirical nature clearly documenting the efficacy of interventions.

An example of a line of inquiry that should be rigorously pursued by the profession is the issue of assessment. A set of fundamental questions must be created to set course. These will certainly spawn other questions. From these questions, interest groups could gather together to parcel out tasks so that strategic plans might be developed to secure answers to the questions. Research of an applied and basic nature should be commissioned to competitors who would submit proposals to a panel of experts charged with the responsibility to oversee a seed grant program. One could launch this line of inquiry around the Leisure Diagnostic Battery (LDB) as an instrument for assessment. Much of the essential background work has been completed in regard to the theoretical bases for the LDB and could be updated by the investigators. From this line of inquiry, one might begin to examine the validity of the continuum model. Are the results of an assessment of one's leisure behavior really relevant if a client has suffered several relapses, but has potential to regain or surpass his/her previous level of functioning? Further, is it possible to plot human performance in cognitive, affective, and psycho-motor domains along the same continuum, especially with the more severely and profoundly disabled individuals we are seeing in the hospitals and clinics today? These questions might lead an investigator or team of investigators to examine alternatives to the accepted theoretical construct. It just may be that the continuum is not a valid premise or theory. What are the alternatives?

Associated with this line of inquiry in assessment are questions of utility. While the theoreticians advance a given concept or theory, its application in the practice may be confounding or nearly impossible. Early versions of the LDB were met with questions about its utility due to the length of administration of each assessment. This led to the refinement of the item pool and other streamlining into Version "B" and a short form without compromising the validity and reliability of the instrument. In addition, Ellis and Niles (1985), and Ellis and Compton (1985) utilized the same theoretical constructs validated in the LDB to create a rating scale approach. These instruments, while showing some evidence of validity, need further replication and validation. Recently, Gary Ellis, Carlos Ramos and I have been dabbling with a time diary approach utilizing many of the original LDB constructs with severely and profoundly handicapped youth. The purpose of the study is to determine if this non-obtrusive approach to measuring leisure behavior can reliably chronicle time use, perceived mood states, perceived freedom and several other items relevant to leisure functioning. Early indications suggest that this approach could be utilized by special educators, parents, case workers and therapeutic recreation specialists in an efficient and effective manner.

While progress on the LDB has been quite good over the past few years, much work needs to be done in the future. Ellis and Witt (1986) indicate that there are some major unanswered questions. A sample of these questions include the following:

1. With what populations is the LDB useful?
2. To what extent are the correlations among the measures of perceived freedom a result of "common method" variance?

3. Is the depth of involvement concept stable? That is, does it remain generally constant over time?
4. Can a valid measure of knowledge of leisure opportunities be developed?

The LDB is a clear example of a line of inquiry that can and should be followed by professionals seeking answers to fundamental questions regarding the efficacy of therapeutic recreation. Additional lines of inquiry should be developed around such items, issues and instruments as:

1. The "What Am I Doing?" (WAID) instrument developed by Neulinger (1986). An excellent primary meta-analysis offers cogent information about the utility, reliability and values for the WAID. (Hultsman and Black, 1989) The utilization of meta-analysis is somewhat new to the field of therapeutic recreation but should be employed more often.

2. Single-subject research methodology is another approach to examining issues of the efficacy of our intervention with clients in therapeutic recreation. Dattilo (1986) describes this approach by stating, "Typically, single-subject research experiments examine a few cases extensively, via repeated measurement, in order to verify functional relationships between an individual's behavior and environmental changes. This procedure stresses inferences pertaining to the individual and findings applicable to the individual." This method holds great promise as an approach to address the issues of accountability and efficacy of clinical intervention in our discipline.

3. Leisure education has often been referred to as a basis for the cultivation of values, beliefs and lifestyle. If this is true, then does it not stand to reason that a variety of learning theories should be examined to determine which is most effective in achieving the Individual Educational Objectives (IEP) of the special education teacher? Numerous other questions and vectors could be explored in relation to education for leisure. Another tangential line of inquiry that is worthy of exploration is the "quality of life" issue. What is this for the person with a disability, the severely and profoundly disabled, and those who are attempting to transition back into the community?

Computers and the Research Agenda

Over the past decade the computer has changed the modus operandi of the average worker. Today word processing is so sophisticated when completed on a computer that it has made the typewriter almost obsolete. The ability of a skilled operator to create, alter, display text for complex reports and produce camera ready documents is phenomenal. Word processing is but one application of today's personal computer. Data based management systems allow the therapeutic recreation professional to store, sort and retrieve data pertinent to a given file. Information can be recalled instantly and various reports generated which may be useful in the daily activities of the therapist. Brasile, et al suggest that, "Data bases can be used to file and manipulate client records, library resources, community referral resources, equipment inventories, and information for volunteer utilization." In addition, the personal computer is able to manage large volumes of information for planning purposes. Data on client participation and performance, costs per treatment, and overall budgeting may be accomplished on the personal computer. The computer can also link the individual or client with many data bases through telecommunication technology such as a modem. One need not have the most sophisticated or expensive computer available on the market. A small personal computer with a built in modem will suffice. Utilization of a system such as SCHOLE, a telecommunication system developed by Boston University, could link many therapeutic recreation professionals together, especially those who might have a similar group of clients. Common programs, problems and planning efforts could be shared with immediate feedback to the initiator of the request.

Other applications of the personal computer include accounting programs, planning programs (eg) Mac Project II, graphics packages (eg) Harvard graphics, Mac Draw, etc., desk top publishing and games. While there are numerous models of computers it appears that the most popular systems center around the IBM and MacIntosh personal computers. Each has a large number of software applications in each of the aforementioned categories. Utilization of the computer in the office as a management device requires careful planning and skilled operators. Both Apple and IBM, and a host of other companies offer classes, seminars and camps in hopw to get the most out of your computer. Universities, community colleges and even companies also offer additional training to upgrade skills and learn new applications. To survive in today's competitive world the practitioner, researcher and student must become adept at operating a personal computer. The computer opens up new vistas to every individual. It also promotes greater efficiency in the day to day operations of any unit.

Conclusion

Therapeutic recreation research has made steady and marked improvement in the production of research over the past five years. Much needs to be done to develop and sustain a national agenda if we are to reach a level of respectability from others. The profession does not currently have a passion for the production of research but is anxious to secure the answers to justify its existence. Attention to repeated calls for a comprehensive and strategic research plan in therapeutic recreation must be heeded by the professional organizations. Universities must change curricula and requirements to accelerate the research agenda. Practitioners must join hands with skilled researchers and students to carry out research in practice. Lines of inquiry must be articulated and aggressively attacked by individuals and teams of researchers. Rewards and funds to support the national agenda must be forthcoming- and soon! Competence in conducting research must be widespread among educators and practitioners. Ongoing training and skill development should be the responsibility of all members and organizations- not just a handful of individuals who already know the ropes. Finally, the federal, state and private sectors should be rigorously courted to provide the necessary funding to carry out the national agenda as articulated in this, and several other articles in the past.

Study Questions

1. Examine selected chapters' study questions in the book and identify three researchable topics. Then write 2-3 questions that should be examined in detail. Identify how you would approach the study of this question by stating a hypothesis.

2. Visit a local therapeutic recreation practitioner and inquire about their need for information about the efficacy of therapeutic recreation with their clients. In your discussion, see if it is possible to jointly examine an identified issue, problem or area of need.

3. Go to the library and pick up a copy of the *Therapeutic Recreation Journal*, *Journal of Leisure Research*, *Leisure Sciences* or a journal focused on a particular disability group. Read a research article or two. If possible, work with your adviser or supervisor in trying to replicate the study.

4. Does leisure exist (as defined by the LDB) in the most severely or profoundly disabled person? If so, is it measurable? And if so, is the LDB sensitive enough to detect differences?

5. Investigate how the continuum model was adopted as the standard bearer for the philosophical statement of NTRS. Is the model valid and reliable? What are the inherent problems with its use in a clinical intervention context?

6. Examine several methods of research such as single-subject designs, naturalistic inquiry, meta-analysis, and various empirical strategies and identify a line of inquiry you might pursue with a particular method. The work of Dattilo is an excellent starting point.

7. Develop a paper on how you would: (a) establish a national clearinghouse for therapeutic recreation research; or (b) propose to train practitioners to become competent in research protocols and methods; or (c) find funds to support the national research agenda of therapeutic recreation.

References

Aguilar, T.E., Elliot, L., Kaufman, J., Lucas, M., & Munson, W. (1987). NTRS Research and Development Committee: Final Report (1986-1987). Mimeographed paper submitted to the National Therapeutic Recreation Society Board of Directors, Officers, and the membership.

Barnett, L.A. (1988). *Research About Leisure: Past, Present and Future*. Champaign, IL: Sagamore Publishing.

Brasile, F.M., Conway-Callahan, M.K., Dager, D., & Kleckner, D.J. (1986). Computer Applications in Therapeutic Recreation. *Therapeutic Recreation Journal, 20*(2), 9-11.

Bullock, C.C., McGuire, F.M., & Barch, E.M. (1984). Perceived Research Needs of Therapeutic Recreators. *Therapeutic Recreation Journal, 18*, 17-24.

Burdge, R.J. (1985). The Coming Separation of Leisure Studies from Parks and Recreation Education. *Journal of Leisure Research, 17*(2), 133-141.

Burdge, R.J. (1983). Making Leisure and Recreation Research a Scholarly Topic: Views of a Journal Editor, 1972-1982. *Leisure Sciences, 6*(1), 99-126.

Compton, D.M. (1984). Research Priorities in Recreation for Special Populations. *Therapeutic Recreation Journal, 18*(1), 9-17.

Dattilo, J. (1986). Single-subject Research on Therapeutic Recreation: Applications to Individuals with Disabilities. *Therapeutic Recreation Journal, 20*(1), 76-7.

Ellis, G.D. & Compton, D. M. (1985). *Project LIFE: Analysis of data from pilot testing of the Comprehensive Leisure Rating Scale.* Denton, TX: David M. Compton and Associates.

Ellis, G.D. & Niles, S. (1985). Development, Reliability, and Preliminary Validation of a Brief Leisure Rating Scale. *Therapeutic Recreation Journal, 18*, 50-61.

Ellis, G.D. & Witt, P.A. (1986). The Leisure Diagnostic Battery: Past, Present and Future. *Therapeutic Recreation Journal, 20*,31-47

Hultsman,J.T. & Black, D.R. (1989). Primary Meta-analysis in Leisure Research: Results for Neulinger's "What Am I Doing?" Instrument. *Journal of Leisure Research, 21*(1), 18-31.

Iso-Ahola, S.E. (1980). *The Social Psychology of Leisure and Recreation.* Dubuque, IA: Wm. C. Brown.

Iso-Ahola, S.E. (1988). Research in Therapeutic Recreation. *Therapeutic Recreation Journal, 22*(1), 7-13.

Mannell, R.C. (1983). Research Methodology in Therapeutic Recreation. *Therapeutic Recreation Journal, 17*(4), 9-16.

Neulinger, J. (1986). What Am I Doing? *The WAID.* Dolgeville, NY: The Leisure Institute.

Rickards, W.H. (1985). Perspectives on Therapeutic Recreation Research: Opening the Black Box. *Therapeutic Recreation Journals, 19*(2), 15-23.

Riddick, C.C., DeSchriver M., & Weissinger, E. (1984). A Methodological Review of Research in Journal of Leisure Research from 1978 to 1982. *Journal of Leisure Research 16*, 311-321.

Schleien, S.J. & Yermakoff, N. (1983). Data-based Research in Therapeutic Recreation: State of the Art. *Therapeutic Recreation Journal, 17*, 17-26.

Witt, P.A. (1988a). Therapeutic Recreation Research: Past, Present, and Future. *Therapeutic Recreation Journal, 22*(1) 14-23.

Witt, P.A. (1988b). Leisure Programs and Services for Special Populations. In L.A.Barnett (Ed.) *Research About Leisure: Past, Present, and Future.* Champaign, IL: Sagamore Publishing.

UNIQUE HORIZONS IN RESEARCH:
SINGLE-SUBJECT DESIGNS

John Dattilo

Introduction

Single-subject research designs have been used in many areas of research, including psychology, psychiatry, education, rehabilitation, social work, counseling, and other disciplines (Kazdin, 1982). The distinguishing feature of these designs is that they provide the investigator with a method to rigorously evaluate the effect of interventions on the individual. Because therapeutic recreation interventions are determined by the needs and desires of the individual participant, an individualized research strategy that examines the impact of services on the individual appears warranted (Dattilo, 1986). Therefore, theoretical and practical information on single-subject research is presented in this chapter.

This chapter is divided into five major sections. The first section provides an explanation of how therapeutic recreation specialists can begin to demonstrate cause-and-effect relationships between their interventions and client behavior. A description of the two types of experimental research designs is also included in this section. A discussion of some advantages of single-subject research is presented in the second section of the chapter. The feasibility of implementing and understanding single-subject research, an examination of the treatment process, demonstration of experimental control, and therapeutic recreation program accountability will be highlighted in this section. In the third section, internal validity, external validity, and reliability requirements for single-subject research designs are addressed. Information relative to data analysis is introduced in the fourth section of this chapter. This section includes information on procedures for developing graphic data, characteristics of visual inspection, and criteria used when visually inspecting graphic data.

Finally, general conclusions about single-subject research are presented at the end of the chapter.

Experimental Research: Beyond Evaluation

Systematic data collection on client progress allows the therapeutic recreation specialist to make important observations about client behavior. These data and observations provide the therapeutic recreation specialist with an opportunity to evaluate the client's progress and draw conclusions relative to the direction and magnitude of behavior change. However, Alberto and Troutman (1982) warned that these procedures do not provide sufficient information to indicate a cause-and-effect relationship between an intervention and the behavior in question. Data collection must be conducted under rigorous conditions in order for the therapeutic recreation specialist to begin to make some assumptions about cause-and-effect. To determine the relationship between a leisure intervention and a behavior, the therapeutic recreation specialist must implement experimental research designs. These designs assist the therapeutic recreation specialist in determining the relationship between a leisure intervention and client behavior, and increase the confidence of the investigator that the intervention effected client behavior.

Experimental research requires the manipulation of variables and the measurement of their effects on other variables (Campbell & Stanley, 1966). Experimental research contrasts with descriptive and correlational research, which essentially describes or examines relationships about what is observed but in which no manipulation of variables occurs (McReynolds & Kearns, 1983). Primarily, experimental research is divided into "between-group" and "single-subject" design categories (Alberto & Troutman, 1982).

Traditional between-group research designs focus on group performance using post hoc statistical significance testing to estimate group differences relative to variability. Often, a pattern arises when the results of between-group research reports are read by professionals (Dattilo, 1985). This pattern involves practitioners attempting to apply the group procedures to individuals with the expectation that similar results will be forthcoming (Dattilo, 1986). Unfortunately, results obtained from these designs represent the "average" performance, and often this average performance is the exception rather than the rule. Emphasis on the average may be misleading when a wide range of behaviors exists (Kunstler, 1985).

Single-subject methodology, as the name implies, is designed to evaluate the effect of interventions on the individual (Dattilo, 1985). The essential features of single-subject designs are that all conditions are applied to the same subject and that the results of the change in behavior are analyzed with respect to that individual (Repp, 1981). Typically, single-subject research experiments examine a few cases extensively, via repeated measurement, to verify functional relationships between an individual's behavior and environmental changes (Dattilo & Nelson, 1986). This procedure allows for inferences and/or findings that are applicable to the individual. Inferences made in single-subject research experiments should not be confused with those drawn from groups of individuals. Single-subject research requires careful identification and measurement of dependent variables (behaviors in need of treatment) that are influenced by the systematic application of independent variables (treatments) in applied therapeutic settings. The goal of this methodology is to design investigations that allow the therapeutic recreation specialist to determine an individual's performance and to infer with confidence that a functional relationship between planned interventions and behavior changes exists (Dattilo, 1986).

Advantages of Single-Subject Research

McReynolds and Thompson (1986) have noted that there are many advantages associated with single-subject research that diminish the separation between practitioners and researchers. Because of the advantages associated with single-subject research, there is increasing use of and interest in employing these research designs in the behavioral sciences (Kratochwill, 1978). Single-subject research allows practitioners to consume new research discoveries and apply this information to practice, to empirically evaluate interventions in an effort to increase accountability, and to conduct and disseminate research employed in the therapeutic environment (Kent, 1985). Advantages such as the feasibility of implementing and understanding single-subject research, understanding the treatment process, demonstration of experimental control, and therapeutic recreation program accountability are highlighted in this section of the chapter.

Feasibility

Single-subject research is designed to be used in an applied setting. Therefore, the application of single-subject methodology provides a

feasible procedure for therapeutic recreation practitioners to implement. This methodology does not require elaborate recording and
scoring procedures, and it can occur without disrupting therapeutic
recreation programming. The implementation of single-subject research procedures frequently increases the effectiveness of leisure
services by encouraging the therapeutic recreation specialist to develop
and implement systematic programming procedures. Single-subject
research allows the practitioner to meet the needs of people with limitations and at the same time contribute to the collective knowledge of
the profession (Kent, 1985).

Many therapeutic recreation practitioners who are conducting
research encounter difficulty when attempting to locate a large homo-
geneous sample, which is required to implement a between-group
design. In traditional between-group research, when a treatment is
administered consistently across a sample of individuals, the researcher
can infer with confidence that similar results will occur with other
subjects. However, this conclusion assumes a great deal of treatment
and subject stability, which is often present in a laboratory yet typically
absent in a therapeutic environment (Dattilo, 1987). Because the
application of single-subject research designs requires intense
measurement of an individual or a small sample of people, this
approach appears suited for research investigations conducted by
therapeutic recreation specialists.

Siegal and Spradlin (1985) observed that the provision of services
for people with limitations is most useful when the practitioner organ-
izes and integrates research-produced knowledge with knowledge
drawn from other sources into a comprehensive therapeutic recreation
program that effects a positive change in the behavior of clients.
Frequently, single-subject research investigations are more easily
interpreted by the practitioner than traditional between-group research
(Smith, 1983). Single-subject research facilitates an understanding of
the individual and the evaluation of therapeutic interventions on an
individual's behavior (Dattilo, 1986). The ability of the therapeutic recreation specialist to interpret and implement single-subject research investigations will result in improved and innovative leisure programming for persons with limitations.

Treatment process

A distinctive feature of single-subject research is that it requires
repeated measurements of an individual's performance. As a result, the
therapeutic recreation specialist employing single-subject research

designs can examine the behavioral process as well as the experimental product. Because single-subject research designs require several observations while the intervention is being administered, the therapeutic recreation specialist is able to collect data while the subject's behavior is changing. The concern of the therapeutic recreation specialist for the process of change that occurs with the subject is an important strength of the multiple data points gathered in the continuous measurement procedures required for single-subject designs (Drew, 1976).

Therapeutic recreation specialists are concerned with facilitating the development of appropriate lifestyles for individuals who possess limitations that create barriers to their leisure involvement. Individuals with limitations vary tremendously in terms of cognitive, emotional, physical, and social skills. As a result of the heterogeneity of persons with limitations, practitioners should develop specialized interventions (McReynolds & Thompson, 1986) and predict their effects on each individual client. Because single-subject research is concerned with the effect of an intervention on the individual, this methodology provides therapeutic recreation specialists with the procedures to make inferences pertaining to the individual and thus contributes to the development of more effective specialized interventions.

Single-subject research is a procedure that allows practitioners to avoid withholding helpful treatment from clients participating in a therapeutic recreation program. Frequently, intervention research requires the administration of treatment to one group of participants while not allowing another group (the control group) to receive the treatment. The action of withholding useful services from clients in need of treatment may create an ethical dilemma for therapeutic recreation practitioners attempting to conduct systematic research (Dattilo, 1986). One of the virtues of single-subject designs is that they require that each individual act as his or her own control (Walker, 1983), thus ensuring that each person participating in the research investigation receives the therapeutic recreation intervention.

Experimental control

Perhaps the most central idea in research, basic to all experimental designs, is the concept of experimental control (Drew, 1976). Once an investigation has been conducted, it is important for the therapeutic recreation specialist to be able to attribute the results of the study to the treatment. To accomplish this with any confidence, other possible explanations of the results must be minimized. For example, the distinguishing feature of single-subject methodology is the provision of a means for the therapeutic recreation specialist to rigorously evaluate the effects of interventions on individual participants by allowing each individual to receive the identified treatment yet also serve as his or her own control. The individual is observed when treatment is withheld (control period) and when the intervention is administered (experimental period).

Effects of interventions are examined through observations of treatment performance of the same person. Repeated assessment of performance is required in single-subject research because of the need to examine intervention effects over an extended time period, avoiding the attribution of change to historical accidents (Dattilo, 1986). These procedures allow the investigator to examine trend, variability, and stability of an individual's performance. Experimental control is established by accounting for changes in level and trend through observation of the effect of treatment on the performance of the same person. As a result, these designs assist in the prediction of effects for individuals and they facilitate individualized instruction.

Accountability

There has been an increasing demand by the consumers of therapeutic recreation services, administrators, accrediting bodies, and third-party funding agencies for therapeutic recreation specialists to demonstrate the effectiveness of their therapeutic interventions. One potential benefit of the implementation of single-subject research designs is an increase in accountability related to the provision of effective leisure services for persons with limitations. Because single-subject research is treatment oriented, its application by practitioners interested in working with people with disabilities may result in information that will assist these practitioners in becoming more accountable (McReynolds & Kearns, 1983). The results of single-subject research investigations will provide therapeutic recreation specialists with data that can result in the development of more effective treatment.

Research Requirements

To better understand the research procedure associated with single-subject designs, the requirements for all research and their applications for single-subject methodology are now described. The three primary requirements for empirical research are internal validity, external validity, and reliability (Isaac & Michael, 1981). Internal validity relates to the extent to which a study eliminates alternative explanations of results, while external validity is concerned with the generalizability of the results beyond the experimental conditions. Reliability reflects the degree to which a measurement instrument yields similar results for the same subjects under different conditions.

Internal validity

The task for therapeutic recreation specialists is to examine the influence of a particular intervention in such a way that extraneous factors will not interfere with the reported conclusions. After examining the threats to internal validity, Kazdin (1982) and Kratochwill (1978) concluded that single-subject investigations can readily reduce and eliminate these threats.

The presence of extraneous variables that influence the individual and are difficult to evaluate may introduce rival reasons that could account for change not attributable to therapeutic intervention (Cook & Campbell, 1979). The reduction or elimination of this threat to internal validity can be achieved in single-subject research through the systematic application of experimental designs that are based on objective, continuous, and reliable data collection (Dattilo, 1986). As a result of using individual subjects as their own controls, the therapeutic recreation specialist alleviates the problem of differences among individuals prior to the experiment and facilitates examination of individual differences.

The purpose of single-subject research designs is to demonstrate that the manipulation of the treatment (independent variable) results in change in the behavior (dependent variable). Single-subject research designs are employed to demonstrate that a functional relationship exists between variables (Alberto & Troutman, 1982). The goals of the research designs are to increase experimental control while decreasing extraneous variables that may influence the subject's behavior. According to McReynolds and Kearns (1983), the effort to prevent extraneous variables from confounding the effect of an independent variable introduces the concept of control into the design of an experimental study. As previously stated, experimental control facilitates the belief that changes in dependent variables are those environmental conditions that are not controlled by the therapeutic recreation specialist but may affect behaviors.

The requirements of single-subject designs include operational specificity, continuous assessment, baseline performance, and implementation of an intervention. Operational specificity relates to the precise and complete description of behaviors being measured (dependent variables) and the treatment (independent variables) to facilitate replication. Continuous assessment, on the other hand, requires the repeated and regular observations of one or more subjects over an extended period of time to determine behavior patterns before and after the intervention (Birnbauer, Peterson, & Solnick, 1974).

Because of the complexity of baseline and intervention phases, these two requirements will now be described in considerable detail. Prior to demonstrating the effect of an intervention, it is necessary for the researcher to determine the performance level of the subject without influence from the intervention (Drew, 1976). The observation period of examining the target behavior that occurs before the intervention is termed the *baseline*. The baseline data measures the level of behavior (dependent variable) as it naturally occurs. The function of the baseline is twofold (Kazdin, 1982). First, baseline is descriptive in nature, that is, baseline allows the therapeutic recreation specialist to describe the existing level of behavior. Second, baseline has a predictive function, which is used to project the future occurrence of the behavior.

To effectively describe existing behaviors and predict the future of them, therapeutic recreation specialists must measure the identified behaviors often enough to develop an accurate picture of them. Therefore, it is imperative to obtain a representative sample of the target behaviors as they occur in the natural environment. A representative sample of the target behaviors will allow practitioners to determine whether behaviors have stabilized (Alberto & Troutman, 1982).

Behavior stability is characterized by variability and trend. Variability measures the amount of fluctuation in the behaviors from one measurement to the next. The more behaviors fluctuate, the more difficult it is to describe and predict them. In essence, the picture of the behaviors becomes fuzzy or distorted (Dattilo, 1986). Although this procedure may distort daily performance, it reduces the number of data points and may clarify the graphic display.

The second characteristic of behavioral stability, trend, describes the distinctive direction in which the behaviors are occurring. When a clear trend occurs during baseline, therapeutic recreation specialists would predict that without treatment the behaviors would continue following the same trend. Therefore, if the trend changes when intervention is initiated, comparisons between baseline and intervention phases can occur.

After baseline data are collected, the fourth requirement of single-subject designs, an intervention phase, must be employed. The single-subject experimental designs incorporate several baseline and intervention phases in the design that are administered across time, behaviors, subject, and/or settings. The purpose of changing from one phase to another is to demonstrate that the behavior change is a result of the condition (Drew, 1976). There are a variety of single-subject experimental designs available to answer therapeutic recreation research questions. According to Barlow, Hayes, and Nelson (1984), the choice of which design to use depends on factors such as the nature of the target behaviors, the setting in which a study is conducted, the availability of additional subjects, and other practical concerns. The reader is referred to Barlow and Hersen (1984), Kazdin (1982), Kearns (1986), McReynolds and Kearns (1983), and Tawney and Gast (1984) for detailed descriptions of various single-subject designs.

With the implementation of single-subject designs, experimental control can be attained (Siegel & Spradlin, 1985). Single-subject designs not only incorporate objective measures, repeated assessments of performance over time, information regarding performance stability, and the association of marked changes in behavior with an intervention, but also arrange the administration of the intervention to reduce further threats to internal validity (Kazdin, 1982).

External validity

In addition to demonstrating the relationship between the intervention and behavioral changes, the goal for therapeutic recreation specialists is to demonstrate that findings can be generalized to different people, settings, and situations. External validity refers to the extent to which the results of an investigation can be generalized beyond the experimental condition (Kratochwill, 1978). One procedure that enhances the external validity of an investigation is the replication of intervention effects (McReynolds & Thompson, 1986). Through replication, the therapeutic recreation specialist can examine the extent to which results can be generalized across behaviors, settings, investigators, and measures.

Direct replication, one of two different methods for replication of experimental findings, involves the application of the same procedures across a number of different subjects (usually in the same investigation). This procedure assists the therapeutic recreation specialist by determining whether findings are restricted to the subjects that were included in the original demonstration.

To determine the generalizability of findings across a variety of different conditions, an alternative replication method could be employed. The therapeutic recreation specialist can conduct systematic replications by repeating the investigation and systematically varying different features of the original experiment. If the results of direct and systematic replication research show that the intervention affects behaviors in new subjects across different conditions, the generalizability of the results has been demonstrated (Kazdin, 1982).

Reliability

The degree to which a measurement instrument yields similar results for the same subject under different conditions (reliability) is addressed through data collection procedures. Measurement instruments used to collect research data must be designed to accurately record behavior change in order for them to be considered reliable. Therefore, it is critical that therapeutic recreation specialists conducting single-subject research define client behavior (dependent variable) with observable and measurable terms (Dattilo & Murphy, 1987). This requirement appears compatible with systematic programming guidelines that encourage therapeutic recreation practitioners to use behavioral terminology when developing client objectives and performance measures (Peterson & Gunn, 1984).

The method of data collection most often used in single-subject investigations involves behavioral observations. Observational procedures are the primary method to obtain information on what is actually happening in a situation (Pelegrino, 1979). The observation data collection procedures must ensure observer accuracy and inter-observer agreement.

Observer accuracy requires that the observations reflect the actual behavior. This is achieved by establishing a standard or criterion (Kazdin, 1982). One procedure that may assist the development of a criterion is the use of videotaping equipment (Dattilo, 1986). The investigator could videotape the participant and then review the tape on numerous occasions, using an observational checklist. The findings recorded on the observational checklist would then become the standard for the actual observers. Once this criterion is established, observers should then be trained to reach this criterion.

When the therapeutic recreation specialist relies on direct observation to obtain assessment and evaluative data, the possibility exists that observers will not record behavior consistently. Therefore, the evaluation of the correspondence of the data obtained by separate observers (inter-observer agreement) is necessary when applying single-subject methodology. Two or more individuals independently observing a behavior are required for inter-observer agreement (Kratochwill, 1978). A comparison then is calculated to determine the correspondence between their observations. Using more than one observer and analyzing the observer agreement allows the researcher to detect inconsistencies in observer analysis of subject response. If agreement between observers is demonstrated, confidence in the data will increase.

High inter-observer agreement does not necessarily mean the observers are measuring the behavior accurately. Observer accuracy is a separate issue and, as previously stated, must be considered in relationship to established criteria. The rationale for inter-observer agreement is to ensure consistency between observations and individuals (McReynolds & Kearns, 1983). Through accurate and specific definitions of terms, the establishment of inter-observer agreement should result in minimizing observational biases.

Although inter-observer agreement checks on each data-recording session would be extremely informative, it is unlikely that therapeutic recreation specialists possess adequate personnel to make this practice feasible (Dattilo, 1986). Therefore, Kazdin (1982) suggested that inter-observer agreement probes be used. Inter-observer probes require designating one trained observer as the primary observer to examine a particular situation. Systematic involvement of another trained observer must then occur to facilitate periodic examination of some sessions. Inter-observer agreement can then be calculated between the corresponding data of the two observers.

Data Analysis: Emphasis on Visual Inspection

Single-subject research is designed to control for variances by experimental design rather than by relying on statistical procedures (Kratochwill, 1978). The strength of the investigator's conclusions lies in the degree of experimental control established during the investigation (Dattilo, 1986). Although statistical analysis may be used, visual inspection of graphic displays is often the most effective method by which the effects of an intervention may be determined (Parsonson & Baer, 1978). Visual inspection of graphed data provides the basis for judgment about reliability or consistency of intervention effects and permits determination of dramatic effects (Kazdin, 1982). In this section the procedure for developing graphic data, characteristics of visual inspection, and the criteria used when visually inspecting data are presented.

Procedures

Visual inspection requires therapeutic recreation specialists to plot the data graphically to allow them to reach a decision about the data patterns (Dattilo, 1987). According to Pelegrino (1979), graphic presentation is simply depicting numerical data in visual form. Each target behavior should be graphically displayed across the intervention. The graphs should provide a detailed and compact summary of the data. Pelegrino suggested the utilization of a line graph consisting of a grid upon which the relationship of two variables is plotted to dramatize fluctuation or a definite trend over continuous time, distance, weight, or similar data. To promote accurate and efficient data display, Jones, Vaught, and Weinrott (1977) recommended that researchers provide concise titles describing the nature and purpose of the study, develop explicit captions communicating the identity and meaning of variables, and use appropriate scale units on the ordinate and abscissa scales.

Characteristics

The visually depicted data should reflect systematic interventions and result in a consistency of judgment about the impact of the intervention. Visual inspection is used because significant effects should be obvious when the graphically portrayed data are examined. Therefore, the therapeutic recreation specialist will be more likely to accept those interventions that have major effects and dismiss those which are weak. Visual inspection then can be viewed as a screening device for powerful interventions.

Although there are many advantages associated with visual inspection, there are also some concerns that must be addressed (Dattilo, 1987). Visual inspection lacks concrete decision rules related to significance of the intervention. As a result, different investigators may not agree on the interpretation of the results. In addition, there are many criteria that must be considered when judging the impact of interventions. The multitude of concerns creates difficulty in interpreting graphic data. Because visual inspection can serve to identify only powerful effects, those procedures that provide some, but minimal, assistance may be overlooked.

Criteria

When visual inspection is implemented, there is often a problem in determining the impact of the intervention when the behavior is highly variable (Dattilo, 1987). Therefore, the following criteria involving the magnitude and rate of change have been established for therapeutic recreation specialists to follow when employing visual inspection procedures. The magnitude of change involves the amount of behavior change that has occurred and can be affected by the mean and the level of behavior. Change in mean performance is defined as the change in the ratio of the number of times the target behavior occurs per unit of observation time (Parsonson & Baer, 1978). A change in mean of the behavior relates to the shift in the average rate of the behavior. Determination of the discontinuity of performance from the end of one phase to the beginning of the next phase is referred to as a change in level (Kazdin, 1982). Therefore, determination of a level change requires the therapeutic recreation specialist to observe the shift in the dependent variable from the end of one phase to the beginning of the next phase.

The rate of change involves the change in the trend or the latency of behavior. Trend, or slope of the behavior, relates to the tendency of the behavior to change after the intervention has been implemented (Dattilo, 1987). Examination of trend allows the therapeutic recreation specialist to determine the tendency of the data to increase or decrease systematically over time. Latency refers to the period of time between the beginning or end of one condition and changes in an individual's performance (Dattilo, 1986). Examination of latency allows the therapeutic recreation specialist to determine how long it takes the subject's behavior to change after the intervention has been implemented. Reporting changes in the behavior's mean, level, trend, and latency period will encourage consumers of the research to more effectively apply visual inspection of graphic data and develop a more thorough understanding of the results of the investigation.

Conclusion

There are advantages as well as disadvantages associated with both single-subject and traditional between-group experimental designs. Neither should be systematically viewed as being preferable over the other (Drew, 1976). In addition, there are numerous problems and situations within a therapeutic recreation setting where research may be conducted. The selection of an experimental design should be dictated by the experimental question that the therapeutic recreation specialist is attempting to answer and the anticipated effects of the treatment. Often these determinants of design selection are bypassed by the unquestioned reliance on tradition as a guide (Kazdin, 1980). An understanding of the various design characteristics will prepare therapeutic recreation specialists to become better producers and consumers of research.

Individuals participating in therapeutic recreation programs can be carefully examined by repeatedly measuring their performance during baseline and intervention phases (Dattilo, 1987). Single-subject research represents a viable method for making informed decisions about the quality of therapeutic recreation programs and provides a context for understanding the behavioral dynamics of individuals with limitations. Single-subject designs, used alone or in conjunction with other research designs, can be responsive to various practical dilemmas in the field of therapeutic recreation.

Study Questions

1. How do experimental designs allow therapeutic recreation specialists to move beyond program evaluation and demonstrate cause-effect relationships?

2. What are the two primary design categories of experimental research, and how are they different?

3. Why is single-subject research a feasible procedure for therapeutic recreation specialists to implement and understand?

4. How can single-subject research provide therapeutic recreation specialists with the opportunity to understand the treatment process?

5. What is experimental control, and how do single-subject research procedures increase external validity?

6. How do single-subject designs reduce threats to internal validity?

7. How can therapeutic recreation specialists who employ single-subject research procedures increase external validity?

8. How does inter-observer agreement relate to reliability?

9. What is an advantage and a disadvantage of using visual i n - spection of data to evaluate the effects of an experimental research investigation?

10. What are the four criteria that should be considered by therapeutic recreation specialists when visually inspecting graphic data?

11. What factor should determine selection of an experimental design?

References

Alberto, P.A., & Troutman, A.C. (1982). *Applied Behavior Analysis for Teachers* (2nd ed.) Columbus, OH: Charles E. Merrill.

Barlow, D.H., Hayes, S.C., & Nelson, R.O. (1984). *The Scientist Practitioner; Research and Accountability in Clinical and Educational Settings.* New York: Pergamon Press.

Barlow, D.H., & Hersen, M. (1984). *Single-Case Experimental Designs: Strategies for Studying Behavior Change.* New York: Pergamon Press.

Birnbauer, J.S., Peterson, C.R., & Solnick, J.V. (1974). Design and Interpretation of Studies of Single Subjects. *American Journal of Mental Deficiency, 79,* 191-203.

Campbell, D.T., & Stanley, J.C. (1966). *Experimental and Quasi-Experimental Designs for Research.* Chicago: Rand McNally.

Cook, T.D., & Campbell (1979). *Quasi-Experimentation, Design and Analysis Issues for Field Settings.* Chicago: Rand McNally.

Dattilo, J. (1985). An Alternative to Studying Individuals with Disabilities: Single-Subject Research. *Leisure Information Quarterly, 17,* 11.

Dattilo, J. (1986). Single-Subject Research in Therapeutic Recreation: Implications to Individuals with Limitations. *Therapeutic Recreation Journal, 20* (1), 76-87.

Dattilo, J. (1987). Encouraging the Emergence of Therapeutic Recreation Research-Practitioners Through Single-Subject Research. *Journal of Expanding Horizons in Therapeutic Recreation, 2.*

Dattilo, J., & Murphy, W.M. (1987). *Behavior Modification in Therapeutic Recreation.* State College, PA: Venture.

Dattilo, J., & Nelson, G. (1986). Single-Subject Evaluation in Health Education. *Health Education Quarterly, 13* (3), 249-259.

Drew, C.F. (1976). *Introduction to Designing Research and Evaluation.* St. Louis: C.V. Mosby.

Isaac, C., & Michael, W.B. (1981.) *Handbook in Research and Evaluation: For Education and the Behavioral Sciences.* San Diego: Edits.

Jones, R.R., Vaught, R.S., & Weinrott, M. (1977). Time-Series Analysis in Operant Research. *Journal of Applied Behavior Analysis, 10,* 151-166.

Kazdin, A. (1980). *Research Design in Clinical Psychology.* New York: Harper and Row.

Kazdin, A. (1982). *Single-Case Research Designs: Methods for Clinical and Applied Settings.* New York: Oxford University.

Kearns, K.P. (1986). Flexibility of Single-Subject Experimental Designs: Part 2. Design Selection and Arrangement of Experimental Phases. *Journal of Speech and Hearing Disorders, 51,* 204-214.

Kent, R.D. (1985). Science and the Clinician: The Practice of Science and the Science of Practice. *Seminars in Speech and Language, 6,* 152-163.

Kratochwill, T.R. (1978). *Single Subject Research: Strategies for Evaluating Change.* New York: Academic Press.

Kunstler, R. (1985). Research Update. *Parks and Recreation, 20,* 24-27.

McReynolds, L.V., & Kearns, K.P. (1983). *Single-Subject Research: Strategies for Evaluating Change.* New York: Academic Press.

McReynolds, L.V., & Thompson, K. (1986). Flexibility of Single-Subject Experimental Designs: Part I. Review of the Basics of Single-Subject Designs: *Journal of Speech and Hearing Disorders, 51,* 194-203.

Parsonson, B.S., & Baer, D.M. (1978). The Analysis and Presentation of Graphic Data. In T.R. Kratochwill (Ed.), *Single-Subject Research Strategies for Evaluating Change* (pp.101-166). New York: Academic Press.

Pelegrino, D.A. (1979). *Research Methods for Recreation and Leisure: A Theoretical and Practical Guide.* Dubuque, IA: William C. Brown.

Peterson, C.A., & Gunn, S.L. (1984). *Therapeutic Recreation Program Design: Principles and Procedures.* Englewood Cliffs, NJ: Prentice-Hall.

Repp, A.C. (1981). *Teaching the Mentally Retarded.* Englewood, Cliffs, New Jersey: Prentice-Hall.

Siegel, G.M., & Spradlin, J.E. (1985). Therapy and Research. *Journal of Speech and Hearing Disorders, 50,* 226-230.

Smith, H. (1983). Single Subject Research: Application in Leisure Services. *Impact, 10,* 7-8.

Tawney, J. & Gast, D. (1984). *Single-Subject Research in Special Education.* Columbus, OH: Charles E. Merrill.

Walker, C.E. (1983). *The Handbook of Clinical Psychology: Theory, Research and Practice.* Homewood, IL: Dow Jones-Irwin.

International Issues

photo courtesy of City of Las Vegas

Play, recreation, and leisure are universal terms that should be utilized as instruments of peace, freedom, and human dignity.

—David M. Compton

INTERNATIONAL ISSUES IN THERAPEUTIC RECREATION:
A Latin American Perspective

Miguel A. Albarrán

Latin America has long been conceptualized in many ways. Sometimes the term *Latin America* refers only to Western Hemisphere countries whose native language is Spanish, other times to those whose language simply has etiological roots in Latin (i.e., French, Portuguese, Spanish). Latin America has been spoken of as a multinational culture with a Spanish influence, but it sometimes includes the British- and Dutch-influenced countries of the Caribbean as well. The world's economic communities have spoken of these countries as being Third World, underdeveloped, subdeveloped, and developing.

This chapter addresses the Latin American concept from a holistic perspective, referring to all American countries and territories south of the United States of America. Thus, Latin America includes Mexico, Central America, the Caribbean, and South America, regardless of an individual area's language, historical background, or economic condition.

The Latin American issue is one that goes beyond all religious, political, economical, and cultural factors. Perhaps it is more an issue on how to be good neighbors. Even though there seems to be a sense of unity, this is only a perception, because the cultures and governments are individually and collectively very pluralistic.

Technological progress in Latin America has led to an expansion of free time (Special Report on Latin America, 1981). Thus, more and more people are engaging in leisure experiences—and the special population is no exception. Due to economic factors and the nature of recreation services, compared by North American standards, a great deal of all Latin American government recreation programs are therapeutic recreation or special population service programs. For example, Brazil has developed programs to educate toward creative leisure (Requixa, 1981). Colombia is providing urban recreation programs to solve urban problems. Mexico, Peru, and Venezuela are trying to service industrial, community, and family needs through recreation (Juarez, 1981; National Institute for Recreation Physical Education and Sports, 1981; Ministry of Youth, 1981).

Table 1
Latin American Academic Institutions
in Leisure, Recreation, and Related Fields

Country	Institution					Type of Training					
	GD	I	PA	U	Y	STP	C	TSP	AD	B	GP
Argentina	1						X				
Brazil		1									X
Chile	1					X	X				
Colombia	1	1				X	X				
Costa Rica				2						X	
Cuba		1								X	
Dominican Rep.	1					X	X				
Mexico	1	1	1	1			X			X	
Netherland Antilles	1						X	X			
Panama				1			X				
Puerto Rico				3					X	X	
Venezuela					1		X				
Total	6	4	1	7	1	3	8	1	1	4	1

Key:
GD: Government department   I: Institute
PA: Professional association   U: University
STP: Short-term program   C: Certificate
TSP: Technical skill prog.   AD: Associate degree
B: Bachelor's degree   GP: Graduate program
Y: YMCA

Source: International Directory of Academic Institutions in Leisure, Recreation and Related Fields by Max D-Amours (Ed.), 1986, Commission on Education of the World Leisure and Recreation Association.

Recreational services for the handicapped and/or special populations have been influenced by different countries throughout Latin

America. Also, countries like Canada, Great Britain, Holland, the Soviet Union, Spain, the United States, and West Germany have influenced the delivery of recreational services. These countries have been influential primarily through formal education programs in which Latin American students receive professional training. Also, there have been seminars, institutes, workshops, and short-term programs that do not lead toward professional degrees, but provide some hands-on experience. Professional preparation in the recreation field is becoming more and more important in the Latin American countries (See Table 1).

D'Amours's (1986) publication on academic institution in leisure, recreation, and related fields gives a good review of programs throughout Latin America, the United States, and Canada. Some other programs that are not affiliated with neither the World Leisure and Recreation Association nor the Latin American Leisure and Recreation Association also have recreation or adapted recreation degrees or courses.

A great deal of the university institutions have courses dealing with recreation, leisure, and physical education for special populations. These courses are mainly taken by students and professionals in the education, rehabilitation, and health fields.

The concept of therapeutic recreation as conceived by North American scholars is almost a nonexistent one for the Latin American countries. Delivery systems as designed by Gunn and Peterson (1978) are far from becoming a reality.

Latin American (Spanish and Portuguese) literature does not have a consensus on how to refer to the therapeutic recreation field. Recreation is mainly seen as an area within physical education that has very heavy ties with sports. Recreation has not yet emerged as a profession by itself. Taking the prior statement in consideration, what can one expect from the therapeutic field?

Like the United States, Latin America has labeled therapeutic recreation in various manners. It seems that the way each country addresses therapeutic recreation is a result of the field from which it emerges. The Latin American Group of Professional Rehabilitation (GLARP) has demonstrated a special interest in the therapeutic recreation field. This is probably why, in some instances, therapeutic recreation programs have a clinical perspective, with physicians, occupational therapists, physical therapists, and psychologists advocating and delivering services. These fields tend to believe that recreation plays an important role in the rehabilitation process of ill and handicapped individuals. This belief is possibly based on what they have seen from other countries, but each country has a lack of empirical evidence that can prove the general belief. Many think that participating in recreational activities alone will provide adequate experiences for rehabilitation. Social workers, teachers, counselors, and clerical personnel are commonly found as recreational service providers in communities and institutions. In Latin America, services for special populations are often the result of collaboration among several different agencies (Arias, Albarrán, & Aguilar, 1982).

Table 2
Terms Used in Latin America to Refer to
Therapeutic Recreation Services

Spanish Term	English Translation
deportes adaptados	adapted sports
deportes especiales	special sports
deportes en silla de ruedas	wheelchair sports
deportes para impedidos	sports for the unable
deportes para lisiados	sports for the handicapped
deportes para el incapacitado	sports for the disabled
recreación adaptada	adapted recreation
recreación correctiva	corrective recreation
recreación especial	special recreation
recreación fisica	physical recreation
recreación para el incapacitado	recreation for the disabled
recreación para el excepcional	recreation for the exceptional
recreación para el físicamente limitado	recreation for the physically handicapped
recreación para el impedido	recreation for the unable
recreación para el nino excepcional	recreation for the crippled child
recreación para poblaciones especiales	recreation for special populations

Spanish Term	English Translation
recreación terapéutica	therapeutic recreation
terapia habilitativa	abilitative therapy
terapia de juego	play therapy
terapia de recreación	recreation therapy
terapia de rehabilitativa	rehabilitative therapy
terapia recreativa	recreational therapy

Government Support for Recreation and Leisure

Public recreation services are found throughout the entire hemisphere. Even though some countries do not have any structured services, others do have recreation and park systems. The organization of these services vary from country to country.

Public and private institutions and associations are advocating recreational services for general and special populations. United Nations General Secretary Alfredo Penalosa has reported that recreational programs are seen in many Latin American countries as the only way the economically deprived populations can obtain some experiences that they cannot afford (WLRA, 1978).

Public recreation programs have been organized under different philosophies. We find national organizations that coordinate the recreation events in each country. Special attention has been given to the creation of a leisure and free-time policy. In some countries, public institutions and private enterprise have worked together to create a leisure policy. The main emphasis of this policy is to improve sports, folklore, handcrafts, culture, arts, and social development. This trend has already started in Argentina, Brazil, Chile, Colombia, Costa Rica, and Puerto Rico.

Sports for Special Populations in Latin America

Sport participation is an important and controversial issue. In most of the Latin American countries, this is the only form of recreational therapy "treatment." The sports programming area seems to be in the highest point of human existence for many Latin American countries. In some cases the elite athletes thus receive the best of the opportunities, but the rest of the population is deprived of the sport experience.

Table 3
Some Organizations that Coordinate Recreational Services in Latin American Countries

Spanish name	English translation	Country
Coldeportes	Colsports	Colombia
Comité Nacional de Recreación Chilena	Chilean National Comm. on Rec.	Chile

Departamento de Asuntos de la Juventud	Dept. of Youth Affairs	Curaczao
Departamento de Recreación y Deportes	Dept. of Rec. & Sports (Asst. Secretariat for Adapted Rec.)	Puerto Rico
Fundeporte	Sports Foundation	Ecuador
Instituto Nacional de Deportes y Recreación	National Sports Institute	Venezuela
Instituto Nacional de Deportes y Recreación	National Institute of Sports and Recreation	Cuba
Instituto Nacional de Recreación, Educacion Física y Deportes	National Institute of Recreation, Physical Education and Sports	Peru
Ministerio Nacional de la Familia y la Juventud	National Ministry of the Family and Youth	Argentina
Secretaría de Estado de Deportes, Educación Física y Recreación	Secretariat of State for Sports, Physical Ed. and Recreation	Dominican Republic
Servicio Social de Comercio	Social Service for Commerce	Brazil

International sports movements have been campaigning for the participation of the masses. The "Life—Be in It," "Volksports," and "Sports for All" movements have caught the attention of many recreation agencies and associations. This type of sports propaganda is not appropriate for some Latin American programs. It is very difficult to advocate "Sports for All" when there is not "Health, Food, Education, or Work" for all. Thus, the participation in sports activities is a luxury and extremely cherished. So, if advocating for "Sports for All" is inadequate, what can we say about "Sports for All the Disabled"?

Despite this situation, the handicapped population is involved in sport competition, as this is in many cases the form of treatment in reference to leisure services. The Special Olympic movement is getting stronger for the mentally retarded population, and other disability groups such as the deaf and the blind also engage in regional and international games.

The physically handicapped is the largest group that participates in sports. Almost every country has a handicapped, disabled, or wheelchair sports association. Evidently this is a result of the internationally known doctor Ludgwin Guttman and his philosophy of sports for the disabled. Benjamin Lipton's work has also influenced this sports movement throughout the New World. The Pan American Wheelchair Association was founded in 1966 and held its first games on August 8, 1967 in Canada. Six countries attended this first event (Argentina, Canada, Jamaica, Mexico, Trinidad-Tobago, and the United States). Puerto Rico was the host of the last games in 1986 and Venezuela has petitioned to host the 1990 games.

Sports for the blind has obtained an important position in the rehabilitation process. The Latin American Union for the Blind has appointed a sports committee to advocate the sports movement for the blind. As a result of this Union, a sports association has been founded. The Latin American Blind Sports Association (LABSA) is affiliated with the International Blind Sports Association. They organize sport competitions for blind athletes in four different sport modalities—chess; track and field, swimming, and wrestling).

South America

Argentina: Recreational services for the handicapped population are mostly offered in Buenos Aires. The existence of a children's play program in a Buenos Aires hospital and the participation of disabled athletes in wheelchair sports seem to be the most structured services for the handicapped.

Table 4
Latin American Members of the
Pan American Wheelchair Association

Country	\\			Host				
	Can. 1967	Arg. 1969	Jam. 1971	Per. 1973	Mex. 1975	Bra. 1978	Can. 1982	P.R 1986
Argentina	X	X	X	X	X	X	X	X
Bahamas							X	X

Table 4 (cont.)

Country	Host							
	Can. 1967	Arg. 1969	Jam. 1971	Per. 1973	Mex. 1975	Bra. 1978	Can. 1982	P.R 1986
Bolivia					X	X		X
Brazil		X	X	X	X	X	X	X
Chile		X	X	X		X	X	X
Colombia				X	X	X	X	X
Cuba				X	X			X
Dominican Rep.			Obs	X	X	X	X	X
Ecuador					X	X		X
El Salvador			X		X			X
Guatemala					X	X		X
Guyana			Obs	X			X	
Haiti			X					
Jamaica	X	X	X	X	X	X	X	X
Mexico	X	X	X	X	X	X	X	X
Panama								Obs
Paraguay		X						
Peru		X	X	X	X	X	X	X
Puerto Rico							X	X
Trinidad-Tobago	X	X	X		X			
Uruguay		X				X	X	X
Venezuela			X			X	X	X

Obs= Observer

Sources:

Ramírez, H.E. (Enero, 1986) *Síntesis Histórica de los Juegos Panamericanos Sobre Silla de Ruedas.* Buenos Aires, Argentina

Comité Organizador JUPASIRU (Noviembre, 1986) *Programa VIII Juegos Pan Americanos Sobre Silla de Ruedas.* Aguadilla, Puerto Rico

Formal preparation in therapeutic recreation does not exist. Courses are being taught in the area of adapted physical education and recreation as a part of an undergraduate degree in physical education (Cassione, 1986).

Table 5
Countries Attending the Second Latin American Games for the Blind in the Dominican Republic (1988)

Region	Country
Caribbean	Cuba Dominican Rep. Puerto Rico (obs)
Central America	Panama
South America	Colombia Venezuela

Brazil: A private organization provides recreational activities as a means of recreation for different disability groups in Sao Paulo. The staff of this program has formal academic preparation in physical education.

Recreational services for " the Third Age" is an important service in Brazil. The Social Service for Commerce has established programs to serve the elderly. Some programs for seniors, particularly in the state of Sao Paulo, are provided by social organizations (Gaelzer, 1986).

Chile: The issue of providing recreational services for the elderly is a new one for many Latin American countries. In Chile, recreation "was reference synonymous to youngsters, children and in some exceptional cases to adults" (Emeres, 1986). The YMCA has created awareness for this type of programming and has established camps, special activities, and clubs for the elderly and committees to provide services.

Colombia: Wheelchair sports is the most structured form of recreation service in Colombia. The interest for sports participation for the handicapped is supported by the Colombian Wheelchair Sports Association. Colombian scholars have even written textbooks for the practice of wheelchair sports.

The government has demonstrated an interest for recreation programs for the economically deprived and senior citizens. Conferences, workshops and seminars have been held in Colombia that address these issues.

Ecuador: Jesse Caudillo (1983) reports on the status of Ecuador's first municipal parks and recreation program. This program has been established in Quito and serves many low-income participants. Municipal recreation programs do not exist, but private clubs are available for the wealthy. The Special Olympics movement provides services for the mentally retarded. Cooperative efforts between agencies provide services through the education system.

Central America

Costa Rica: The National Council of Rehabilitation and Special Education has celebrated seminars and workshops to improve the recreational services for the handicapped. Also, the University of Costa Rica, San Jose, has included a recreation degree program at the undergraduate level.

Summer camps and activities for the handicapped are being offered by private and public associations. Hospitals and institutions are providing recreation services for their populations.

El Salvador: Wheelchair sports is one of the areas of growth and interest. Recreation for special populations is coordinated by the Ministry of Education. This agency has performed workshops in adapted physical education. The adapted physical education services are offered by physical therapists or clinical personnel.

Recently El Salvador has asked for information and training in the therapeutic recreation field. Professional personnel within the area of adapted physical education from Puerto Rico have offered workshops for the Salvadorans (Lopez, 1988). The need for services increases even while the country undergoes its military conflicts.

Mexico: Recreation programs in Mexico City follow the trend of the rest of the Latin American countries. Programs for the handicapped are a public and private endeavor. The focus of these programs are directed toward youth, the physically handicapped, senior citizens, and low-socioeconomic-status communities.

An innovative program was established after Mexico's last earthquake. Children and youths were provided with special recreation services at the emergency villages that assisted the victims. This population was given recreation and art materials. The drawings of the victims initially represented the disasters (Aguilar, 1987). As a result of this program, the recreation staff could assess the psychological state of the victims through sessions of art therapy. This emergency plan has been presented to some Latin American countries, and there are plans to incorporate it into civil defense and Red Cross emergency plans.

Wheelchair sports are also popular in Mexico, where they have one of the best teams in the Pan American Wheelchair Association.

The Carribean

***Cuba*:** All adapted recreation services are delivered by the government. Most of these services are provided by the National Institute of Sports, Physical Education and Recreation (INDER). An adapted physical education and recreation program exists for the needy, and senior citizens are treated in hospitals and institutions.

Wheelchair sports, blind sports, and handicapped sports programs are being focused on by the government as well as the sports-for-all policy. This later emphasis is used as an aspect of preventive medicine (Xiques, 1988).

Curazao: Government recreational services are aimed especially toward youth. This is so due to social problems of this population has. The Department of Youth Affairs is providing programs to assist this population. One of the programs that has been structured is the "Moving Theatre Program," providing arts and drama experiences to low-socioeconomic-status communities. The objective of this program is to represent social and community problems and experiences through drama. The social drama technique is used as a problem-solving exercise for the youth community (Augusta, 1986).

***Jamaica*:** Recreation for the disabled has been integrated with the rehabilitation services. The Caribbean Association for the Rehabilitation of the Disabled has organized conferences in which Jamaica has participated. It is known that services for the elderly, the blind, and the physically handicapped are a prime concern for the Jamaican government. This country is one of the founders of the Pan American Wheelchair Association.

***Puerto Rico*:** Puerto Rico has developed some programs for the handicapped population. The public and private sectors are working to provide adapted recreation services. Even though services are being provided in some institutions, they are still in the initial phase of development.

Programs from universities such as the National University of Puerto Rico and Bayamon Technological University College are serving the handicapped. The American University has an aerobic program for the handicapped and they provide workshops to prepare personnel to serve the handicapped community. The Bayamon Technological University College has a Handicapped Perceptual Motor Skills Laboratory. This program offers physical and motor assessment for the handicapped. They also prescribe and perform treatment with the special population.

The private sector has also started to provide services for the handicapped with the Physical Education Resource Center (PERC), which treats the handicapped population by the means of physical activity. This privately operated agency works on a fees basis, providing swimming, fitness, and perceptual motor skill activities. Assessment and treatment is a part of the program. Another privately operated institution is the Roberto Clemente Sports City (RCSC). They have an adapted recreation program that serves the handicapped community and a youth program that takes place every day within the RCSC. The staff has been trained to provide special services for the population.

Public agencies such as the Recreation and Sports Department have developed programs such as (a) outdoor recreation and education for children in low-socioeconomic-status areas, (b) physical fitness programs for the elderly, (c) physical activities and assessment for Head Start participants, and (d) recreation and sports for the handicapped. The Department of Recreation and Sports has recently created the position of assistant secretariat of adapted recreation. This new assistant secretariat provides recreational services for the handicapped in Puerto Rico.

Virgin Islands: The Commission for the Handicapped of the USVI is concerned with the recreational opportunities of the population. The commission has started to work on conferences, interest groups, and public awareness for recreation for the handicapped (Finch, 1985). A study of barriers for leisure in the Virgin Islands will be conducted in order to assess this situation.

Conclusion

Latin American countries have recognized the need for recreational services for special populations. The Latin American Recreation and Leisure Association (ALATIR) has coordinated conferences, workshops, and seminars regarding this matter. Some of the events have been held in conjunction with the World Leisure and Recreation

Association, which has provided valuable assistance. ALATIR has created the Center for the Study of Leisure at the American University of Puerto Rico. Recreation services for special populations in Latin America tend to program activities in the areas of physical recreation and social involvement. Psychological well-being has not been reported as an important consideration up until now.

Recreation participation seems to be the main goal of these programs. Leisure counseling and leisure education still need to enter the adapted recreation arena in order to provide individualized services.

Unfortunately, the development of programs for the handicapped and recreational services projects are not always adapted and are instead fit into institutions and agencies that cannot sustain them. Many of the programs and projects performed within the TR spectrum are copies, or adopted from North American programs. The adoption of these programs brings a great gap in the delivery system because it does not account for social, economical, environmental, cultural, or ethnical differences.

We believe that the development of therapeutic recreation in Latin America will increase as soon as the academic institutions provide the new professionals with the skills to deal with special populations. Latin America will need to recruit and prepare university teachers and researchers to study the dynamics of their special populations. Until this happens, recreation services will be provided by allied fields, and programs will be copied from models of other countries.

Let us work together to initiate and improve the quality of therapeutic recreation in America, Latin America, and the rest of the world. Practitioners and researchers must be willing to contribute their experience and knowledge, but they need to create awareness in reference to cultural and social differences. Before exporting programs and concepts, we must adapt them in accordance with each country's reality.

Study Questions

1. Enumerate at least four causes of the lack of professional therapeutic recreation in Latin America.

2. Why can't Gunn and Peterson's model for therapeutic recreation function in most of Latin America?

3. What is the main trend in Latin America in the therapeutic recreation field?

4. If you would have to develop a "therapeutic recreation model for Latin America," which one would you select? Why?
    a. Clinical model
    b. Institutional model
    c. Community model
    d. Others

References

Aguilar, L. (1987). Personal communication, Guatemala City, Guatemala.

Albarrán, M.A. (1987). *The Development of Therapeutic Recreation in Latin America.* Paper presented at the 1987 Midwest Symposium on Therapeutic Recreation, St. Louis, MO.

Arias Madrigal, F. de M. Albarrán, M.A., & Aguilar, T.E. (1982). *Therapeutic Recreation Journal, 16*(2), 44-47.

Augusta, M. (1986). Personal communication, San Juan, Puerto Rico.

Cassione, E. (1986). Personal communication, Sao Paulo, Brazil.

Caudillo, J. (1983). Fundeporte: A Noble Dream. *World Leisure and Recreation Association Journal , 25*(2), 4-6.

Comité Organizador JUPASIRU (Noviembre, 1986) *Programa VIII Juegos Panamericanos Sobre Silla de Ruedas.* Aguadilla, Puerto Rico.

D'Amours, Max (Ed.). (1986). *International Directory of Academic Institution in Leisure, Recreation and Related Fields.* Achevé d'ímprimer au Canada, Commission on Education of the World Leisure and Recreation Association.

Emeres, H, (1982) Chile Applies Leisure to Elderly. Summarized by Richard Ortiz in *World Leisure and Recreation Association Journal,24*(6), 16.

Finch, U. (1986). Personal communication, Saint Thomas, Virgin Islands.

Gaelzer, L. (1986). Personal communication, Sao Paulo, Brazil.

Gunn, S.L., & Peterson, C.A. (1978).*Therapeutic Recreation Program Design, Principles and Procedures.* Englewood Cliffs, New Jersey: Prentice-Hall, 10-26.

Juarez, A.G. (1981) Mexico Develops Industrial Recreation. *World Leisure and Recreation Association Journal, 23*(3), 10-11.

Lopez, M. de L. (1988). Personal communication, San Juan, Puerto Rico.

Ministry of Youth, National Institute for Minors. (1981). Venezuela Emphasizes Underprivileged Youth. *World Leisure and Recreation Association Journal,23*(3), 14-15.

National Institute for Recreation, Physical Education and Sports in Peru. (1981).Peru Provides for Diverse Needs. *World Leisure and Recreation Association Journal, 23*(3), 12-13.

National Recreation Commission of Costa Rica. (1982). National Recreation Commission of Costa Rica Promotes Public Leisure. *World Leisure and Recreation Association Journal,* 24(1), 8-10.

Peñalosa, E. (1977). Statement for the INTERCALL Conference on Human Settlements, Habit, In *Proceedings and Papers, The First World Conference of Experts of Leadership for Leisure.* Pub. World Leisure and Recreation Association. Vancouver, Canada.

Ramirez, H.E. (Enero, 1986). *Sintesis Historico de los Juegos Panamericanos Sobre Silla de Ruedas.* Mimeographed paper. Buenos Aires, Argentina.

Requixa, R. (1981) Brazil Expounds Leisure Through Education. *World Leisure and Recreation Association Journal, 23*(3), 4-6.

Xiques, E. (1988). Personal communication, Santo Domingo, Dominican Republic.

photo courtesy of City of Las Vegas

Unless each day can be looked back upon by an individual as one in which he/she has had some fun, some joy, some real satisfaction, that day is a loss.

—Dwight D. Eisenhower

PART IV

National and International Issues

Summary

Patrick, Park and Hillman provide the reader an excellent history of the legislation pertinent to therapeutic recreation. Citing federal law which created a parcel of land for the Kentucky Deaf and Dumb Asylum in 1827, the authors cite law after law which in some form relates or creates a role for therapeutic recreation. Specific attention is paid to the Rehabilitation Act, Developmental Disabilities Act and Education of Handicapped Children Act. Millions of dollars have been provided colleges and universities over the past two decades to train professionals and conduct research. Section 316 of the Rehabilitation Act authorized demonstration projects in the community for recreation with handicapped children and adults. Outdoor recreation and camping has also benefitted immensely from federal government involvement and sponsorship. Direct patient care by the federal government has essentially been limited to the Veterans Administration and the National Institutes of Health. Each of these federal organizations has piloted quality assurance systems which will serve to assist the profession in the quest for excellence in service. The federal government is a central figure in shaping health care policy and the future of therapeutic recreation may be determined in laws, regulations, research and clinical practices advanced in the aforementioned agencies.

Bullock discusses non-traditional practice issues especially as they relate to Public Law 94-142, the Education for All Handicapped Act. He discusses the role therapeutic recreation assumes in special education as a related service. "Who is eligible" to receive services is discussed. Where services may be delivered is also described. A rationale for inclusion of therapeutic recreation services in the transition goals of school systems is advanced. With high unemployment of the disabled populations once they leave the school system, it is clear that some form of leisure education and services are necessary to accommodate the individual in the transition process. The status of therapeutic recreation as a related service in the school systems is quite disappointing. In spite of litigation, accolades and national position statements, there has been little progress in securing a place in the Individualized Educational Plan (IEP) of handicapped children and youth across the nation.

Shank and Compton discuss legislative, regulatory and political imperatives for the profession. Both authors suggest that the profession has done little to profoundly influence the political process. Faced with relying on the voluntary efforts of members of the professional organizations to carry out lobbying eforts, the profession often finds itself being reactive rather than proactive. Some political efforts have been successful in influencing selected laws (eg) Rehabilitation Act and the Education for All Handicapped Children Act.

Shank discusses the political process and how it should be influenced. Compton points to problems of organization and the inability of the profession to marshall its forces on issues pertinent to its survival. The fundamental issues facing the profession will more than likely require advocacy on behalf of the membership and unification of purpose. Compton calls for the establishment of a federation to enjoin the forces that exist under the aegis of therapeutic recreation.

Another rather fundamental issue is that of research in therapeutic recreation. Compton asserts that there is little empirical evidence to convince policy makers, agencies, higher education authorities, lawyers or others of the efficacy of therapeutic recreation in the clinical or commumity settings. While there has been decided progress in theory development, this may wane with the birth of incoming researchers. Our institutions of higher learning are beginning to focus on research and the creation of knowledge more than any time in history but it may be too late. We still lack a valid and reliable model for clinical or community practice. There are no accepted intervention protocols. While several key individuals possess knowledge and skill necessary to examine critical and profound questions, the majority of the profession gropes to ask the right questions. Many seem enamored with the internal machinations of organizations rather than building a base of knowledge essential for survival. Datillo offers hope for many by the introduction of the single subject design method of inquiry.

Albarran gives us a glimpse of the international scene and the role therapeutic recreation plays from a Latin American perspective. The issues facing developing countries are vastly different than those in developed countries. One of the major issues is that of terminology. In Latin America therapeutic recreation is almost synonymous with the term sport. It is through sport that it derives its legitimacy. There are a variety of individuals who deliver recreation services to handicapped or disabled individuals and most are not professionally trained in therapeutic recreation because of the few programs or courses of study available in the region. Numerous agencies in Latin American countries have emerged to provide recreation and sport opportunities for the handicapped and disabled. Economic difficulties facing the nations and regions may curtail the rapid development of these programs in the future. More trained professionals are needed and stronger ties with the professional preparation programs in the United States would do much to assist in this process.

photo courtesy of Bradford Woods

Issues confronting therapeutic recreation often seem impossible to overcome, yet with perseverance, clarity of thought, and sincerity of purpose, they are resolvable.
—David M. Compton

EPILOGUE:
ON SHAPING A FUTURE FOR THERAPEUTIC RECREATION

David M. Compton

Introduction

Throughout the brief history of therapeutic recreation, the discipline has been marked by continual efforts to clarify its mission, terms, and identity. Nothing has been more problematic than arriving at a clear statement of philosophy and scope of practice. While emerging professions rarely face issues that are life threatening, they are usually drawn early on into debating issues of identity, terminology, and scope of practice. While these issues in and of themselves are usually friendly sparring matches, they eventually must be resolved or become major sources of confusion and anger. Therapeutic recreation has followed suit as an emerging profession. The issues presented in previous chapters have, hopefully, served to focus readers on some of the most critical issues facing the profession. In addition, the authors have attempted to incite the reader to search for the right questions, thoughtfully and systematically address the issues, and develop answers to the most critical of these issues.

This chapter attempts to digest the major issues facing the profession. It offers some questions worthy of further inquiry, debate and resolution. It also offers some possible solutions from the author's perspective. These creative options merely represent starting points for any serious reader. They are offered without regard to one's preference for professional affiliation, education level, role, or years of experience. They are influenced by my own beliefs and convictions about the necessity to change our present status and move forward with our essential contributions to the quality of life of every human being. They are also reflective of a growing sense of urgency that suggests if something is not done to control our own destiny through proactive resolutions, it will be determined by others. There appears to be little time to act on several of the critical issues before grave conseequences are forthcoming, such as third-party payment systems and higher education programs. With this in mind, we start with a brief sketch of our attempts to become a discipline.

On Becoming a Professional Discipline

Over the years as the profession strived for respect from health care and human service sectors, several activities were undertaken to earn the title of a professional discipline. Efforts to create a respectable credentialing system have taken considerable time and energy, but have born fruit with nearly 10,000 credentialed professionals circa 1989. This national system, operated by the National Council on Therapeutic Recreation Certification (NCTRC) under the able tutelage of Dr. Peg Connolly, has emerged as the principal voice for the profession in matters of federal policy, encroachment, and ethics. Parallel efforts to create a nationally recognized system of accreditation for programs in higher education have resulted in the approval of more than 25 programs with specializations in therapeutic recreation at the bachelor's level. In keeping with a mandate to create a body of knowledge and produce scholarly works, the *Therapeutic Recreation Journal* (TRJ) has emerged as a highly respected publication. Under the able guidance of Dr. Peter Witt, the *TRJ* became the clarion voice for research and improved scholarly works. Continuing education efforts have blossomed with the creation of several symposia and management schools, each designed to provide some facet of continuing education to professionals. The Mid-West Symposium on Therapeutic Recreation under the direction of Mr. Gerald Hitzhusen, Extension Specialist, has emerged as the largest and most comprehensive continuing education effort in the world. The symposium has also been largely responsible for the development of therapeutic recreation in the international community through a variety of innovative programming efforts.

In a major thrust for national recognition, quality control, and standardization of knowledge, the NCTRC has commissioned a written national job analysis project that will serve as the basis for a written examination to test entry-level professionals' knowledge. (*NCTRC Newsletter*, 1988) This examination will certainly mark a new era in the credentialing of professionals in therapeutic recreation. Without question, this action will require a response from higher education and the public/private agencies who employ these individuals. Stricter interpretation of accreditation standards, coupled with a tightening of the credentialing process will obviously signal to governmental bodies, professionals in other disciplines, and consumers, that the practice of therapeutic recreation requires a technical and well-defined process of preparation. The question remains as to whether these actions will have an adverse reaction on a diminishing pool of students and drastic shortage of professors.

Therapeutic recreation has come a long way in a short period of time. The aforementioned highlights point to a series of positive activities. This is not to suggest that the profession has by any stretch of the imagination become a recognized professional discipline. Much work remains to be done in several critical areas before the profession will have the stature it desires and the respect it deserves.

Is It the Horse We Have Been Riding All Along?

In emerging professions, especially those who have several focii, there appears to be confusion early in their life as to who they are, what they do (or do not do), and who can belong? Reaching conclusions on these questions usually takes considerable time and requires rigorous examination. Over the past quarter century, therapeutic recreation has engaged in dialogue, debate, and numerous forums to arrive at resolutions on some of the aforementioned questions. Unfortunately, we have recycled many of the same questions, often arriving at the same conclusion. It is rather ironic that the great therapy debate of the early 1980s, which apparently led to the emergence of ATRA, was the very same debate that occurred over twenty years earlier, leading rival clinical and community professional groups to form NTRS! The words of Harvey Cox seem poignant at this point. "What we are seeking so frantically elsewhere may turn out to be the horse we have been riding all along." While we continue a search for meaning and value, numerous pragmatic, as well as philosophical issues are raised.

Major Questions Facing the Profession

From the material presented in this book, my own perspective, and the salient issues facing our nation, society and profession, it appears that there are some major questions that must be addressed by the profession if it is to propel itself into a new era of responsiveness. These in no way represent the totality of questions that must be asked or answered. They are merely representative of the major issues facing the profession, and in that context will hopefully provoke some in-depth inquiry.

What is therapeutic recreation?

We continue to be asked to explain the terms, and much to the chagrin of readers, professionals, parents, and consumers, there is little clarity on the issue. There seem to be as many different answers as there are individuals who ask the questions. After a quarter of a century of inquiry and debate, we continue to have difficulty defining terms and precisely describing what we do in therapeutic recreation. We still use terms such as therapeutic recreation and recreation therapy interchangeably. And in some cases, the adjective "recreation" is replaced with the substitute adjective "recreational" thus confounding the situation even further. Who can blame third-party payors, legislative personnel, students, professionals, and consumers if they seem confused about our explanations? Some state organizations use different terms to title their organizations. Universities, colleges and communities have vastly different viewpoints on the content of the therapeutic recreation curriculum, in spite of national accreditation standards. The only similarity may be in the title of the course, certainly not in the learning outcomes or competencies required of the student. All of this suggests a need for clarity and uniformity in our terms.

The use of the term "therapeutic recreation" by the National Therapeutic Recreation Society was first challenged by Elliot Avedon (1970) in his widely discussed paper entitled "A Critical Analysis of the National Therapeutic Recreation Society Position Statement." The literature is replete with "definitional sparring" but few definitions and terms have been decided once and for all. Ball (1970), Shivers (1971), Rusalem (1973), Witt (1977), O'Morrow (1976), the National Therapeutic Recreation Society (1982), Mobily (1985), and Sylvester (1985) represent a few of the concerned professionals to advance a position defining therapeutic recreation. While the definitional debates have festered from time to time over the past decade there still appears to be little widespread attention to the issue or acceptance of a given position. Evidence of this continued fractionalization over philosophy, terms and definitions is illustrated in the founding of the ATRA, and the existence of several other organizations operating in the arena of therapeutic recreation. In spite of some valiant attempts at reaching clarity in recent years, the term *therapeutic recreation* remains unclear and widely misunderstood today

Why does therapeutic recreation exist?

The question of why therapeutic recreation exists appears at first to be rather naive or very dumb. When examined a bit more carefully, the question is quite penetrating. If we cannot define what we do, do not have a well-articulated philosophy, have a body of knowledge that is questioned and positions that are often considered peripheral or secondary to the primary mission of the agency, then is it any wonder that the question is posed? Numerous outcome-oriented statements dot the literature suggesting that therapeutic recreation is an integral part of the human service delivery system, as well as a part of a "holistic health movement" (Howe, Murphy, and Charboneau, 1987). Therapeutic recreation probably exists because of premises far removed or radically different from those imagined by our own profession. While the profession may think that the reason for therapeutic recreation's existence is the amelioration of disease, disability, or some functional deficit, this may be radically different from the consumer's perception. And both of these perceptions may differ from that of the care provider, federal or state regulator, or the third-party payor. Little data exists to corroborate either position.

In any event, the bottom line is that until we can put to rest the notion that we have an authentic philosophical basis, questions regarding our existence will abound. In our future deliberations, is it not prudent to examine the question of *why* we exist? The underlying problem is that we have few individuals who are in a position to conduct such an inquiry. Even fewer of our lot write in scholarly journals where the test of philosophical positions can be carried out in a scientific fashion. Faculty today are not blessed with sufficient time to ponder philosophical issues because of excessive demands on their time from students, committee assignments, or scholarly requirements. The tenure process often requires the publication of data based articles, and discourages such musings. The problem is further confounded by the fact that there are few universities or colleges where two or more faculty in therapeutic recreation exist in one department. Students are often engaged in superficial philosophical discussions, but little indepth inquiry is required.

There must be an imperative for the discipline. The imperative may well be couched in medical, humanistic, or economic terms. Whatever the case, it seems apparent that if we are unable to create an overriding demand for the discipline, it will continue to remain adjunctive and peripheral—not a primary or essential part of any delivery system.

It is apparent that the discipline must be able to define its terms and gain widespread support for this action. These terms must be rooted in a philosophical statement that emanates from well-defined theory and motives. Above all, those orgnizations and individuals who claim they are *therapeutic recreation* must set aside differences and agree that the terms and statement accurately represent the discipline. The current state of affairs is one of confusion and uncertainty. Critical work in joint committees (with representatives from ATRA, NTRS, AALR, NAAP, etc.) will be required to reach a consensus on these matters. If a committee could develop tight rationale statements from several vectors (eg) medical, humanistic, economic, etc., and validate these with solid scientific inquiry, would we be better off defending our existence as a discipline to the health care, public service, third-party payors, or consumers?

Further, no uniform interpretation of the discipline exists. National, regional, and state organizations do not use the same definitions or interpretive material when addressing the issue of just what is *therapeutic recreation.* Universities, colleges, and community colleges have vastly different viewpoints on the content of the therapeutic recreation curriculum. They often teach many versions of a standard or introductory course. The only similarity may be the title—certainly not the content or learning outcomes.

The philosophy underlying these terms appears rather shallow and without firm foundation. While the National Therapeutic Recreation Society (1982) attempted to develop a statement of philosophy, the effort by many accounts, falls short of articulating a true philosophy. (Mobily, 1985) Recent attempts by ATRA to create a statement of philosophy also fall short. The clear delineation of a philosophy for therapeutic recreation seems at best problematic. What is it we do? Why do we do it? What are the moral and ethical canons that underlie its provision? What impact does it have on the welfare, well being and quality of life of individuals? When is it necessary? Is the same product provided to individuals who are functioning independently in a community setting that is provided to individuals who are totally dependent and institutionalized? If not, why? These and numerous other questions need to be posed and answered by scholars, students, and practitioners if we are to create a moral, medical or economic demand for services in the future.

What is to be provided and by whom?

Born out of the recreation and park movement, social work, and volunteerism, therapeutic recreation has come to mean different things to different individuals. As discussed earlier, the definition one assumes has a significant bearing on what types of service are provided, who provides them, and to whom they are provided. Where one provides therapeutic recreation services also becomes a question. The widely accepted conceptual model of service delivery advanced by Peterson and Gunn (1984) articulates three domains of service: treatment; leisure education; and recreation participation. It seems reasonable that each of these three domains of service could be provided in clinical as well as community-based settings. This premise is advanced by Halberg earlier in this text. The fact is that there is less than a full spectrum of services in both the clinical and community sectors.

What should be provided under the aegis of therapeutic recreation is not circumscribed by public policy or philosophy, but by the expressed needs of those who are defined as clients or consumers. Halberg (Kelly 1985, Compton 1985) points to a significant gap in the provision of therapeutic recreation and recreation services at the community level. It is a fact that public recreation has not fulfilled its responsibility to meet the play, recreation. and leisure needs of those special populations who reside in their communities. Reasons given are varied and quite vague. Over the past decade, public recreation has seemingly lost its sense of responsibility. Programs that are based on high physical skills, are team-oriented, and highly competitive, are the maven of public recreation today. Those who are skilled, affluent, and prefer a particular style engagement are catered to because of growing needs to commercialize the services. This approach excludes many from participating in a functionally integrated manner. As Hubert H. Humphrey, former Vice President of the United States once said, "The moral test of government is how it treats those in the dawn of life (children), those in the shadow of life (disabled, disadvantaged, handicapped) and those in the twilight of life (elderly) (Note: bracketed information is author emphasis).

At a time when selected populations need therapeutic recreation services the most, the public sector has, in a broad sense, ignored their needs. Where are the programs to assist the chemically dependent back into the mainstream of life in the community? The same could be said of the millions of mentally ill who now reside in the community, AIDS victims, adjudicated youth, and the homeless. Our communities are filled with those individuals who are either attempting to return to a normalized way of life, those being partially supported by some aspect of the health care system, or those who have been abandoned entirely. Is there any greater responsibility for the public agency than to meet the critical needs of the people it serves? While many succumb to the "malignancy of idleness", the public agencies have turned their attention to less controversial constitutents who have the means to pay for services.

A wide array of sequential, tiered program offerings should be provided to these populations. The overriding philosophy should be one that guarantees access to areas, facilities, and program opportunities. While there should be programs that are of low risk, there should be those that challenge each individual physically, intellectually, and socially. All activities and programs must be guided by high standards related to age appropriateness, respect for individual differences, personal dignity, the diligent pursuit of freedom of choice, and the cultivation of a leisure ethic.

In the public sector, credentialed therapeutic recreation personnel should be hired to ensure the overall quality and integrity of a comprehensive program. This does not suggest that individuals who have "special recreation" skills, or for that matter, just plain program planning skills, could not be involved in delivering services to clients or consumers. In fact, this is the case at present in many communities. What it does require is a strong commitment from administrators, boards, consumers, and parents to ensure that funding is available and programs are delivered. The fact that increasing numbers of individuals who were heretofore institutionalized or incarcerated now reside in the community, presents ominous challenges to the public recreation agency. The severity of the condition of many individuals residing in the community will require professionals trained in programming and managing their affairs. It will also require a closer articulation with hospitals, clinics, and residential treatment facilities.

In clinical and rehabilitative settings, therapeutic recreation will of necessity, need to move from a diversionary, entertainment, and amusement theme to one based on clinical protocols. We must begin to develop clearer insight into the leisure based problems of clients, and be in a position to select with some certainty a protocol for intervention. Currently we do little to enhance our image in the clinical setting because of the absence of a theoretical basis, varied professional preparation programs, and an absence of valid and reliable assessment instrumentation. Determining the efficacy of our treatment has become the paramount issue facing our discipline. To this end, it seems prudent to be certain that our continuing education programs, credentialing efforts, and accreditation of professional preparation programs develop a clinical focus that could improve our collective efforts to become recognized in the health care arena.

Over the past two decades, there has been an evolution in the type of clients in clinical and rehabilitation settings. The moderate and sometimes even severe cases are being discharged to residential care facilities in the community. What is left in the institution are the severe and acute cases. These clients often represent a level of chronicity for which there is difficulty ascertaining whether leisure, as a concept, even exists within them. This situation challenges the most skilled professional in developing programs, assessing levels of functioning and developing a course of intervention.

Clinical and rehabilitation personnel will need to extend themselves into the community where their clients become consumers of public and commercial recreation services. Successful transition programs from the clinic, rehabilitation center, or hospital will require much more attention than has been paid in the past. We cannot simply discharge people and hope they make it. The process requires cooperation across settings and among different professionals. The cause is the same—optimal human functioning. Financing the entire transition aspect of treatment is still not clear in many cases, but is it not incumbent on the health care and human service sectors to cooperatively address this issue?

The principal activities of the clinical and rehabilitative settings are to diagnose, assess, treat, counsel, educate and successfully support the transition of the client as he moves into the next phase of his life. Therapeutic recreation personnel deliver services from all three domains described by Peterson and Gunn (1984)—treatment, leisure education, and recreation participation. While they are responsible for all three domains, the therapist should be more involved in treatment and leisure education than the provision of recreation services. Support personnel and volunteers should be employed to carry out the recreation service aspect.

Individualized clinical intervention to promote independent leisure functioning is the cornerstone for the therapist of the future. While the therapist may work in small or large groups, in an era of cost containment and accountability there is a compelling argument to individualize services. This individualization will require a shift in many agencies' current focus. Other allied health disciplines such as occupational therapy and physical therapy, etc. are not driven by entertaining the masses but funded almost exclusively of individual client treatments. In the future, there appears to be a strong indication that only a few therapists will be provided the privilege of intervening with clients. Becoming a viable member of the treatment team, in many cases, will require the acquisition of "clinical privilege" credentials. These will more than likely be provided by a given facility or the director of clinical operations. As the health care industry attempts to deal with rapidly rising costs, the therapeutic recreation specialist may either be eliminated from the reimbursement process or subsumed under some other discipline if clinical privileges are not secured. Obtaining clinical privileges in hospitals, clinics and other rehabilitation settings then will be critical to survival in the future. This is, in my opinion, predicated on having a theoretically sound and effective set of treatment protocols and assessment tools.

Is our quest for quality and recognition succeeding?

Several chapters in this text focused on standards, requirements, and credentials. Over the years, the therapeutic recreation profession has, by and large, paid great attention to the critical dimensions of an emerging profession (education vis-a-vis regulatory agencies and laws). These central aspects of the profession were the center of much committee work in the mid-1970s and early 1980s resulting in such items as the language in PL94-142 describing therapeutic recreation as a related discipline, NTRS Field Placement Guidelines (1975), guidelines for both community and clinical setings (1979), a Philosophical Statement on Therapeutic Recreation (1981) and a Model Practice Act (1981) (Wilson, 1988).

During the decade from 1975-85, considerable attention was paid to the credentialing process. The creation of an independent credentialing body in 1981 marked a critical period in the evolution of therapeutic recreation credentialing. Severing ties with the NRPA and NTRS ensured compliance with federal regulatory statutes and other legal opinions relative to the separation of credentialing bodies and their professional organizations. (see Carter and Folkerth, appendices of this text) Today the credentialing process appears to be at its strongest point in its brief history. The quest for quality through a rigorous credentialing program is evidenced in the forthcoming written examination that will be required of all therapeutic recreaion personnel who desire to be credentialed. Stumbo and Carter aptly describe the process leading to the creation of a national examination in this text. Of particular interest is the potential impact this process will have on university curricula, state credentialing efforts (especially those where a practice act is in place or licensure exists), the long-term care industry, where for years the industry has turned its back on the hiring of professionals, and the existing credentialing system. While I applaud the profession for this step forward, it will require considerable political acumen to bring in major segments of the health care industry. I also wonder what implications there are for the public recreation sector who have lagged behind in hiring qualified professionals, and might view this as just another attempt to control their service delivery system. How will the

NCTRC propose to influence or force the adoption of this credentialing program in various state personnel regulations, in the private sector health care system, the federal government, and especially the Veteran's Administration, the single largest employer of therapeutic recreation personnel in the nation?

One major effort over the past fifteen years has been the development and implementation of accreditation standards for curricula in higher education. Representatives from therapeutic recreation were intimately involved in the early stages of creating accreditation standards. Since 1976, NTRS has formally participated in the adoption of curriculum standards. (O'Morrow, 1976) Revision of the standards in 1981 aided significantly in focusing the curricular efforts of colleges and universities. (Council on Accreditation, 1981) While the standards have served to focus the development and standardization of curricula, there remain serious questions regarding the diversity of instruction across programs. A study by Peterson and Connolly (1981) indicated there was an amazing diversity of courses and little consistency in regard to knowledge, skills, or abilities as evidenced in competencies. Couple the course diversity with many faculty who have little or no preparation in therapeutic recreation, and one wonders why the system works at all. (Smith and McGowan, 1982) Further concerns over the large credit hour obligations to fulfill the degree requirements in parks and recreation cloud the uniqueness of this approach to professional preparation. Alternative locations for an independent department of therapeutic recreation or affiliation with another allied health discipline seem distant given the current economic climate on campuses. The tendency is to consolidate and cut back, rather than expand or create new entities. This may require operating within the current structure of parks and recreation for the foreseeable future. One of the major threats to the existence of professional preparation programs in therapeutic recreation is the diminishing number of quality doctoral programs and students. There are only a handful of programs where more than two faculty members in therapeutic recreation are employed. This makes it extremely difficult to conduct a viable graduate program, especially at the doctoral level. The pool of available doctoral students in 1989 has diminished to the point that many jobs in higher education are going unfilled. Demand has far exceeded our ability to produce the product. With no new programs on the horizon, the outlook is somewhat frightening. The ripple effect is that without qualified and experienced instructors, the pool of entry level professionals (bachelor degreed personnel) will be even further diluted in terms of their quality.

Solutions to these problems are not easy, nor are they immediate. The profession must turn its attention once again to higher education. While the issues facing the practice arena are important, if there are inferior or limited numbers of personnel coming into the profession, and these individuals are not able to meet increased standards for credentialing, a major crisis could occur in the profession.

In my opinion, therapeutic recreation has yet to reach a level of respectability enjoyed by our sister professions, occupational therapy and physical therapy, etc. Much of this is due to our inability to focus on the most significant of the long list of issues before the profession. It is confounded by the fractionalization of the profession into two major camps (NTRS and ATRA), a small base from which to derive operating capital, diversity of purpose (community and clinical), and a tenuous base in higher education.

Seven Keys to Shaping the Future of Therapeutic Recreation

While I am reticent about offering a prescription for the future health and well being of the profession, these suggestions are made with the intent that they might provoke or incite some action. They are based on a review of the papers contained in this text, a review of the literature, and my own personal convictions based on my experience as a member of several national, regional, and state organizations, my role as an officer in many of the organizations and my current role as Dean in an institution that contains an accredited therapeutic recreation emphasis area. Some of these thoughts have appeared in personal correspondence to colleagues, organizations, and federal officials. Others have appeared in articles in various journals.

When sitting down to present this list, I was reminded of the words of James DePreist, "On the edge of a precipice, only a fool does cartwheels." Hopefully, these offerings are not cartwheels but carefully balanced handstands. They are portions from a much bigger agenda—the pursuit of excellence for our profession.

1.   *Lay the philosophical cornerstones to the profession*

Recent efforts by Sylvester (1985), Mobily (1985) and (Sylvester et al. 1987) to address the philosophical issues facing the profession are refreshing and provocative. More of this line of thinking must be promoted and underwritten by the profession, universities and organizations. Papers that attempt to advance models, definitions and theoretical constructs should be encouraged. There should be an annual forum for the presentation of papers on matters of a philosophical nature. An annual monograph should be published of these works and widely disseminated.

2. *Define and solidify relationships between credentialing, accreditation and regulatory bodies*

Currently there is little coordination between and among the critical organization charged with shaping policy, establishing standards or regulating practice and the profession. NCTRC, COA and regulatory agencies (eg) HCFA, CARF, etc. in concert with the principal professional organizations must jointly address issues of representation, policy formulation, standards, etc. The current ad hoc fashion of an individual serving as a liaison with an organization is not only ineffective but an inefficient use of personnel. Long-term representation by an individual should be strongly encouraged. Regular meetings between NCTRC, COA, NTRS, ATRA, and others would facilitate more effective strategic planning in determining where representation is critical, essential, or merely ceremonial. The basic issue is that there is little coordination between and among essential groups who purport to represent or control the profession.

3. *Determine the status of the profession*

From the literature, there appear to be fragments of a comprehensive data set to determine the status of the profession. What is critically needed is valid and reliable demographic data on the status of the profession. It is essential to future financing, professional preparation efforts and a host of other reasons to know the stability or volatility of the job market. We need information on career mobility, composition of the work force, etc. In addition, information on the nature and extent of public and private programs serving which groups of disability would be helpful. Understanding the financing of these programs would also be helpful.

Perceptions of the profession from the perspective of the consumer, parents, and other professionals would be helpful in understanding our public image. Knowing how federal, state and regulatory representatives feel about the profession would likewise help in developing strategies to address our image and prioritize activities of boards and committees.

4. *Commission a study of higher education*

It has been nearly a decade since the last major study of professional preparation programs was undertaken. (Peterson and Connolly) We need to determine the efficiency and effectiveness of the current programs, both accredited and non-accredited. Determining the needs of existing professional preparation programs will be essential if a case is to be made to upgrade what we currently have, or add other programs. Central to this study should be an examination of the production of doctorally prepared individuals to carry on the programs. A critical examination of curricula should also take place. This study would be most effective if it were coordinated with, or commissioned by the COA, NCTRC, and Society for Park and Recreation Educators with representation from the profession.

5. *Actively seek federal support for research and training in therapeutic recreation*

Over the past decade, federal funds for research and training in therapeutic recreation have dropped dramatically. (Hillman, 1989) From the late 1970s through the mid 1980s these funds were keys to building the graduate programs in therapeutic recreation across the nation. Without support for graduate students, research possibilities are limited and manpower needs go unfilled. These funds provide the fiscal resources to support additional faculty and create depth in a given department. Research funding is also necessary to determine the efficacy of therapeutic recreation. A recent effort by the National Institute for Disability and Rehabilitation Research (NIDRR) appears to be a singular effort rather than a part of a long-term plan of research.

6. *Coordinate and upgrade continuing education efforts*

Throughout the brief history of therapeutic recreation, there have been continuing education efforts. Regional symposia, conferences, institutes, seminars, and management schools have all contributed to the improvement of therapeutic recreation personnel. What appears to be missing in current continuing education efforts is the identification and coordination of a national agenda. Regional symposia offer a potpourri of programs aimed at their constituencies. One recent conference sponsored by ATRA focused on quality assurance, but this thematic and focused effort is rare. A second or follow-up conference, again sponsored by ATRA, aimed at assuring competence for the trainees. A publication of key material from the conference was a refreshing addition to the improvement of the knowledge base. If the profession, credentialing, and regulatory bodies intend on keeping the profession current and competent, then much more attention must be paid to what is offered under the aegis of continuing education. All conferences should have rigorous training sessions aimed at developing competencies required for credentialing. Competence testing in areas such as assessment, ethics, third-party reimbursement methods, consulting practices, clinical protocols, diagnostic procedures, etc. should be commissioned.

7. *Create a federation to optimize resources and increase power base*

The current arrangement of several organizations representing therapeutic recreation is not only debilitating but duplicative. Philosophical differences aside, the profession is too small to effectively carry out battles for diminishing health care and human service resources. Separately there is no organization that has more than 3000 members (excluding the NCTRC, which is not chartered to carry out certain aspects of the profession). Collectively, however, the organizations could amass some 30,000 professionals. Bringing together organizations such as the NTRS, ATRA, the National Association of Activity Professionals, the National Correctional Recreation Association, the National Consortium on Physical Education , Recreation for the Handicapped, the American Association for Recreation and Leisure, and a host of other activity or disability specific organizations would create an amalgam with political clout. Today we stand divided, often working in a counterproductive fashion on many matters. A federation would allow the autonomy desired by different factions while marshalling allied forces together necessary to create political support for programs, research, and training efforts.

Conclusion

The seven keys presented above suggest a course of action to shape the future of therapeutic recreation. Without strategic and long-range planning, though, the profession may continue to drift into oblivion. While I am not a doom and gloom prognosticator, I firmly believe that we must take charge of our destiny soon. New leaders must surface and seize the opportunity to chart a more defined course for the profession. Rigorous study of critical issues must result in substantive change. Accreditation, credentialing, and regulatory representatives must work in concert with each other to avoid major logistical problems in the implementation of their respective standards. Continuing and higher education must become more sharply focused than ever before to meet the challenges facing the profession. Above all, we must be willing to change. We must be willing to take the first step. As Eudora Welty once said, "All serious daring starts from within."

References

Avedon, E.M. (1970). A Critical Analysis of the National Therapeutic Recreation Society Position Statement cited in Reynolds, R.P., & O'Morrow, G.S. (1985) *Problems, Issues and Concepts in Therapeutic Recreation,* Englewood Cliffs, NJ: Prentice-Hall, 42.

Ball, E.L. (1970). The Meaning of Therapeutic Recreation. *Therapeutic Recreation Journal 4*(1), 17-18.

Compton, D.M. (1985). The Status of Recreation Participation by Disabled Persons in America. In J.D. Kelley (Ed.). *International Forum: Leisure, Sports, Cultural Arts, and Employment for Persons with Disability.* Washington, D.C.: Inspire '85.

Council on Accreditation. (1981). *Standards and Evaluative Criteria for Recreation, Park Resources and Leisure Services Baccalaureate Curricula.* Alexandria, VA: National Recreation and Park Association.

Hillman, W.A. Jr. (1989). Personal correspondence summarizing the status of funding of therapeutic recreation by the Office of Special Education and Rehabilitative Services (January 15, 1989)

Howe-Murphy, R., & Charboneau, B.G. (1987). *Therapeutic Recreation Intervention: An Ecological Perspective.* Englewood Cliffs: Prentice-Hall.

Mobily, K.E. (1985a). A Philosophical Analysis of Therapeutic Recreation: What Does It Mean to Say "We Can Be Therapeutic"? Part I. *Therapeutic Recreation Journal, 19*(1), 14-26.

Mobily, K.E. (1985b). A Philosophical Analysis of Therapeutic Recreation; An Invitation to Philosophize. *Therapeutic Recreation Journal,* 19(2), 7-14.

National Council on Therapeutic Recreation Certification (1988). The National Job Analysis Project. *NCTRC Newsletter,* August/September (p.4). Spring Valley, N.Y. National Council on Therapeutic Recreation Certification.

National Therapeutic Recreation Society. (1982). Philosophical Position Statement of the National Therapeutic Recreation Society. Arlington, VA: National Recreation and Park Association.

O'Morrow, G.S. (1976). *Therapeutic Recreation: A Helping Profession.* Englewood Cliffs, N.J.: Prentice-Hall.

Olsson, R.H., Jr. (1986). The Prospective Payment System: Implications for Therapeutic Recreation. *Therapeutic Recreation Journal,* 20(1) 7-17.

Peterson, C.A., & Connolly, P. (1981). Professional Preparation in Therapeutic Recreation. *Therapeutic Recreation Journal,* 15(2) 39-45.

Peterson, C.A., & Gunn, S.L. (1984). *Therapeutic Recreation Program Design: Principles and Procedures.* Englewood Cliffs: Prentice-Hall.

Reitter, M.S. (1984). Third-Party Reimbursement: Is Therapeutic Recreation Too Late? *Therapeutic Recreation Journal,* 18(4) 13-19.

Reynolds, R.P., & O'Morrow, G.S. (1985). *Problems, Issues and Concepts in Therapeutic Recreation.* Englewood Cliffs:Prentice-Hall.

Rusalem, H. (1973). An Alternative to the Therapeutic Model in Therapeutic Recreation. *Therapeutic Recreation Journal,* 7(1), 8-15.

Smith, S.H., & McGowan, R.W. (1982). A Study to Determine the Educational Levels and Practical Experience of College Teachers in Therapeutic Recreation: 1980, in *Extra Perspectives: Concepts in Therapeutic Recreation,* Neal, L.L., and Edginton, C.R. (eds.), Eugene, OR, Center of Leisure Studies, University of Oregon.

Sylvester, C.D. (1985). Freedom, Leisure and Therapeutic Recreation: A Philosophical View. *Therapetic Recreation Journal,* 19(1), 6-13.

Sylvester, C.D. (1986). Wonder, Doubt, and Thoughtfulness in Therapeutic Recreation: An Invitation to Philosophize. *Therapeutic Recreation Journal,* 20(3), 6-10.

Sylvester, C., Hemingway, J.L., Howe-Murphy, R., Mobily, K., & Shank, P. (1987). *Philosophy of Therapeutic Recreation : Ideas and Isuses.* Alexandria, VA: National Recreation and Park Association.

Wilson, J. (1988). NTRS Report , Combined newsletter of the Nationnal Therapeutic Recreation Society. Mimeographed paper, 2-3.

Witt, P.A. (1977). Therapeutic Recreation : The Outmoded Label. *Therapeutic Recreation Journal, 11*(2), 39-41.

photo courtesy of Bradford Woods

Recreation as a related service is rarely made available because many education and related services personnel are not aware of the role of recreation and its contributions in the educational process for students with handicapping conditions.

—Charles C. Bullock

Appendix A

National Therapeutic Recreation Society
Code of Ethics

Introduction

The National Therapeutic Recreation Society (NTRS), a branch of the National Recreation and Park Association (NRPA), is a professional organization committed to the provision of recreation services for all persons regardless of age, race, sex, national origins, religious beliefs, or physical, social or mental abilities. NTRS maintains open membership to all persons employed in an occupation that provides recreation services for special populations (e.g., mentally ill, retarded, physically handicapped, aged, correctionally incarcerated, socially disadvantaged, etc.), and who subscribe to the professional standards and ethical practices endorsed by the governing board of the society.

The National Therapeutic Recreation Society affirms its commitment to the goals of the park and recreation movement as represented by the Constitution of the National Recreation and Park Association and acknowledges its a priori adherence to standards and principles embodied in the related health disciplines from which it draws much of its heritage of concern and standards of practice.

In this spirit, the therapeutic recreation professional subscribes not only to the ethical code adopted by NRPA, but equally subscribes to those general principles of ethical conduct endorsed by all health related disciplines.

The Statement

I. The therapeutic recreation professional believes in the value and importance of special recreation services for persons who are limited in their opportunities because of physical, social or mental disabilities. He/she is committed to the continuous task of learning and self-improvement to increase his/her competency and effectiveness as a professional.

II. Above all else, the therapeutic recreation professional is guided by the accepted responsibility of encouraging and providing quality service to the client/consumer. He/she demonstrates respect for the dignity of the client/consumer as an individual human being. He/she makes an honest effort to meet the habilitative, rehabilitative and leisure needs of the client/consumer and takes care that the client/consumer is not exploited or otherwise abused. This includes but is not limited to the guarantee of basic human rights under law.

III. The therapeutic recreation professional engages only in those activities that bring credit to himself/herself and to the profession. He/she shows respect for fellow colleagues in word and deed. When he/she becomes aware of unethical conduct by a colleague or fellow professional, appropriate and prescribed professional channels will be followed in reporting said conduct.

IV. The therapeutic recreation professional observes the principle of confidentiality in all written and verbal communications concerning clients/consumers, fellow colleagues and/or matters of professional privilege.

V. The therapeutic recreation professional serves as an advocate for therapeutic recreation by intepreting the purposes and values of the profession to clients/consumers, other professionals, and the community at large, He/she accepts responsibility for improving communications and cooperative effort among the many professional fields serving special populations. He/she encourages and participates in demonstration and investigative projects aimed at upgrading professional services and communicates the results of his/her efforts.

VI. The therapeutic recreation professional obligates himself/herself to providing consultation service to consumers, other professionals, community agencies and institutions. Fees for services, where appropriate, are made known to clients/consumers prior to entering into any contractual relationships.

Appendix B

The Evolution of the National Council for Therapeutic Recreation Certification, Inc.

Marcia Jean Carter
Jean E. Folkerth

A Brief History

The year 1981 marked the 25th anniversary of a voluntary therapeutic recreation cerdentialing program, the first national standard in existence for the profession of parks, recreation, and leisure services. This same year saw the creation of a new governing body, the National Council for Therapeutic Recreation Certification, Inc. (NCTRC, or "the Council"), to manage the operation of the therapeutic recreation personnel credentialing program.

Prior to 1981, a fragmented approach to the development of credentialing tools was in evidence. Actions of professional committees were reactive and issue-oriented, with minimal communication between societies and associations addressing the various aspects of professional competence. A need to systematically address credentialing surfaced during the late 1970s. The former Registration Board of the National Therapeutic Recreation Society (NTRS) surveyed professionals to ascertain the status of the voluntary registration plan as a regulatory plan, and surveyed private and federal health care agencies to determine credentialing requirements of professional regulatory bodies (Carter 1978, 1979). Results indicated there was (a) a lack of literature and statistical information on registration, and (b) a need to investigate whether therapeutic recreators required a stronger credentialing program. Simultaneously, some NTRS members expressed concern for the operation of the voluntary registration plan within NTRS.

An open NTRS board meeting held October 30, 1979, during the New Orleans Congress of the National Recreation and Park Association (NRPA), explored the formation of an independent credentialing body for NTRS. The NTRS board of directors received a recommendation that an administratively independent certification program for therapeutic recreators be guided by the criteria of the National Commission for Health Certifying Agencies. During a follow-up meeting January 29, 1980, representatives of NTRS and NRPA considered the structural and philosophical links between NTRS and NRPA. Mutually independent issues were the administrative independence of credentialing bodies, the cost of developing national examinations, and alternative credentialing approaches. Two options for the therapeutic recreation credentialing program surfaced: a cooperative credentialing mechanism within NRPA and NTRS, operating as an administratively and financially autonomous body;

or the formation of an independent extension of NTRS similar to the Council for the Advancement of Hospital Recreation (CAHR), the first governing body of the "National Voluntary Registration for Hospital Recreation Personnel." In February 1980, these options were presented by the Credentialing Task Force to the NTRS Board, which directed the Task Force to prepare documents supporting the second option.

As a result, a "Proposal for the Creation of an Administratively Independent Council for Therapeutic Certification" and the "By-Laws for the National Council for Therapeutic Recreation Certification" were drafted. During the 1980 NRPA Congress in Phoenix, the NRPA executive staff endorsed the creation of an independent credentialing program outside the governance of both NRPA and NTRS. Following several revisions, the documents were approved by the NTRS board of directors in February 1981 and forwarded to the NRPA Trustee Constitution and By-Laws Committee, with approval by the NRPA trustees on May 22, 1981, during their midyear meeting. The NTRS trustees were renamed the "Certification Review Board" (CRB) to imply that a credential would be issued only following review of prerequisite criteria. The CRB prepared the operational procedures to activate the Council. Accordingly, nominations for NCTRC directors were presented to the NTRS Executive Committee, which appointed board members to assume responsibilities during the inaugural meeting of the Council.

National Council for Therapeutic Recreation Certification, Inc.

On October 29, 1981 the first meeting of the board of directors of the National Council for Therapeutic Recreation Certification was held in Minneapolis. The purposes of the Council are to

> 1) establish national evaluative standards for the certification and recertification of individuals who attest to the competencies of that profession; 2) grant recognition to individuals who voluntarily apply and meet the established standards; and 3) monitor the adherence to the standards by the certified therapeutic recreation personnel. (By-laws, 1981)

The nine members of the new board of directors and their representations were Reginald Ayala, (NRPA representative); Marcia Jean Carter, chair, (professional); Jean Dickinson (paraprofessional); Patrick Griffin (professional); Lenore Hersh (employer representative); Donnell Langston (professional); Lee Meyer (NTRS representative); Marlene Reid (paraprofessional); and Norma Stumbo (consumer representative).

Two standing committees appointed from the new board of directors were a finance committee and a nominations and elections committee. The Test Development and Research Committee and the Procedures Manual Committee were established as ad hoc committees. Ms. Yvonne Washington was contracted as a part-time administrative officer through NRPA.

Two other standing boards of the Council are the CRB and the Appeals Board. Although the name changed, the purpose of the CRB remained the same as it was under the CAHR and NTRS . . .—to review applications and certify those applications, and certify those applicants who meet the current standards. The CRB was comprised of Robert Parker, chair, Mead Jackson, and Lou Powell. Operational procedures for the standing committees and boards were accepted by the directors in October 1984; until that time, the NTRS Executive Committee served as the Appeals Board. Appointed Appeals Board members included John McGovern, chair, Laura Kelly, Robert Connor, and alternate Johnette Whitaker.

Immediate Council tasks included the continuation of a Council newsletter, first prepared by the former NTRS Registration Board in May of 1980; continuation of a national registry, which was printed in July 1983; and the formulation of a management plan. Council goals focused on securing full fiscal and managerial autonomy from NRPA, gathering and disseminating credentialing information, revising certification standards, and exploring alternative credentialing processes, including examination development.

The first election by the certified membership was held in the fall of 1983, when professional and paraprofessional positions on the board were elected. The determination was made to seek further autonomy from the membership organizations; therefore, when the terms of office of the representatives of NRPA and NTRS were completed, the positions were not refilled. Thus, in the fall of 1984, the board was comprised of three professional-level representatives, two paraprofessional-level representatives, an employer representative, and a consumer representative. The professional membership organizations established official liaisons with the board, but without voting privileges.

With legal and financial assistance, the directors drafted a "Memorandum of Agreement Between the National Recreation and Parks Association and the National Council for Therapeutic Recreation" (MOA) during 1981-82, with signatures by both parties in October 1982 for fiscal year 82-83. This document summarized the history and research preceding the Council's creation and outlined criteria for enabling complete fiscal and managerial autonomy of Council operations. While operating under the MOA and subsequent appendums (February 1984, June 1984, and April-May 1985), fiscal autonomy was completely achieved July 1, 1984, and began the process to achieve the status of a tax-exempt nonprofit body through incorporation.

On July 1, 1984, a mailing was sent to all certified members, requesting their proxy vote on the articles of incorporation of NCTRC, Inc. At the October 1984 meeting of the board in Orlando, the constitution and bylaws were approved, and a meeting of the membership was held to explain the need for the proxy vote. In April 1985, the process of collecting the necessary number of proxy votes was complete. The legal documents enabling official recognition as a nonprofit corporation were filed in Austin, Texas, May 1985. In

Dallas, in October 1985, the official incorporation papers were presented by former NCTRC Chair Marcia Jean Carter to the NCTRC board of directors.

With certification continuing to gain recognition as a viable credential, more individuals began to make application. The growth in the number of NCTRC members and applications held many ramifications for the board. First of all, the sheer number of members and applicants, with their diverse service needs, became too much for a part-time executive director. Thus, in April 1986, the board of directors voted to hire a full-time executive director; in September 1986, Dr. Peg Connolly was hired. Also, NCTRC was still operating out of a small office in NRPA headquarters in Virginia. It was felt by the board that a larger office space in a less costly area was needed to continue the overall work of the Council. In February 1987, the office was officially moved to its current location in Spring Valley, New York.

The board found its own work overwhelming at times. Each board member was expected to head several important committees, with other tasks also being required. To ease some of the work load, the board of directors was expanded to nine members in April of 1987, with the addition of two professional-level members. In October 1987, it was also decided to change one of the paraprofessional-level positions to a professional-level position in order to more accurately reflect the overall composition of NCTRC's membership.

The CRB also felt the impact of the field's acceptance of certification. During 1982, NCTRC's first year of operation, a total of only 848 applications were reviewed all year; by 1987 over 900 applications were being reviewed each review period. Thus, it was necessary to expand the CRB from its orignial three-member board to four members in 1987, then to five members by April 1988.

By October 1987, the office staff found that they, too, needed additional assistance due to the amount of work and research being required by the board. In February 1988, Marie Gutjahr was hired as the credentialing specialist. Thus, the office staff was comprised of two full-time office workers and two full-time professional staff members.

In 1985, an ad hoc committee was established to begin seeking information on the important issue of ethics. With this committee specifically, cooperative committee work was established with the professional organizations, NTRS and ATRA. In October 1987, the ethics committee became a standing committee of the NCTRC.

Certification Levels and Standards, 1982 to Present

Commencing with the February 1982 Certification Review Board meeting, a person requesting renewal as either a therapeutic recreation leader, a therapeutic recreation specialist, or a masters therapeutic recreation specialist was automatically given the professional-level title *therapeutic recreation specialist*. A person seeking to be a therapeutic recreation assistant, a therapeutic recreation technician I, or a therapeutic recreation technician II was given the paraprofessional-level title *therapeutic recreation assistant.*

Since the evolution of NCTRC, the only additional standard that has been accepted was a new "provisional" standard. This standard allowed provisional certification if the person had been awarded a degree in therapeutic recreation or a degree in recreation with an option in therapeutic recreation, but for some reason did not meet the accepted number of courses or credit hours in recreation or therapeutic recreation that would allow the person to become certified. The provisional certification was nonrenewable and lasted only 2 years, during which time the perosn was expected to complete the necessary coursework.

Two standards have been deleted. No longer can a person be awarded certification with only a degree in recreation and 2 years of experience in the field of therapeutic recreation. Nor can a person be awarded provisional certification with simply a degree in recreation.

The majority of activity that has occurred in the area of standards has been the clarification of specific items. After January 1, 1986, all professional-level field experiences must be completed under an agency fieldwork supervisor who is a NCTRC-certified therapeutic recreation specialist, while all paraprofessional-level field placement experiences must be completed under an agency fieldwork supervisor who is NCTRC-certified at either the paraprofessional level or the professional level.

The definitions of options, both professional and paraprofessional, were revised. For the first time, options were defined by number and content of courses, and the equivalency process was redefined to include therapeutic recreation and recreation upper division "coursework" rather than "competence." The minimum degree requirements were made applicable regardless of degree level; thus, persons pursuing master's degrees and doctorates were to satisfy the requirements of the bachelor's degree as defined by professional option.

Further clarification continued to be sought by those in the field. Thus, it was decided that therapeutic recreation and recreation courses must be a minimum of three semester units each. The internship must be a minimum of ten consecutive weeks. Within definition of a major, the requirements were changed to stipulate coursework from three of the six areas in supportive coursework. The internship requirement for paraprofessionals was reduced from 400 hours to 200 hours. It is anticipated that further standard clarification will continue. Also, a job analysis is currently being completed in order to begin the process of test development.

Certification has become a significant credential in the field of therapeutic recreation, as evidenced by the growth in the number of certified personnel and requests for further clarification and information. Today's credentialing plan has a solid foundation due to the early efforts of the initial CAHR registration program. The dedication, perseverance, and integrity of many professionals has enabled the growth of a viable credentialing plan that contnues to assist the scope and practice of therapeutic recreation.

References

Carter, M.J. (1978). [Status of the NTRS Voluntary Registration Plan as a professionally identified regulatory plan]. Unpublished raw data.

Carter, M.J. (1979). [Study to determine the registration, certification, and licensure requirements of professional regulatory bodies]. Unpublished raw data.

Folkerth, J.E. (1986). Certification, Historical Perspectives: The First Thirty Years, 1956-1986 [Monograph]. *Twentieth Anniversary National Therapeutic Recreation Society*, 51-59.

Appendix C
Related Professional and Activity Resources for Therapeutic Recreation

Associations and Organizations Serving Special Populations

Government

Administration on Aging and
Mental Retardation
Washington, D.C. 20201
(301) 496-4000

Architectural and Transportation
Barriers Compliance Board
Barriers Compliance Board
330 C.St., SW, Room 1010
Washington, D.C. 20036

National Clearinghouse on Post-
Secondary Education for Disabled People
1 DuPont Circle
Washington, D.C. 20036
(301) 732-4550

National Council on the Aging, Inc.
600 Maryland Ave., SW, West Wing 100
Washington, D.C. 20024
(202) 479-1200

National Institute of Health
9000 Rockville Pike
Bethesda, Maryland 20010
(301) 496-4000

National Institute of Mental Health
11A-20 Parklawn Bldg.
5600 Fisher Lane
Rockville, Maryland 20857
(301)443-4515

National Park Service
Division of Special Popula-
tions and Programs, Department of Interior
18th and C St., NW
Washington, D.C. 20240
(301) 343-1100

President's Committee on Mental Retardation
7th and D Sts., SW
Washington, D.C. 20201

President's Committee on Employment of the Handicapped
1111 20th St., NW Room 606
Washington, D.C. 20036

U.S. Public Health Service
5600 Fisher Ln.
Rockville, Maryland 20857
AIDS Hotline
1-800/324-AIDS

Veterans Administration
Recreation Services
810 Vermont Ave. NW
Washington, D.C. 20420

Professional Organizations

American Alliance of Health,
Physical Education, Recreation
and Dance
1900 Association Drive
Reston, Virginia 22090
(703) 476-3400

American Art Therapy Assoc.
1980 Isaac Newton Square, So.
Reston, Virginia, 22090

American Association for
Music Therapy
PO Box 359
66 Morris St.
Springfield, New Jersey 07081
(201) 379-1100

American Association for
Rehabilitation Therapy
Box 93
N. Little Rock, Arkansas 72216
(501)725-9100 ext. 469

American Association of University
Affiliated Programs for the Developmentally Disabled
1234 Massachusetts Ave., NW
Suite 813
Washington, D.C. 20005
(202) 333-7880

American Camping Association
Bradford Woods
5000 State Rd., 67 North
Martinsville, Indiana 46151
(317) 342-8456

American Correctional Association
4321 Hardwick Rd., Suite L 208
College Park, Maryland 20740
(301) 997-4040

American Health Care Association
1200 15th St., NW
Washington, D.C. 20005
(202) 833-2050

American Psychiatric Association
1400 K St., NW
Washington, D.C. 20005
(202) 682-6000

American Therapeutic Recreation Assn.
2021 L St., NW, Suite 250
Washington, D.C. 20036
(202) 457-0232

Commission on Accreditation of
Rehabilitation Facilities
2500 North Pontano Rd.
Tucson, Arizona 87515
(602) 886-8575

Council for Exceptional Children
1920 Association Drive
Reston, Virginia 22031
(703) 620-3660

Gerontological Society of America
1411 K St., NW, Suite 300
Washington, D.C. 20005
(202) 393-1411

Joint Commission on Accreditation
of Hospitals
875 North Michigan Ave.
Chicago, Illinois 60611
(321) 642-6061

National Association of Activity
Professionals
PO Box 274
Park Ridge, Illinois 60068
(312)692-2564

National Association of Activity
Therapy and Rehabilitation Program
Directors
Box 111
Independence, Iowa 50644
Not listed

National Association of Vocational
Education for Special
Needs Personnel
University of Nebraska
300 West Nebraska Hall
Lincoln, Nebraska 65888
(402)472-3417

National Consortium on Physical
Education and Recreation for the
Handicapped
University of Virginia
221 Memorial Gymnasium
Charlottesville, Virginia 22903
(804) 924-6194

National Correctional Recreation
Association
Blackburn Correctional Complex
311 Spurr Rd.
Lexington, Kentucky 40511
(606) 254-2971

National Council for Therapy and
Rehabilitation through Horticulture
92220 Wightman Rd., Suite 300
Gaithersburg, Maryland 20877
(301) 948-3010

National Recreation and Park Association
3101 Park Center Drive
Alexandria, Virginia 22302
(703) 820-4940

National Rehabilitation Association
633 South Washington St.
Alexandria, Virginia 22314
(703) 836-0850

National Therapeutic Recreation Society
3101 Park Center Drive
Alexandria, Virginia 22302
(703) 820-4940

Advocate Organizations

Alcoholics Anonymous
PO Box 459
Grand Central Station
New York, New York 10017
(212) 686-1100

Alzheimer's Disease and
Related Disorders Assn. Inc.
70 E. Lake St.
Chicago, Illinois 60601
1-800-621-0379 or
(312)-853-3060

American Association for the Deaf
PO Box 105
Talladega, Alabama 35160
Phone not listed

American Association of Retired Persons
1909 K St., NW
Washington, D.C. 20049
(202) 872-4700

American Association on Mental
 Deficiency (AAMD)
510 Wisconsin Ave., NW
Washington, D.C. 20016
(202) 686-5400

American Coalition of Citizens
with Disabilities
1346 Connecticut Ave., NW Room 817
Washington, D.C. 20036
(202) 785-4265

American Council on Alcoholism
8501 Lasalle Rd., Suite 301
Towson, Maryland 21204
(301) 296-5555

American Diabetes Association
PO Box 25757
1660 Duke St.
Arlington, Virginia 22313
(703) 549-1500

American Foundation for the Blind
15 East 16th St.
New York, New York 10019
(212) 620-2000

American Spinal Injury Assn.
250 East Superior St., Room 619
Chicago, Illinois 60611
(312)980-3425

Arthritis and Rheumatism Found.
1314 Spring St., NW
Atlanta, Georgia 30309
(404) 872-7100

Association for Children with
Learning Disabilities
4156 Library Rd.
Pittsburgh, Pennsylvania 15234
(412)341-1515

Association for Retarded Citizens
PO Box 6109
Arlington, Texas 76006
(817)640-0204

Braille Institute
741 North Vermont Ave.
Los Angeles, California 90020
(213)663-1111 Ext. 275

Council for Learning Disabilities
PO Box 40303
Overland Park, Kansas 66204
(913) 492-3840

Down's Syndrome Congress
1640 W. Roosevelt Rd., Rm 156E
Chicago, Illinois 60608
(312) 823-7550

Epilepsy Foundation of America
4351 Garden City Drive
Landover, Maryland 20785
(301)459-3700

Federation of the Handicapped, Inc.
211 W. 14th St.
New York, New York 10011
(212) 242-9050

Foundation for Children with Learning
Disabilities
PO Box LD 2929
Grand Central Station
New York, New York 10016

Information Center for Individuals
with Disabilities
20 Park Plaza, Room 330
Boston, Massachusetts 02116

Muscular Dystrophy Assn. of America
810 7th Ave.
New York, New York 10016
(212) 586-0808

National Amputation Foundation
12-45 150th St.
Whitestone, New York 11357
(718) 767-0596

National Association of the Deaf
814 Thayer Ave.
Silver Spring, Maryland 20910
(301) 587-1788

National Association of Developmental
Disabilities Council
1234 Massachusetts Ave., NW
Suite 203
Washington, D.C. 20005
No phone listed

National Assn. for Retarded Citizens
2709 Avenue E, East
PO Box 6109
Arlington, Texas 76011
(817) 261-4961

National Assn. of the Physically
Handicapped, Inc.
76 Elm St.
London, Ohio 43140
(614) 852-1664

National Congress of Organizations
for the Physically Handicapped, Inc.
1627 Deborah Ave.
Rockford, Illinois 61103
(815) 877-4900

National Council on Senior Citizens
925 15th St., SW
Washington, D.C. 20005
(202) 347-8800

National Easter Seals Society
for Crippled Children and Adults
2023 West Ogden Ave.
Chicago, Illinois 60612
(312) 243-8400

National Foundation for Neuro-
muscular Diseases
250 East 5th St.
New York, New York 10019
(212) 586-5800

National Head Injury Foundation
280 Singletary Lane
Framingham, Massachusetts 01701
(617) 485-9950

National Hospice Organization
1901 North Fort Myer Dr. Ste. 307
Arlington, Virginia 22209
(703) 243-5900

National Information Center
on Deafness
Gallaudet College
Kendall Green
Washington, D.C. 20002
(202) 651-5005 voice & TTY

National Inst. for Advanced Study in
Teaching Disadvantaged Youths
Room 112, 1126 16th St., NW
Washington, D.C. 20036

National Institute of Senior Centers
c/o National Council on the Aging
600 Maryland Ave., SW, West Wing 100
Washington, D.C. 20024
(202) 479-1200

National Mental Health Association
1021 Prince St.
Arlington, Virginia 22312
(703) 528-6404

National Multiple Sclerosis Society
205 E. 42nd St.
New York, New York 10017
(212)986-3240

National Rehabilitation Info. Center
(NARIC)
Catholic University of America
4407 8th St., NE
Washington, D.C. 20064
(202) 653-5826

Orton Dyslexia Society
724 York Rd.
Baltimore, Maryland 21204
(301) 29-0232

Paralyzed Veterans of America
801 18th St., NW
Washington, D.C. 20006
(202) USA-1300

United Cerebral Palsy Association
66 E. 34th St.
New York, New York 10016
(212) 481-6300

Recreation and Competitve Sport Organizations

American Athletic Assn. of the Deaf
3916 Lantern Drive
Silver Spring, Maryland 20902

American Camping Association
Bradford Woods
5000 State Rd., 67 North
Martinsville, Indiana 46151
(317) 342-8456

International Committee of the Silent
Sports, Gallaudet College
Florida Avenue and 7th St. NE
Washington, D.C. 20001
(202) 651-5005 voice & TTY

Indoor Sports Club
1145 Highland St.
Napoleon, Ohio 43545
(419) 592-5756

National Arts and the Handicapped
Information Service
Arts and Special Constituencies
Project
National Endowment for the Arts
2401 E St., NW
Washington, D.C. 20506
(301) 682-5400

National Assn. of Sports for Cerebral
Palsy
United Cerebral Palsy Assn. Inc.
66 E. 34th St.
New York, New York 10016
(212) 481-6300

National Committee/Arts for
the Handicapped
1701 K St., NW Suite 801
Washington, D.C. 20006
(202)223-8007

National Handicapped Sports and
Recreation Assn.
Box 33141 Farragut Station
Washington, D.C. 20033
(301) 652-7505

National Park Service
Division of Federal and State
Liaison
Department of Interior
Washington, D.C. 20240

National Wheelchair Athletic Assn
3617 Betty Dr., Suite S
Colorado Springs, Colorado 80917
(303) 597-8330

Outdoor Recreation Technical Assistance
Clearinghouse, Heritage Conservation
and Recreation Service
Department of Interior
Washington, D.C. 20201
phone Assoc. for Fitness in Business
Stamford, CT
(203) 359-2188

Special Recreation
362 Koser Ave.
Iowa City, Iowa 52240
(319) 337-7578

Special Olympics, Inc.
1350 New York Suite 500
Washington, D.C. 20005
(202) 628-3630

Special Activity Areas

Aerobics/Physical Fitness

National Handicapped Sports and
Recreation Assn.
1145 19th St., NW Suite 717
Washington, D.C. 20036
(301) 652-7505

Air Guns

National Wheelchair Shooting
Federation/NWAA
3617 Betty Dr. Suite S
Colorado Springs, Colorado 80907
(303)597-8330

All Terrain Vehicles

Wheelchair Motorcycle Association
101 Torrey St.
Brockton, Massachusetts 02401
(617)583-8614

Archery

Wheelchair Archery Sport Section/NWAA
3617 Betty Dr., Suite S
Colorado Springs, Colorado 80917(303) 597-8330

U.S. Amputee Athletic Assn.
4024 Nolensville Rd., Suite B
Nashville, Tennessee 37311
(615) 832-4242

Baseball

National Beep Ball Assn
730 Hennepin Ave., Suite 301
Minneapolis, Minnesota 55403

Basketball

American Athletic Assn. for the Deaf
10604 E. 95th St. Terrace
Kansas City, Missouri 64134
(816)765-5520

Natl. Wheelchair Basketball Assn.
110 Seaton Bldg.
University of Kentucky
Lexington, Kentucky 40506
(606) 257-1623

Special Olympics International
1350 New York Ave., NW Suite 500
Washington, D.C. 20005
(202) 628-3630

Biking

BOLD, Inc.
Blind Outdoor Leisure Development
533 E. Main St.
Aspen, Colorado 81611
(303) 925-8922

The Funway Co.
15940 Warwick Rd.
Detroit, Michigan 48223

Western Electric Co.,
Hawthorne Works
Medical Engineering Division
Cicero and Cermak Rd.
Chicago, Illinois 60650

Bowling

American Blind Bowling Assn.
67 Bame Ave.
Buffalo, New York 14215

American Wheelchair Bowling Assn.
N54 W15858 Larkspur Ln.
Menomonee Falls, Wisconsin 53051
(414) 781-6876

National Assn. of Sports for Cerebral Palsy
United Cerebral Palsy Assn of CT.
1 State St.
New Haven, Connecticut 06511

National Deaf Bowling Association
9244 E. Mansfield Ave.
Denver, Colorado 80237
(303) 771-9018

National Deaf Women's Bowling Assn.
Meadow Lark Ln.
Erwin, South Dakota 57233

Special Olympics International
1350 New York Ave., NW Suite 500
Washington, D.C. 20005
(202) 628-3630

Camping

American Camping Association
Bradford Woods
5000 State Rd., 67 North
Martinville, Indiana 46151
(317) 342-8456

BOLD, Inc.
Blind Outdoor Leisure Development
533 E. Main St.
Aspen, Colorado 81611
(303) 925-8922

Office of Special Programs and
Populations
National Park Service
U.S. Department of Interior
PO Box 371127
Washington, D.C. 20013
(202) 343-3674

Canoeing

American Canoe Association
PO Box 248
Lorton, Virginia 22079
(703) 550-7523

Cycling

Wheelchair Motorcycle Association
101 Torrey St.
Brockton, Massachusetts 02401
(617) 583-8614

Diving

Amputee Sports Association
PO Box 60412
Savannah, Georgia 31420
(912) 927-5406

Fishing

Fishing Fact Sheet
Outdoors Forever
PO Box 4811
East Lansing, Michigan 48826

Flying

American Wheelchair Pilots Assn.
3953 W. Evans Drive
Phoenix, Arizona 85023

California Wheelchair Aviators
1117 Rising Hill Way
Escondido, California 92025
(619)746-5018

Freedom's Wings International
277 Malapardis Rd.
Mooris Plains, New Jersey 07950
(201) 267-0479

Football

City of Santa Barbara Rec. Dept.
PO Drawer P-P
Santa Barbara, California 93102
(805) 962-1474

Recreation and Athletics
Rehabilitation Education Center
University of Illinois
1207 South Oak St.
Champaign, Illinois 61820
(217) 333-4606

Golf

Amputee Sports Association
PO Box 60412
Savannah, Georgia 31420
(912) 673-1135

John Klein
Singing Hills Country Club
3007 Dehesa Rd.
El Cajon, California 92921
(619)422-3425

National Amputee Golf Association
PO Box 1228
Amherst, New Hampshire 03031
(603) 673-1135

Peter Longo
PO Box 27283
Tempe, Arizona 85282
(602) 893-2092

Gymnastics

Special Olympics International
1350 New York Ave.,NW Suite 500
Washington, D.C. 20005
(202) 628-3630

Hiking

BOLD, Inc.
Blind Outdoor Leisure Development
533 E. Main St.
Aspen, Colorado 81611
(303) 925-8922

Horseback Riding

Cheff Center for the Handicapped
Augusta, Michigan 49012

BOLD Inc.
Blind Outdoor Leisure
Development
533 E. Main St.
Aspen, Colorado 81611
(303) 925-8922

National Center for Therapeutic Riding
PO Box 42502
Washington, D.C. 20015
(202) 966-8004

National Foundation for
Happy Horsemanship for
the Handicapped
Box 462
Malvern, Pennsylvania 19355
(215) 644-7414

North American Riding for
the Handicapped Assn.
Box 100
Ashburn, Virginia 22011
(703) 471-1621 or 777-3540

Winslow Therapeutic Riding
Unlimited
340 A 5 Route 94
Warwick, New York 10990

Kayaking

Rick Ciccotto
Route 2, Box 589
Moncks Corner, SC 29461

Nantahala Outdoor Center
Star Route, Box 68
Bryson City, NC 28713

Racquetball

National Wheelchair
Racquetball Association
c/o AARA
815 N. Weber, Suite 203
Colorado Springs, CO 80903
(714)861-7312

U.S. Wheelchair Racquet Sports
Association/American Amateur
Racquetball Association
1941 Viento Verano Drive
Diamond Bar, California 91765
(714) 861-7312

Road Race

International Wheelchair Road
Racer Club
30 Myano Ln.
Stamford, Connecticut 06902
(203) 967-2331

Wheelchair Athletics of the USA/NWAA
3617 Betty Drive., Suite S
Colorado Springs, Colorado 80907
(303)597-8330

Rowing

U.S. Rowing Association
201 S. Capitol, Suite 400
Indianapolis, Indiana 46223
(317) 237-2769

Rugby

United States Quad Rugby Association
811 Northwestern Drive
Grand Forks, North Dakota, 58201
(701) 775-0790

Sailing

American Wheelchair Sailing Association
512 Thirtieth St.
New Port Back, California 92662

American Sailing Foundation
c/o American Sailing Association
13922 Marquesas Way
Marina Del Rey, California 90292
(213) 822-7171

Shake-a-Leg
PO Box 1002
Newport, Rhode Island 02840
(401) 849-8898

Scouting

National Advisory Commit-
tee on Scouting for the
Handicapped
1325 Walnut Hill Ln.
PO Box 152079
Irving, Texas 75015
(214) 580-2127

Scuba

Handicapped Scuba Assn.
1104 El Prado
San Clemente, CA 92672
(714) 498-6128

Shooting

National Wheelchair Shooting Federation
545 Ridge Rd.
Wilbraham, MA 01095
(413)596-4407

Skating

BOLD, Inc.
Blind Outdoor Leisure
Development
533 E. Main St.
Aspen, Colorado 81611
(303) 925-8922

Special Olympics Inter-
national
1350 New York Ave., NW
Suite 500
Washington, D.C. 20005
(202) 628-3630

Skiing

American Blind Skiing
Foundation
610 S. William St.
Mt. Prospect, IL 60056
(312) 652-7505

National Amputee Skiing Assn.
c/o NHSRA
1145 19th St., NW, Suite 717
Washinton, D.C. 20036
(301) 652-7505

National Handicapped Sports
and Recreation Association
1145 19th St. NW, Suite 717
Washington, D.C. 20036

National Wheelchair Athletic Association
3617 Betty Drive, Suite S
Colorado Springs, Colorado 80917
(303) 597-8330

New England Handicapped
Sportsmen's Assn.
PO Box 2150
Boston, Massachusetts 02106

Ski for Light
1455 W. Lake St.
Minneapolis, Minnesota 55408
(612) 827-3232

U.S. Deaf Skiers Association
8980 Rossman Hwy
Diamondale, Michigan 48821
(517) 646-6811

Winter Park Handicapped Skier Program
Winter Park Recreational Association
PO Box 36
Winter Park, Colorado 80482

Slalom

Wheelchair Athletics of the
USA/NWAA
3617 Betty Drive, Suite S
Colorado Srings, Colorado 80907
(303)597-8330

Softball

American Athletic Assn. for the Deaf
10604 E. 95th St. Terrace
Kansas City, Missouri 64134
(816) 765-5520

National Wheelchair Softball
Association
PO Box 22478
Minneapolis, MN 55422
(612) 437-1792

Swimming

Amputee Sports Association
PO Box 60412
Savannah, Georgia 31420
(912) 673-1135

BOLD, Inc.
Blind Outdoor Leisure
Development
533 E. Main St.
Aspen, Colorado 81611
(303) 597-8330

Physically Challenged
Swimmers of America
3617 Betty Dr. Suite S
Colorado Springs, CO 80907

Special Olympics Inter-
national
1350 New York AVE., NW
Suite 500
Washington, D.C. 20005
(202) 628-3630

U.S. Amputee Athletics
Association
4024 Nolensville Rd., Suite B
Nashville, TN 37311
(615) 832-4242

U.S. Synchronized Swim-
ming, Inc.
201 S. Capitol, Suite 510
Indianapolis, IN 46223
(317) 237-5700

Table Tennis

Amputee Sports Assn.
PO Box60412
Savannah, GA 31420
(912) 927-5406

National Wheelchair Athletics
Association
3617 Betty Drive, Suite S
Colorado Springs, Colorado 80917
(303) 597-8330

U.S. Amputee Athletics Association
4024 Nolensville Rd., Suite B
Nashville, Tennessee 37311
(615) 832-4242

U.S. Wheelchair Table Tennis
Association/NWA
3617 Betty Drive, Suite S
Colorado Springs, Colorado 80907

Tennis

National Foundation of Wheelchair Tennis
Bradley Park, Press
15441 Red Hill Ave. Suite A
Tustin, California 92680
(714) 259-1531

Peter Burwash International
Special Tennis Programs
2203 Timberloch Place
Woodlands, Texas 77380
(731) 363-4707

Track and Field

Achilles Track Club
Nine E. 89th St.
New York, New York 10128
(212) 967-6496

Amputee Sports Association
PO Box 60412
Savannah, Georgia 31420
(912) 927-5406

National Wheelchair Athletics of
the USA/NWAA
3617 Betty Drive, Suite S
Colorado Springs, Colorado 80917
(303) 597-8330

Special Olympics Inter-
national
1350 New York Ave. NW,
Suite 500
Washington, D.C. 20005
(202) 628-3630

U.S. Amputee Athletics Assn.
4024 Nolensville Rd., Suite B
Nashville, Tennessee 37311
(615) 832-4242

Trampoline

Amputee Sports Association
PO Box 60412
Savannah, Georgia 31420
(912) 927-5406

Volleyball

Amputee Sports Association
PO Box 60412
Savannah, Georgia 31420
(912) 927-5406

Water Skiing

American Water Ski Assn.
799 Overlook Drive
PO Box 191
Winter Haven, Florida 33882
(813) 324-4341

Amputee Sports Association
PO Box 60412
Savannah, Georgia 31420
(912)927-5406

Kan Ski
2704 Hwy. 99
Biggs, California 95917
(916) 989-4541

Weight Lifting

Natl. Wheelchair Athl. Assn.
3617 Betty Dr., Suite S
Colorado Springs, CO 80917

U.S. Amputee Athletics Association
4024 Nolensville Rd., Suite B
Nashville, Tennessee 37311
(615) 832-4242

Weight Training

Casa Colina/Work it Out Program
255 Bonita Ave.
Pomona, California 91767
(714)593-7521

National Institute of Health
Fittness Center
9000 Wisconsin Ave., Bldg. T-39
Bethesda, Maryland 20205
(301) 496-TRIM

Wilderness Activity Programs

Blue Spruce Lodge/Guest Ranch
451 Marten Creek Rd.
Trout Creek, Minnesota 59874
(406) 827-4762

Breckenridge Outdoor Education
Center
PO Box 697
Breckenridge, Colorado 80424
(303) 453-6422

Cooperative Wilderness
Handicapped Outdoor Group
Idaho State University
Box 8118
Pocatello, Idaho 83209
(208) 236-3912

Vinland National Center
PO Box 308
Loretto, Minnesota 55357
(612) 479-3555

Voyager Outward Bound School
10900 Cedar Lake Rd.
Minnetonka, Minnesota 55343
1-800-328-2943 or (612) 542-9255

Wilderness Inquiry II
1313 Fifth St., SE. Suite 327A
Minneapolis, Minnesota 55414
(612) 379-3858

International Recreation and Competitive Sport Organizations

Cerebral Palsy-International
Sport and Recreation
Association (CP-ISRA)

International Blind Sports
Association (IBSA)
Heijneoordesweg 5
NL06813 GG Arnhem
Netherlands

International Blind Sports Assn.
DDR-1020 Berlin, Germany
Democratic Republic

International Committee of
Sports for the Deaf (CISS)
Langaaveg 41
DK-2650 Hvidovre, Denmark

International Foundation for
Wheelchair Tennis (IFWT)
Peter Burwash, International
2203 Timberloch, Texas 77380

International Sports Federation
for Persons with Mental Handicaps (INAS-FMH)
248 Avenue Louise, boite 17
B-1050 Brussels, Belgium

International Sports Organiza-
tion for the Disabled (ISOD)
SHIF
S-12 387 Farsta, Sweden

Sports for All ClearingHouse
Galerij Ravenstein 4-27
B-1000 Brussels, Belgium

International Stoke-Mandeville
Games Federation (ISMGF)
Lidwig Guttmann Sports Centre
for the Disabled
Stoke-Mandeville
Harvey Road
Aylesburg, Buckinghamshire,
England

International Wheelchair Road
Racers Club
30 Myano Lane
Stamford, Connecticut 06902
(203) 967-2231

Ski for Light
1455 W. Lake St.
Minneapolis, Minnesota 55408
(612)827-3232

World Leisure and Recreation
Organization
599 King Edward Ave.
Room 108
University of Ottawa
Ottawa, Ontario, Canada
K1N 7N6

Resources

*Access America: An Atlas and Guide to the
National Parks for Visitors with Disabilities*
Northern Cartographic
Dept. AA PO Box 133
Burlington, Vermont 05405 $89.95

Access to Recreation Catalog
Access to Recreation
2509 E. Thousand Oaks Blvd., Sutie 430
Thousand Oaks, California 91360 Free

*California Park and Recreation Society
Directory Service* California Park and
Recreation Society PO Box 161118
Sacramento, California 95816
Published: Annually in October $65.00

*Directory of Agencies and Organizations
Serving Deaf-Blind Individuals*
Helen Keller National Center
111 Middle Neck Rd.
Sands Point, New York 11050 $10.00

*Directory of Recreation Resources
for the Handicapped*
Mickey A. Christiansen, MS RTR
11066 G on Salves Place
Cerritos, California 90701

Disabled American Resource Center Catalog
Sheldon, Iowa 51201 Free

Disabled Research Directory
Karen DePauw
Department of Physical Ed.
Washington State Univ.
Pullman, WA 99164 $18.95

Exploration
Cindy Ware
30 Alcott St.
Acton, MA, 01420 $30.00

*Guide to Federal Benefits and
Programs for Handicapped
Citizens and their Families*
Association for Retarded Citi-
zens, National Governmental
Affairs Office
1522 K St. Suite 516
Washington, D.C. 20005

*Handicapped Requirement
Handbook*
Thompson Publishing Group
Federal Programs Advisory
Service
Washington, D.C. 20006 $128.00

*Spinal Network: The Total
Resource for the Wheelchair
Community*, Sam Maddox
PO Box 4162,
Boulder, CO

Leadership Training in Adaptive Physical
Education Information in *Palaestra Magazine:
the Forum of Sport, Physical Education
and Recreation for the Disabled.*
Challenge Publications, Ltd.
549 Meadow Drive, PO Box 508
Macomb, Illinois 61455 $18.00

*Morning/Afternoon Recreation
Programs: A How-To Manual*
Jerry Uppinghouse
West Central Community Center
N. 1603 Belt
Spokane, Washington 99205

Contributors

MIGUEL A. ALBARRÁN received his Ph.D. in College Teaching, Recreation and Leisure Studies from North Texas State University. He is presently Assistant Secretary for Adapted Recreation at the Department of Recreation and Sports of Puerto Rico. He is also a faculty member of the Physical Education Department at the University of Puerto Rico. Professionally he is involved with the Puerto Rico Special Olympics, the Blind Sports Committee of Puerto Rico, and the Latin American Committee of program development, behavioral assessment (physical, motor, and leisure) and services for special populations. He has consulted and participated in programs for the handicapped in Spain, Central and South America, and the Caribbean.

DAVID R. AUSTIN completed his Ph.D. at the University of Illinois. He is a professor of Recreation at Indiana University, Bloomington, where he has been on faculty for thirteen years. Dr. Austin has written widely in therapeutic recreation having authored more than fifty articles. He has written the textbook, *Therapeutic Recreation Processes and Techniques* and coauthored *Special Recreation: Opportunities for Persons with Disabilities.*

CHARLES C. BULLOCK received his Ph.D. from the University of Illinois. He is presently an associate professor in the Curriculum in Leisure Studies and Recreation Administration at the University of North Carolina at Chapel Hill. He is the principal investigator of a funded research project to determine the effects of leisure education on the transition of secondary school special education students from school to adult life. He directs an outpatient/follow-up therapeutic recreation demonstration project called the Community Reintegration Program. Dr. Bullock's scholarly interests lie in the areas of therapeutic recreation integration of persons with disabilities into recreation/play settings, and phenomenological research.

MARCIA JEAN CARTER received her Re.D. from Indiana University. She initiated the processes to create NCTRC Inc., and has served on the National Certification Board of NRPA and the Council on Accreditation of NRPA-AALR. Dr. Carter's interests lie in the areas of credentialing, professional standards, programming, therapeutic recreation in the out-of-doors, and aging. Dr. Carter has received the Professional of the Year Award and the Distinguished Service Award from NTRS.

ROBERT E. CIPRIANO received his Ed.D. in Therapeutic Recreation from New York University. He is currently a full professor in the Recreation and Leisure Department Southern Connecticut State University. Dr. Cipriano has coauthored a textbook with Edith Ball entitled *Leisure Services Preparation: A Competency Based Approach.* He has also written extensively on recreation and corrections. Dr. Cipriano's current research interests lie in the areas of transitional services for disabled children and youth exiting public schools, therapeutic recreation services for severely handicapped individuals, and wellness for the disabled. He is currently the recipient of two federal grants from the U.S. Department of Education, Division of Special Education and Rehabilitation Services.

DAVID M. COMPTON received his Ed.D. from the University of Utah. He is presently Dean, College of Health, University of Utah. He has served as President of the National Therapeutic Recreation Society, National Consortium of Physical Education and Recreation for the Handicapped, and Chairman, Board of Regents, Therapeutic Recreation Management School. He currently directs two federally funded grants (Leisure Learning Systems and TEAM-TR) and has secured nearly $3 million in grants over the last decade. He serves as the Rehabilitation and Human Development Series Editor for Sagamore Publishing. His scholarly interests lie in areas of assessment of leisure behavior in persons with disabilities, leisure consumer behavior, and leisure of selected subcultures.

JOHN DATTILO received his Ph.D. from the University of Illinois. He is currently an assistant professor in the Department of Leisure Studies at Penn State. Dr. Dattilo is a Certified Therapeutic Recreation Specialist who has experience in providing leisure services to individuals with multiple and severe disabilities as well as documenting the effects of interventions through data-based research. His research interests include examination of social-psychological aspects of leisure behavior (i.e., perceived choice, control, challenge, communication, and reference) and applied intervention research design to enhance leisure experience of persons with disabilities.

GARY D. ELLIS received his Ph.D. from North Texas State University. He is presently an associate professor at the University of Utah, where he also serves as Director of the Western Laboratory for Leisure Research. He has served as an Associate Editor for several leading scholarly journals. His interests lie in the areas of measurement and assessment, the social psychology of leisure, and the study of experiential states in daily life.

GERALD S. FAIN received his Ph.D. from the University of Maryland. He is currently Chairman of the Department of Special Education, and Coordinator of Health Education and Leisure Studies program at Boston University. He also created and directs the SCHOLE telecommunications network. Dr. Fain has served as Chairman of the ethics committees for both the National Therapeutic Recreation Society and the American Association on Leisure and Recreation. He is a Past President of NTRS. His scholarly interests focus primarily in the areas of moral philosophy and professional ethics.

JEAN E. FOLKERTH received her Re.D. from Indiana University. She is presently an assistant professor in the Recreation and Park Management Division in the Department of Health, Physical Education, Recreation, and Dance at Eastern Michigan University. She has served on the Board of Directors for the National Council for Therapeutic Recreation from 1984-89. Dr. Folkerth's scholarly interests lie in the areas of families and leisure attitude of parents with handicapped children toward leisure, leisure education for families with handicapped children, certification, and therapeutic recreation curricula.

KATHLEEN J. HALBERG received her Ph.D. from the University of Illinois. Before she assumed her current position as an associate professor at California State University, Long Beach, she worked in the therapeutic recreation field for ten years and served as a faculty member for eleven years. Dr. Halberg's scholarly interests focus upon the effects of social psychological issues on the leisure of individuals with disabilities and older people. She is especially interested in the mainstreaming process and coordinated a national study of the status of services to individuals with disabilities by municipal park and recreation departments.

WILLIAM A. HILLMAN, JR. received his M.S. in Recreation from the University of Maryland. He is presently the Research Coordinator for the Institute for Career and Leisure Development, Washington D.C. Mr. Hillman is also project coordinator for an OSERS funded project in Leisure Learning Systems for the severely handicapped. Mr. Hillman recently retired from the U.S. Department of Education, Office of Special Education and Rehabilitation Services as their Therapeutic Recreation Advocate.

CHRISTINE Z. HOWE received her Ph.D. from the University of Illinois. She is currently a visiting associate professor in the department of Leisure Studies at the University of Illinois. Howe is actively involved in the Leisure Research Symposium and the Society of Park and Recreation Educators. Dr. Howe's scholarly interests lie in the areas of assessment and evaluation, research methods, leisure theory, and adult and older adult leisure behavior.

M. JEAN KELLER received her Ph.D. from the University of Georgia. She is presently serving as a consultant with the Governor's Council on Developmental Disabilities. She has served as Chair of the Southeastern Therapeutic Recreation Symposium, and as a Board Member of the National Therapeutic

Recreation Society. Dr. Keller's scholarly interests are in the area of leisure services with older adults. She is also involved with research on leisure behavior of older mentally retarded individuals.

TERRY KINNEY received his Ph.D. from New York University. He is an associate professor in the Department of Recreation and Leisure Studies at Temple University in Philadelphia, Pennsylvania. Dr. Kinney is currently heading a research project, along with John Shank and Kathy Coyle, from the National Institute for Disability and Rehabilitation Research, examining the efficacy of therapeutic recreation within active treatment.

CHESTER LAND received his M.S. in Therapeutic Recreation from California State University, Northridge. Mr. Land is the Director of Recreation Therapy Department of Rancho los Amigos Medical Center and is on the faculty of California State University, Long Beach, California Polytechnical University, Pomona, and California State University, Northridge. He has served as Director of the Therapeutic Section of the California Park and Recreation Society, Chair, Certification Board of the National Certification of Therapeutic Recreation Board. He is currently the president-elect of the National Therapeutic Recreation Society.

MICHAL ANNE LORD received her M.A. in Therapeutic Recreaion from Texas Woman's University. Having worked as a leader in the area of community-based programs for special populations for the past fifteen years, she is currently a lecturer in the Division of Recreation Administration at Southwest Texas State University in San Marcos. Ms. Lord's interests lie in the areas of recreation mainstreaming, creative arts and their ability to enhance learning and leisure abilities of individuals with disabilities, Special Olympics, and the development of professional organizations and leadership.

RICHARD D. MACNEIL received his Ph.D. in Postsecondary and Continuing Education from the University of Iowa. He presently serves as an associate professor and Undergraduate Coordinator in the Department of Leisure Studies at the University of Iowa. Dr. MacNeil's scholarly interests lie in the areas of aging and development in therapeutic recreation.

KENNETH E. MOBILY received his Ph.D. in Physical Education, majoring in Adaptive Physical Education, with minors in Anatomy and Motor Learning. He is presently an associate professor at the University of Iowa with a joint appointment in the Department of Leisure Studies and Exercise Science. His research interests lie in the areas of aging and leisure, with particular interest in recreation programs in nursing homes, and philosophy and leisure. His current research projects include the study of the meanings of work and play across the lifespan and the study of the effects of a cognitive recreation program on the task responsiveness of Alzheimer's patients.

DAVID C. PARK received his M.S. in Higher Education at George Washington University. He currently is the Chief, Special Programs and Populations Branch, National Park Service, U.S. Department of the Interior where he is responsible for directing the efforts of the National Park Service toward becoming as accessible to disabled persons as possible.

GEORGE PATRICK received his Ph.D. from the University of Illinois. He is presently the Special Assistant for Clinical Affairs in the Patient Activities Department at the National Institute of Health in Bethesda, Maryland. His scholarly interests include clinical research design, the mentor/preceptor/supervisor relationship, quality assurance, and assessment of patient satisfaction.

CAROL ANN PETERSON received her Ed.D. from New York University. She is currently a professor and the Chairperson of the Department of Recreation, Parks, and Tourism at Virginia Commonwealth University in Richmond, Virginia. Dr. Peterson's publications, books and professional presentations have focused on the development of procedures to improve the conceptualization and delivery of therapeutic recreation services and on therapeutic recreation curriculum and professional preparation issues.

MARY S. REITTER received her M.S. in Recreation Administration and Therapeutic Recreation from the University of North Carolina at Chapel Hill. She is currently a Program Coordinator with the Statewide Head Injury Program, Boston, MA. Ms. Reitter is formerly a member and chairperson of the NTRS Third-Party Reimbursement Committee and NTRS/ATRA Reimbursement Coalition representative.

TERRANCE P. ROBERTSON is completing his Ph.D. at the University of Utah. He is presently a clinical instructor in the Department of Recreation and Leisure and the Project Coordinator for a federally funded preservice training grant entitled: "Training, Educating, and Advancement of minorities (or individuals with disabilities) in Therapeutic Recreation" or TEAM-TR. Mr. Robertson's scholarly interests lie in the areas of program and intervention efficacy, issues and trends, mental retardation, and assessment. His dissertation research focuses on the efficacy of sensory stimulation interventions with individuals who are profoundly mentally retarded.

JOHN SHANK received his Ed.D. from Boston University. He is currently an associate professor in the Department of Recreation and Leisure Studies at Temple University. He has taught therapeutic recreation for more than seven years and has been a practitioner for eight years. Dr. Shank's interests lie in the areas of assessment, psychosocial issues of illness and disability, and professionalization.

S. Harold Smith received his Ph.D. from the University of Utah. He currently is an associate professor and coordinator of Therapeutic Recreation at Brigham Young University. He has served in a variety of professional roles, including Chair, Washington Therapeutic Recreation Section, Managing Editor of *Leisure Today*, AAHPERD Board of Governors, and currently serves as the President of the American Association for Leisure and Recreation.

Janiece J. Sneegas received her Ph.D. in Leisure Studies from the University of Illinois. She is currently an assistant professor at the University of Illinois with primary responsibilities in the therapeutic recreation option. Dr. Sneegas's scholarly interests lie in the areas of assessment, social skills, leisure education, and leisure behavior of older adults.

Norma J. Stumbo received her Ph.D. in Leisure Studies with an emphasis in Therapeutic Recreation at the University of Illinois. She is presently an assistant professor in the Recreation and Park Administration program within the Department of Health, Education, Recreation, and Dance, at Illinois State University. She has been on the Board of Directors of the National Council for Therapeutic Recreation Certification since its inception in 1981 and has chaired the Test Development and Research Committee since 1982. Dr. Stumbo's research interests lie in the areas of entry-level knowledge, credentialing, and measurement issues.

Charles D. Sylvester received his Ph.D. in Leisure Studies and Services from the University of Oregon. He is presently an associate professor in the Department of Physical Education, Health, and Recreation at Western Washington University in Belingham, Washington. Dr. Sylvester's scholarly interests include history, philosophy, and social issues.

Michael L. Teague received his Ph.D. in Health, Physical Education, and Recreation from the University of Northern Colorado. He is presently a professor in the Department of Leisure Studies at the University of Iowa. He is currently involved with Comprehensive Health Systems, Inc. in a series of health promotion studies involving public and private organizations. Dr. Teague is also working with Dr. Robert Cipriano of Southern Connecticut State University on health promotion programs for the disabled. Dr. Teague's research interests include gerontology and health promotion programs in work settings.

Joseph L. Wilson received his Ed.D. in Education Administration from Virginia Polytechnic Institute and State University. He is currently an assistant professor in the School of Health, Physical Education, and Recreation at the University of Northern Iowa. He is currently conducting an Efficacy of Therapeutic Recreation study within the state of Iowa. He is also the current editor of *NTRS Report,* a quarterly newsletter of the NTRS. Dr. Wilson's scholarly interests include therapeutic recreation assessment instrumentation.

INDEX

Name Index